GCSE
Biology

Turning cytoplasm into excite-oplasm... this fantastic CGP book explains the facts, theory and practical skills for GCSE Biology with the clearest study notes around!

We've got exam-style practice questions in every topic — plus a set of mock exam papers to *really* test you. And we've included fully-worked answers, so it's easy to mark your work.

You'll also find links to our fantastic online content, with video solutions for practice questions, as well as Retrieval Quizzes to help you nail down all the facts you need to learn.

Unlock your free online extras!

Just go to **cgpbooks.co.uk/extras** and enter this code or scan the QR codes in the book.

2378 6389 1261 7938

By the way, this code only works for one person. If somebody else has used this book before you, they might have already claimed the Online Edition.

Complete
Revision & Practice

Everything you need to pass the exams!

Chiswick School
Burlington Lane
Chiswick
W4 3UN

104

Contents

Throughout this book you'll see grade stamps like these:

Grade 4-6   Grade 6-7   Grade 7-9

These grade stamps help to show how difficult the questions are.

Remember — to get a top grade you need to be able to answer **all** the questions, not just the hardest ones.

In the real exams, some questions test how well you can write (as well as your scientific knowledge).
In this book, we've marked these questions with an asterisk (*).

You'll see **QR codes** throughout the book that you can scan with your smartphone.

A QR code next to a tip box question takes you to a **video** that talks you through solving the question. You can access **all** the videos by scanning this code here.

Video Solutions

A QR code on a 'Revision Summary' page takes you to a **Retrieval Quiz** for that topic. You can access **all** the quizzes by scanning this code here.

Retrieval Quizzes

You can also find the **full set of videos** at cgpbooks.co.uk/GCSEBiologyHigher/Videos and the **full set of quizzes** at cgpbooks.co.uk/GCSEBiologyHigher/Quiz

For useful information about **What to Expect in the Exams** and other exam tips head to cgpbooks.co.uk/GCSEBiologyHigher/Exams

Published by CGP
Editors: Sharon Keeley-Holden, Sarah Pattison and Rachael Rogers.
Contributor: Paddy Gannon.
From original material by Richard Parsons.

With thanks to Emily Smith for the copyright research.

With thanks to EYE OF SCIENCE/SCIENCE PHOTO LIBRARY for permission to reproduce the image on page 248.
With thanks to SCIENCE PHOTO LIBRARY for permission to reproduce the image of a contraceptive implant on page 279.

Printed by Elanders Ltd, Newcastle upon Tyne.
Clipart from Corel®
Illustrations by: Sandy Gardner Artist, email sandy@sandygardner.co.uk

Text, design, layout and original illustrations © Coordination Group Publications Ltd. (CGP) 2021
All rights reserved.

The Scientific Method

*This section **isn't** about how to 'do' science — but it does show you the way **most scientists** work.*

Scientists Come Up With **Hypotheses** — Then **Test** Them

1) Scientists try to explain things. They start by observing something they don't understand.

2) They then come up with a hypothesis — a possible explanation for what they've observed.

3) The next step is to test whether the hypothesis might be right or not. This involves making a prediction based on the hypothesis and testing it by gathering evidence (i.e. data) from investigations. If evidence from experiments backs up a prediction, you're a step closer to figuring out if the hypothesis is true.

Hundreds of years ago, we thought demons caused illness.

Several Scientists Will **Test** a Hypothesis

1) Normally, scientists share their findings in peer-reviewed journals, or at conferences.

2) Peer-review is where other scientists check results and scientific explanations to make sure they're 'scientific' (e.g. that experiments have been done in a sensible way) before they're published. It helps to detect false claims, but it doesn't mean that findings are correct — just that they're not wrong in any obvious way.

3) Once other scientists have found out about a hypothesis, they'll start basing their own predictions on it and carry out their own experiments. They'll also try to reproduce the original experiments to check the results — and if all the experiments in the world back up the hypothesis, then scientists start to think the hypothesis is true.

4) However, if a scientist does an experiment that doesn't fit with the hypothesis (and other scientists can reproduce the results) then the hypothesis may need to be modified or scrapped altogether.

Then we thought it was caused by 'bad blood' (and treated it with leeches).

If **All** the **Evidence** Supports a Hypothesis, It's **Accepted** — For Now

1) Accepted hypotheses are often referred to as theories. Our currently accepted theories are the ones that have survived this 'trial by evidence' — they've been tested many times over the years and survived.

2) However, theories never become totally indisputable fact. If new evidence comes along that can't be explained using the existing theory, then the hypothesising and testing is likely to start all over again.

Now we've collected more evidence, we know that illnesses that can be spread between people are due to microorganisms.

Scientific models are constantly being refined...

The scientific method has been developed over time. Aristotle (a Greek philosopher) was the first person to realise that theories need to be based on observations. Muslim scholars then introduced the ideas of creating a hypothesis, testing it, and repeating work to check results.

Models and Communication

*Once scientists have made a **new discovery**, they **don't** just keep it to themselves. Oh no. Time to learn about how scientific discoveries are **communicated**, and the **models** that are used to represent theories.*

Theories Can Involve Different Types of Models

1) A representational model is a simplified description or picture of what's going on in real life. Like all models, it can be used to explain observations and make predictions. E.g. the lock and key model of enzyme action is a simplified way of showing how enzymes work (see p.47). It can be used to explain why enzymes only catalyse particular reactions.

Scientists test models by carrying out experiments to check that the predictions made by the model happen as expected.

2) Computational models use computers to make simulations of complex real-life processes, such as climate change. They're used when there are a lot of different variables (factors that change) to consider, and because you can easily change their design to take into account new data.

3) All models have limitations on what they can explain or predict. Climate change models have several limitations — for example, it's hard to take into account all the biological and chemical processes that influence climate. It can also be difficult to include regional variations in climate.

Scientific Discoveries are Communicated to the General Public

Some scientific discoveries show that people should change their habits, or they might provide ideas that could be developed into new technology. So scientists need to tell the world about their discoveries.

Gene technologies are used in genetic engineering to produce genetically modified crops. Information about these crops needs to be communicated to farmers who might benefit from growing them and to the general public, so they can make informed decisions about the food they buy and eat.

Scientific Evidence can be Presented in a Biased Way

1) Scientific discoveries that are reported in the media (e.g. newspapers or television) aren't peer-reviewed.

2) This means that, even though news stories are often based on data that has been peer-reviewed, the data might be presented in a way that is over-simplified or inaccurate, making it open to misinterpretation.

3) People who want to make a point can sometimes present data in a biased way (sometimes without knowing they're doing it). For example, a scientist might overemphasise a relationship in the data, or a newspaper article might describe details of data supporting an idea without giving any evidence against it.

Companies can present biased data to help sell products...

Sometimes a company may only want you to see half of the story so they present the data in a biased way. For example, a pharmaceutical company may want to encourage you to buy their drugs by telling you about all the positives, but not report the results of any unfavourable studies.

Issues Created by Science

*Science has helped us **make progress** in loads of areas, from medicine to space travel.*
*But science still has its **issues**. And it **can't answer everything**, as you're about to find out.*

Scientific Developments are Great, but they can Raise Issues

Scientific <u>knowledge is increased</u> by doing experiments. And this knowledge leads to <u>scientific developments</u>, e.g. new technologies or new advice. These developments can create <u>issues</u> though. For example:

> <u>Economic issues:</u> Society <u>can't</u> always <u>afford</u> to do things scientists recommend (e.g. investing in alternative energy sources) without <u>cutting back elsewhere</u>.

> <u>Social issues:</u> Decisions based on scientific evidence affect <u>people</u> — e.g. should alcohol be banned (to prevent health problems)? Would the effect on people's lifestyles be <u>acceptable</u>?

> <u>Personal issues:</u> Some decisions will affect <u>individuals</u>. For example, someone might support <u>alternative energy</u>, but object if a <u>wind farm</u> is built next to their house.

> <u>Environmental issues:</u> <u>Human activity</u> often affects the <u>natural environment</u>. For example, <u>genetically modified crops</u> may help us to produce <u>more food</u> — but some people think they could cause <u>environmental problems</u> (see p.182).

Science Can't Answer Every Question — Especially Ethical Ones

1) We don't <u>understand everything</u>. We're always finding out <u>more</u>, but we'll never know <u>all</u> the answers.

2) In order to answer scientific questions, scientists need <u>data</u> to provide <u>evidence</u> for their hypotheses.

3) Some questions can't be answered <u>yet</u> because the data <u>can't</u> currently be <u>collected</u>, or because there's <u>not enough</u> data to <u>support</u> a theory.

4) <u>Eventually</u>, as we get <u>more evidence</u>, we'll answer some of the questions that <u>currently</u> can't be answered, e.g. what the impact of global warming on sea levels will be. But there will always be the "<u>Should we be doing this at all?</u>"-type questions that experiments <u>can't</u> help us to answer...

> Think about <u>new drugs which can be taken to boost your 'brain power'</u>.
> Some people think they're <u>good</u> as they could improve concentration or memory. New drugs could let people think in ways beyond the powers of normal brains.
> Other people say they're <u>bad</u> — they could give some people an <u>unfair advantage</u> in exams. And people might be <u>pressured</u> into taking them so that they could work more <u>effectively</u>, and for <u>longer hours</u>.

There are often issues with new scientific developments...

The trouble is, there's often <u>no clear right answer</u> where these issues are concerned. Different people have <u>different views</u>, depending on their priorities. These issues are full of <u>grey areas</u>.

Risk

*Scientific discoveries are often great, but they can prove **risky**. With dangers all around, you've got to be aware of hazards — this includes **how likely** they are to **cause harm** and **how serious** the effects may be.*

Nothing is Completely Risk-Free

1) A <u>hazard</u> is something that could <u>potentially cause harm</u>.

2) All hazards have a <u>risk</u> attached to them — this is the <u>chance</u> that the hazard will cause harm.

3) The risks of some things seem pretty <u>obvious</u>, or we've known about them for a while, like the risk of causing <u>acid rain</u> by polluting the atmosphere, or of having a <u>car accident</u> when you're travelling in a car.

4) <u>New technology</u> arising from <u>scientific advances</u> can bring <u>new risks</u>, e.g. scientists are unsure whether <u>nanoparticles</u> that are being used in cosmetics and suncream might be harming the cells in our bodies. These risks need to be considered <u>alongside</u> the <u>benefits</u> of the technology, e.g. improved sun protection.

5) You can estimate the <u>size</u> of a risk based on <u>how many times</u> something happens in a big sample (e.g. 100 000 people) over a given <u>period</u> (e.g. a year). For example, you could assess the risk of a driver crashing by recording how many people in a group of <u>100 000 drivers</u> crashed their cars over a year.

6) To make <u>decisions</u> about activities that involve <u>hazards</u>, we need to take into account the <u>chance</u> of the hazard causing harm, and how <u>serious</u> the <u>consequences</u> would be if it did. If an activity involves a hazard that's <u>very likely</u> to cause harm, with <u>serious consequences</u> if it does, that activity is considered <u>high risk</u>.

People Make Their Own Decisions About Risk

1) Not all risks have the same <u>consequences</u>, e.g. if you chop veg with a sharp knife you risk cutting your finger, but if you go scuba-diving you risk death. You're much <u>more likely</u> to cut your finger during half an hour of <u>chopping</u> than to die during half an hour of <u>scuba-diving</u>. But most people are happier to accept a higher <u>probability</u> of an accident if the <u>consequences</u> are <u>short-lived</u> and fairly <u>minor</u>.

2) People tend to be more willing to accept a risk if they <u>choose</u> to do something (e.g. go scuba diving), compared to having the risk <u>imposed</u> on them (e.g. having a nuclear power station built next door).

3) People's <u>perception</u> of risk (how risky they <u>think</u> something is) isn't always <u>accurate</u>. They tend to view <u>familiar</u> activities as <u>low-risk</u> and <u>unfamiliar</u> activities as <u>high-risk</u> — even if that's not the case. For example, cycling on roads is often <u>high-risk</u>, but many people are happy to do it because it's a <u>familiar</u> activity. Air travel is actually pretty <u>safe</u>, but a lot of people perceive it as <u>high-risk</u>.

4) People may <u>over-estimate</u> the risk of things with <u>long-term</u> or <u>invisible</u> effects, e.g. ionising radiation.

The pros and cons of new technology must be weighed up...

The world's a <u>dangerous</u> place and it's impossible to rule out the chance of an accident altogether. But if you can recognise <u>hazards</u> and take steps to reduce the <u>risks</u>, you're more likely to stay <u>safe</u>.

Designing Investigations

*Dig out your lab coat and dust off your badly-scratched safety goggles... it's **investigation time**.*

Evidence Can Support or Disprove a Hypothesis

1) Scientists <u>observe</u> things and come up with <u>hypotheses</u> to test them (see p.1). You need to be able to do the same. For example:

> <u>Observation</u>: People with big feet have spots. <u>Hypothesis</u>: Having big feet causes spots.

2) To <u>determine</u> whether or not a hypothesis is <u>right</u>, you need to do an <u>investigation</u> to gather evidence. To do this, you need to use your hypothesis to make a <u>prediction</u> — something you think <u>will happen</u> that you can test. E.g. people who have bigger feet will have more spots.

Investigations include experiments and studies.

3) Investigations are used to see if there are <u>patterns</u> or <u>relationships</u> between <u>two variables</u>, e.g. to see if there's a pattern or relationship between the variables 'number of spots' and 'size of feet'.

Evidence Needs to be Repeatable, Reproducible and Valid

1) <u>Repeatable</u> means that if the <u>same person</u> does an experiment again using the <u>same methods</u> and equipment, they'll get <u>similar results</u>.

2) <u>Reproducible</u> means that if <u>someone else</u> does the experiment, or a <u>different</u> method or piece of equipment is used, the results will still be <u>similar</u>.

3) If data is <u>repeatable</u> and <u>reproducible</u>, it's <u>reliable</u> and scientists are more likely to <u>have confidence</u> in it.

4) <u>Valid results</u> are both repeatable and reproducible AND they <u>answer the original question</u>. They come from experiments that were designed to be a <u>fair test</u>...

Make an Investigation a Fair Test By Controlling the Variables

1) In a lab experiment you usually <u>change one variable</u> and <u>measure</u> how it affects <u>another variable</u>.

2) To make it a fair test, <u>everything else</u> that could affect the results should <u>stay the same</u> — otherwise you can't tell if the thing you're changing is causing the results or not.

3) The variable you <u>CHANGE</u> is called the <u>INDEPENDENT</u> variable.

4) The variable you <u>MEASURE</u> when you change the independent variable is the <u>DEPENDENT</u> variable.

5) The variables that you <u>KEEP THE SAME</u> are called <u>CONTROL</u> variables.

> You could find how <u>temperature</u> affects the rate of an <u>enzyme-controlled reaction</u>. The <u>independent variable</u> is the <u>temperature</u>. The <u>dependent variable</u> is the <u>rate of reaction</u>. Control variables include the <u>concentration</u> and <u>amounts</u> of reactants, <u>pH</u>, the <u>time period</u> you measure, etc.

6) Because you can't always control all the variables, you often need to use a <u>control experiment</u>. This is an experiment that's kept under the <u>same conditions</u> as the rest of the investigation, but <u>doesn't</u> have anything <u>done</u> to it. This is so that you can see what happens when you don't change anything at all.

Designing Investigations

The **Bigger** the **Sample Size** the **Better**

1) Data based on small samples isn't as good as data based on large samples. A sample should represent the whole population (i.e. it should share as many of the characteristics in the population as possible) — a small sample can't do that as well. It's also harder to spot anomalies if your sample size is too small.

2) The bigger the sample size the better, but scientists have to be realistic when choosing how big. For example, if you were studying how lifestyle affects people's weight it'd be great to study everyone in the UK (a huge sample), but it'd take ages and cost a lot. It's more realistic to study a thousand people, with a mixture of ages, gender and race.

Your **Equipment** has to be **Right for the Job**

1) The measuring equipment you use has to be sensitive enough to measure the changes you're looking for. For example, if you need to measure changes of 1 cm³ you need to use a measuring cylinder that can measure in 1 cm³ steps — it'd be no good trying with one that only measures 10 cm³ steps.

2) The smallest change a measuring instrument can detect is called its resolution. E.g. some mass balances have a resolution of 1 g, some have a resolution of 0.1 g, and some are even more sensitive.

3) Also, equipment needs to be calibrated by measuring a known value. If there's a difference between the measured and known value, you can use this to correct the inaccuracy of the equipment.

Data Should be **Repeatable, Reproducible, Accurate** and **Precise**

1) To check repeatability you need to repeat the readings and check that the results are similar. You need to repeat each reading at least three times.

2) To make sure your results are reproducible you can cross check them by taking a second set of readings with another instrument (or a different observer).

3) Your data also needs to be accurate. Really accurate results are those that are really close to the true answer. The accuracy of your results usually depends on your method — you need to make sure you're measuring the right thing and that you don't miss anything that should be included in the measurements.
E.g. estimating the amount of gas released from a reaction by counting the bubbles isn't very accurate because you might miss some of the bubbles and they might have different volumes. It's more accurate to measure the volume of gas released using a gas syringe.

4) Your data also needs to be precise. Precise results are ones where the data is all really close to the mean (average) of your repeated results (i.e. not spread out).

Repeat	Data set 1	Data set 2
1	12	11
2	14	17
3	13	14
Mean	13	14

Data set 1 is more precise than data set 2.

Designing Investigations

You Need to Look out for **Errors** and **Anomalous Results**

1) The results of your experiment will always vary a bit because of random errors —
    unpredictable differences caused by things like human errors in measuring.
    E.g. the errors you make when reading from a measuring cylinder are random.
    You have to estimate or round the distance when it's between two marks — so sometimes
    your figure will be a bit above the real one, and sometimes it will be a bit below.

2) You can reduce the effect of random errors by taking repeat readings
    and finding the mean. This will make your results more precise.

3) If a measurement is wrong by the same amount every time, it's called
    a systematic error. For example, if you measured from the very
    end of your ruler instead of from the 0 cm mark every time, all your
    measurements would be a bit small. Repeating the experiment in the
    exact same way and calculating a mean won't correct a systematic error.

    If there's no systematic error, then doing repeats and calculating a mean could make your results more accurate.

4) Just to make things more complicated, if a systematic error is caused by using equipment that
    isn't zeroed properly, it's called a zero error. For example, if a mass balance always reads
    1 gram before you put anything on it, all your measurements will be 1 gram too heavy.

5) You can compensate for some systematic errors if you know about them, e.g. if a mass balance
    always reads 1 gram before you put anything on it, you can subtract 1 gram from all your results.

6) Sometimes you get a result that doesn't fit in with the rest at all. This is called an anomalous result.
    You should investigate it and try to work out what happened. If you can work out what happened
    (e.g. you measured something wrong) you can ignore it when processing your results.

Investigations Can be **Hazardous**

1) Hazards from science experiments might include:

- Microorganisms, e.g. some bacteria can make you ill.
- Chemicals, e.g. sulfuric acid can burn your skin and alcohols catch fire easily.
- Fire, e.g. an unattended Bunsen burner is a fire hazard.
- Electricity, e.g. faulty electrical equipment could give you a shock.

You can find out about potential hazards by looking in textbooks, doing some internet research, or asking your teacher.

2) Part of planning an investigation is making sure that it's safe.

3) You should always make sure that you identify all the hazards that you might encounter. Then you
    should think of ways of reducing the risks from the hazards you've identified. For example:

- If you're working with sulfuric acid, always wear gloves and safety goggles.
  This will reduce the risk of the acid coming into contact with your skin and eyes.
- If you're using a Bunsen burner, stand it on a heat proof mat.
  This will reduce the risk of starting a fire.

Designing an investigation is an involved process...

Collecting data is what investigations are all about. Designing a good investigation is really
important to make sure that any data collected is accurate, precise, repeatable and reproducible.

Processing Data

*Processing your data means doing some **calculations** with it to make it **more useful**.*

Data Needs to be Organised

1) Tables are dead useful for organising data.

2) When you draw a table use a ruler and make sure each column has a heading (including the units).

There are Different Ways of Processing Your Data

1) When you've done repeats of an experiment you should always calculate the mean (average).
To do this add together all the data values and divide by the total number of values in the sample.

2) You might also need to calculate the range (how spread out the data is).
To do this find the largest number and subtract the smallest number from it.

Ignore anomalous results when calculating the mean and the range.

EXAMPLE

The results of an experiment to find the volume of gas produced in an enzyme-controlled reaction are shown below. Calculate the mean volume and the range.

Repeat 1 (cm³)	Repeat 2 (cm³)	Repeat 3 (cm³)	Mean (cm³)	Range (cm³)
28	37	32	(28 + 37 + 32) ÷ 3 = 32	(37 − 28) = 9

3) You might also need to calculate the median or mode (two more types of average).
To calculate the median, put all your data in numerical order — the median is the middle value. The number that appears most often in a data set is the mode.

If you have an even number of values, the median is halfway between the middle two values.

E.g. If you have the data set: 1 2 1 1 3 4 2
The median is: 1 1 1 2 2 3 4. The mode is 1 because 1 appears most often.

Round to the Lowest Number of Significant Figures

The first significant figure of a number is the first digit that's not zero. The second and third significant figures come straight after (even if they're zeros). You should be aware of significant figures in calculations.

1) In any calculation where you need to round, you should round the answer to the lowest number of significant figures (s.f.) given.

2) Remember to write down how many significant figures you've rounded to after your answer.

3) If your calculation has multiple steps, only round the final answer, or it won't be as accurate.

EXAMPLE

A plant produces 10.2 cm³ of oxygen in 6.5 minutes whilst photosynthesising. Calculate the rate of photosynthesis.

rate = 10.2 cm³ ÷ 6.5 min = 1.5692... = 1.6 cm³/min (2 s.f.)

3 s.f.　　2 s.f.　　Final answer should be rounded to 2 s.f.

EXAM TIP

Don't forget your calculator...

In the exam you could be given some data and be expected to process it in some way. Make sure you keep an eye on significant figures in your answers and always write down your working.

Presenting Data

*Once you've processed your data, e.g. by calculating the mean, you can present your results in a nice **chart** or **graph**. This will help you to **spot any patterns** in your data.*

If Your Data Comes in **Categories**, Present It in a **Bar Chart**

1) If the independent variable is <u>categoric</u> (comes in distinct categories, e.g. flower colour, blood group) you should use a <u>bar chart</u> to display the data.

2) You also use them if the independent variable is <u>discrete</u> (the data can be counted in chunks, where there's no in-between value, e.g. number of bacteria is discrete because you can't have half a bacterium).

3) There are some <u>golden rules</u> you need to follow for <u>drawing</u> bar charts:

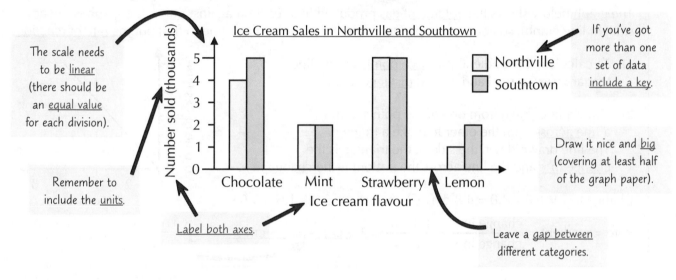

The scale needs to be <u>linear</u> (there should be an <u>equal value</u> for each division).

Remember to include the <u>units</u>.

Label both axes.

If you've got more than one set of data <u>include a key</u>.

Draw it nice and <u>big</u> (covering at least half of the graph paper).

Leave a <u>gap between</u> different categories.

If Your Data is **Continuous**, Plot a **Graph**

1) If both variables are <u>continuous</u> (numerical data that can have any value within a range, e.g. length, volume, temperature) you should use a <u>graph</u> to display the data.

2) Here are the <u>rules</u> for plotting points on a graph:

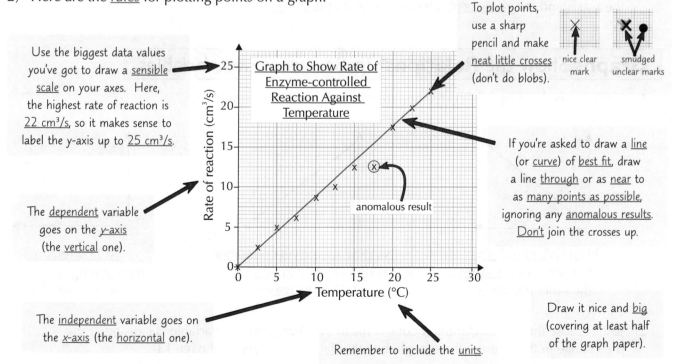

Use the biggest data values you've got to draw a <u>sensible</u> <u>scale</u> on your axes. Here, the highest rate of reaction is 22 cm³/s, so it makes sense to label the y-axis up to 25 cm³/s.

The <u>dependent</u> variable goes on the <u>y-axis</u> (the <u>vertical</u> one).

The <u>independent</u> variable goes on the <u>x-axis</u> (the <u>horizontal</u> one).

To plot points, use a sharp pencil and make <u>neat little crosses</u> (don't do blobs).

nice clear mark

smudged unclear marks

If you're asked to draw a <u>line</u> (or <u>curve</u>) of <u>best fit</u>, draw a line <u>through</u> or as <u>near</u> to as <u>many points as possible</u>, ignoring any <u>anomalous results</u>. <u>Don't</u> join the crosses up.

anomalous result

Remember to include the <u>units</u>.

Draw it nice and <u>big</u> (covering at least half of the graph paper).

More on Graphs

*Graph's aren't just fun to plot, they're also really useful for showing **trends** in your data.*

Graphs Can Give You a Lot of Information About Your Data

1) The <u>gradient</u> (slope) of a graph tells you how quickly the <u>dependent variable</u> changes if you change the <u>independent variable</u>.

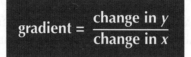

$$\text{gradient} = \frac{\text{change in } y}{\text{change in } x}$$

You can use this method to calculate any rates from a graph, not just the rate of a reaction. Just remember that a rate is how much something changes over time, so x needs to be the time.

The <u>graph</u> below shows the <u>volume of gas</u> produced in a reaction against <u>time</u>. The graph is <u>linear</u> (it's a straight line graph), so you can simply calculate the <u>gradient</u> of the line to find out the <u>rate of reaction</u>.

1) To calculate the gradient, pick <u>two points</u> on the line that are easy to read and a <u>good distance</u> apart.

2) <u>Draw a line down</u> from one of the points and a <u>line across</u> from the other to make a <u>triangle</u>. The line drawn down the side of the triangle is the <u>change in *y*</u> and the line across the bottom is the <u>change in *x*</u>.

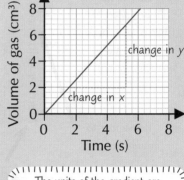

Change in *y* = 6.8 − 2.0 = 4.8 cm   Change in *x* = 5.2 − 1.6 = 3.6 s

Rate = gradient = $\dfrac{\text{change in } y}{\text{change in } x} = \dfrac{4.8 \text{ cm}^3}{3.6 \text{ s}}$ = <u>1.3 cm³/s</u> or <u>1.3 cm³s⁻¹</u>

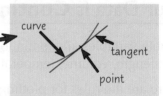
The units of the gradient are (units of y)/(units of x). cm³/s can also be written as cm³s⁻¹.

2) If you've got a <u>curved graph</u>, you can find the rate at any point by drawing a <u>tangent</u> — a straight line that touches a <u>single point</u> on a curve. You can then find the gradient of the tangent in the usual way, to give you the rate at that <u>point</u>.

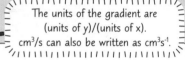

3) The <u>intercept</u> of a graph is where the line of best fit crosses one of the <u>axes</u>. The <u>x-intercept</u> is where the line of best fit crosses the *x*-axis and the <u>y-intercept</u> is where it crosses the <u>y-axis</u>.

Graphs Show the Relationship Between Two Variables

1) You can get <u>three</u> types of <u>correlation</u> (relationship) between variables:

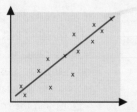

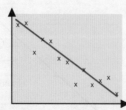

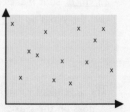

<u>POSITIVE correlation:</u> as one variable <u>increases</u> the other <u>increases</u>.

<u>INVERSE (negative) correlation:</u> as one variable <u>increases</u> the other <u>decreases</u>.

<u>NO correlation:</u> <u>no relationship</u> between the two variables.

2) Just because there's correlation, it doesn't mean the change in one variable is <u>causing</u> the change in the other — there might be <u>other factors</u> involved (see page 13).

Units

*Graphs and maths skills are all very well, but the numbers don't mean much if you don't get the **units** right.*

S.I. Units Are Used All Round the World

1) It wouldn't be all that useful if I defined volume in terms of <u>bath tubs</u>, you defined it in terms of <u>egg-cups</u> and my pal Fred defined it in terms of <u>balloons</u> — we'd never be able to compare our data.

2) To stop this happening, scientists have come up with a set of <u>standard units</u>, called S.I. units, that all scientists use to measure their data. Here are some S.I. units you'll see in biology:

Quantity	S.I. Base Unit
mass	kilogram, kg
length	metre, m
time	second, s

Always Check The Values Used in Equations Have the Right Units

1) Equations (sometimes called formulas) show <u>relationships</u> between <u>variables</u>.

2) To <u>rearrange</u> an equation, make sure that whatever you do to <u>one side</u> of the equation you also do to the <u>other side</u>.

For example, you can find the <u>magnification</u> of something using the equation: magnification = image size ÷ real size. You can <u>rearrange</u> this equation to find the <u>image size</u> by <u>multiplying each side</u> by the real size: image size = magnification × real size

See p.18 for more on magnification calculations.

3) To use an equation, you need to know the values of <u>all but one</u> of the variables. <u>Substitute</u> the values you do know into the formula, and do the calculation to work out the final variable.

4) Always make sure the values you put into an equation have the <u>right units</u>. For example, if you're calculating the magnification of something, but your image size is in <u>mm</u> and the real size is in <u>μm</u>, you'll have to convert both measurements into the <u>same unit</u> (either mm or μm) before you start.

5) To make sure your units are <u>correct</u>, it can help to write down the <u>units</u> on each line of your <u>calculation</u>.

S.I. units help scientists to compare data...

You can only really <u>compare</u> things if they're in the <u>same units</u>. E.g. if the rate of blood flow was measured in ml/min in one vein and in l/day in another vein, it'd be hard to know which was faster.

Converting Units

*You can **convert units** using **scaling prefixes**. This can save you from having to write a lot of 0's...*

Scaling Prefixes Can Be Used for **Large** and **Small** Quantities

1) Quantities come in a huge <u>range</u> of sizes. For example, the volume of a swimming pool might be around 2 000 000 000 cm³, while the volume of a cup is around 250 cm³.

2) To make the size of numbers more <u>manageable</u>, larger or smaller units are used. These are the <u>S.I. base units</u> (e.g. metres) with a <u>prefix</u> in front:

Prefix	tera (T)	giga (G)	mega (M)	kilo (k)	deci (d)	centi (c)	milli (m)	micro (µ)	nano (n)
Multiple of Unit	10^{12}	10^{9}	1 000 000 (10^{6})	1000	0.1	0.01	0.001	0.000001 (10^{-6})	10^{-9}

3) These <u>prefixes</u> tell you <u>how much bigger</u> or <u>smaller</u> a unit is than the base unit. So one <u>kilometre</u> is <u>one thousand</u> metres.

4) To <u>swap</u> from one unit to another, all you need to know is what number you have to divide or multiply by to get from the original unit to the new unit — this is called the <u>conversion factor</u>.

The conversion factor is the number of times the smaller unit goes into the larger unit.

- To go from a <u>bigger unit</u> (like m) to a <u>smaller unit</u> (like cm), you <u>multiply</u> by the conversion factor.
- To go from a <u>smaller unit</u> (like g) to a <u>bigger unit</u> (like kg), you <u>divide</u> by the conversion factor.

5) Here are some conversions that'll be useful for GCSE biology:

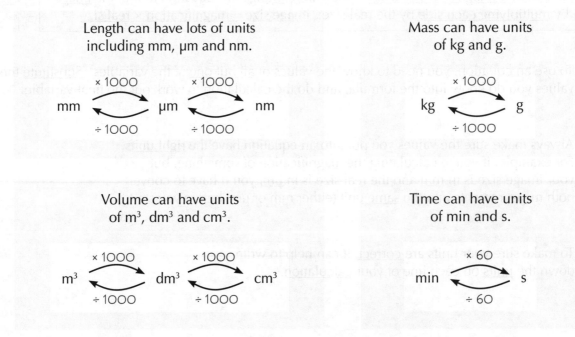

Length can have lots of units including mm, µm and nm.

mm ×1000 → µm ×1000 → nm (÷1000 back)

Mass can have units of kg and g.

kg ×1000 → g (÷1000 back)

Volume can have units of m³, dm³ and cm³.

m³ ×1000 → dm³ ×1000 → cm³ (÷1000 back)

Time can have units of min and s.

min ×60 → s (÷60 back)

To convert from bigger units to smaller units...

...<u>multiply</u> by the <u>conversion factor</u>, and to convert from <u>smaller units</u> to <u>bigger units</u>, <u>divide</u> by the <u>conversion factor</u>. Don't go getting this the wrong way round or you'll get some odd answers.

Drawing Conclusions

*Once you've carried out an experiment and processed your data, it's time to work out **what your data shows**.*

You Can **Only Conclude** What the Data Shows and **No More**

1) Drawing conclusions might seem pretty straightforward — you just <u>look at your data</u> and <u>say what pattern or relationship you see</u> between the dependent and independent variables.

	Fertiliser	Mean growth / mm	

The table on the right shows heights of pea plant seedlings grown for three weeks with <u>different fertilisers</u>.

Fertiliser	Mean growth / mm
A	13.5
B	19.5
No fertiliser	5.5

<u>CONCLUSION</u>: Fertiliser <u>B</u> makes <u>pea plant</u> seedlings grow taller over a <u>three week</u> period than fertiliser A.

2) But you've got to be really careful that your conclusion <u>matches the data</u> you've got and <u>doesn't go any further</u>.

> You <u>can't</u> conclude that fertiliser B makes <u>any other type of plant</u> grow taller than fertiliser A — the results could be totally different.

3) You also need to be able to <u>use your results</u> to <u>justify your conclusion</u> (i.e. back up your conclusion with some specific data).

> Over the three week period, fertiliser B made the pea plants grow <u>6 mm more</u> on average than fertiliser A.

4) When writing a conclusion you need to <u>refer back</u> to the original hypothesis and say whether the data <u>supports it</u> or not:

> The hypothesis for this experiment might have been that adding fertiliser would increase the growth of plants and that different types of fertiliser would affect growth by different amounts. If so, the data <u>supports</u> the hypothesis.

Correlation **DOES NOT** Mean **Cause**

If two things are correlated (i.e. there's a relationship between them) it <u>doesn't</u> necessarily mean a change in one variable is <u>causing</u> the change in the other — this is <u>REALLY IMPORTANT</u> — <u>DON'T FORGET IT</u>. There are <u>three possible reasons</u> for a correlation:

1) <u>CHANCE</u>: It might seem strange, but two things can show a correlation purely due to <u>chance</u>.

> For example, one study might find a correlation between people's hair colour and how good they are at frisbee. But other scientists <u>don't</u> get a correlation when they investigate it — the results of the first study are just a <u>fluke</u>.

2) <u>LINKED BY A 3RD VARIABLE</u>: A lot of the time it may <u>look</u> as if a change in one variable is causing a change in the other, but it <u>isn't</u> — a <u>third variable links</u> the two things.

> For example, there's a correlation between <u>water temperature</u> and <u>shark attacks</u>. This isn't because warmer water makes sharks crazy. Instead, they're linked by a third variable — the <u>number of people swimming</u> (more people swim when the water's hotter, and with more people in the water you get more shark attacks).

3) <u>CAUSE</u>: Sometimes a change in one variable does <u>cause</u> a change in the other. You can only conclude that a correlation is due to cause when you've <u>controlled all the variables</u> that could affect the result.

> For example, there's a correlation between <u>smoking</u> and <u>lung cancer</u>. This is because chemicals in tobacco smoke cause lung cancer. This conclusion was only made once <u>other variables</u> (such as age and exposure to other things that cause cancer) had been <u>controlled</u>.

Uncertainty

*Uncertainty is how sure you can really be about your data. There's a little bit of **maths** to do, and also a formula to learn. But don't worry too much — it's no more than a simple bit of subtraction and division.*

Uncertainty is the Amount of **Error** Your Measurements Might Have

1) When you <u>repeat</u> a measurement, you often get a <u>slightly different</u> figure each time you do it due to <u>random error</u> (see page 7). This means that <u>each result</u> has some <u>uncertainty</u> to it.

2) The measurements you make will also have some uncertainty in them due to <u>limits</u> in the <u>resolution</u> of the equipment you use (see page 6).

3) This all means that the <u>mean</u> of a set of results will also have some uncertainty to it. You can calculate the uncertainty of a <u>mean result</u> using the equation:

$$\text{uncertainty} = \frac{\text{range}}{2}$$

The range is the largest value minus the smallest value (see p.8).

4) The <u>larger</u> the range, the <u>less precise</u> your results are and the <u>more uncertainty</u> there will be in your results. Uncertainties are shown using the '±' symbol.

EXAMPLE

The table below shows the results of a respiration experiment to determine the volume of carbon dioxide produced. Calculate the uncertainty of the mean.

Repeat	1	2	3	mean
Volume of CO_2 produced (cm³)	20.1	19.8	20.0	20.0

1) First work out the range:

Range = 20.1 − 19.8 = 0.300 cm³

2) Use the range to find the uncertainty:

Uncertainty = range ÷ 2 = 0.300 ÷ 2 = 0.150 cm³

So the uncertainty of the mean = 20.0 ± 0.150 cm³

5) Measuring a <u>greater amount</u> of something helps to <u>reduce uncertainty</u>.

For example, in a rate of reaction experiment, measuring the amount of product formed over a <u>longer period</u> compared to a shorter period will <u>reduce</u> the <u>uncertainty</u> in your results.

The smaller the uncertainty, the more precise your results...

Remember that equation for <u>uncertainty</u>. You never know when you might need it — you could be expected to use it in the exams. You need to make sure all the <u>data</u> is in the <u>same units</u> though. For example, if you had some measurements in metres, and some in centimetres, you'd need to convert them all into either metres or centimetres before you set about calculating uncertainty.

Evaluations

*Hurrah! The end of another investigation. Well, now you have to work out all the things you did **wrong**. That's what **evaluations** are all about I'm afraid. Best get cracking with this page...*

Evaluations — Describe **How** Investigations Could be **Improved**

An evaluation is a <u>critical analysis</u> of the whole investigation.

1) You should comment on the <u>method</u> — was it <u>valid</u>?
   Did you control all the other variables to make it a <u>fair test</u>?

2) Comment on the <u>quality</u> of the <u>results</u> — was there <u>enough evidence</u> to reach a valid <u>conclusion</u>? Were the results <u>repeatable</u>, <u>reproducible</u>, <u>accurate</u> and <u>precise</u>?

3) Were there any <u>anomalous</u> results? If there were <u>none</u> then <u>say so</u>.
   If there were any, try to <u>explain</u> them — were they caused by <u>errors</u> in measurement?
   Were there any other <u>variables</u> that could have <u>affected</u> the results?
   You should comment on the level of <u>uncertainty</u> in your results too.

4) All this analysis will allow you to say how <u>confident</u> you are that your conclusion is <u>right</u>.

5) Then you can suggest any <u>changes</u> to the <u>method</u> that would <u>improve</u> the quality of the results, so that you could have <u>more confidence</u> in your conclusion. For example, you might suggest <u>changing</u> the way you controlled a variable, or <u>increasing</u> the number of <u>measurements</u> you took. Taking more measurements at <u>narrower intervals</u> could give you a <u>more accurate result</u>. For example:

> <u>Enzymes</u> have an <u>optimum temperature</u> (a temperature at which they <u>work best</u>).
> Say you do an experiment to find an enzyme's optimum temperature and take measurements at 10 °C, 20 °C, 30 °C, 40 °C and 50 °C. The results of this experiment tell you the optimum is <u>40 °C</u>. You could then <u>repeat</u> the experiment, <u>taking more measurements around 40 °C</u> to a get a <u>more accurate</u> value for the optimum.

6) You could also make more <u>predictions</u> based on your conclusion, then <u>further experiments</u> could be carried out to test them.

When suggesting improvements to the investigation, always make sure that you say why you think this would make the results better.

Always look for ways to improve your investigations

So there you have it — <u>Working Scientifically</u>. Make sure you know this stuff like the back of your hand. It's not just in the lab or the field, when you're carrying out your groundbreaking <u>investigations</u>, that you'll need to know how to work scientifically. You can be asked about it in the <u>exams</u> as well. So swot up...

Cells

*When someone first peered down a microscope at a slice of cork and drew the **boxes** they saw, little did they know that they'd seen the **building blocks** of **every organism on the planet**...*

Organisms can be **Prokaryotes** or **Eukaryotes**

1) All living things are made of cells.

2) Cells can be either prokaryotic or eukaryotic. Eukaryotic cells are complex and include all animal and plant cells. Prokaryotic cells are smaller and simpler, e.g. bacteria (see next page).

You might see the sizes of cells written in standard form — see p.18 for more on this.

3) Eukaryotes are organisms that are made up of eukaryotic cells.

4) A prokaryote is a prokaryotic cell (it's a single-celled organism).

Plant and Animal Cells have Similarities and Differences

Animal Cells

The different parts of a cell are called subcellular structures. Most animal cells have the following subcellular structures — make sure you know them all:

1) Nucleus — contains genetic material that controls the activities of the cell.

2) Mitochondria — these are where most of the reactions for aerobic respiration take place (see page 112). Respiration transfers energy that the cell needs to work.

3) Cytoplasm — gel-like substance where most of the chemical reactions happen. It contains enzymes (see page 47) that control these chemical reactions.

4) Cell membrane — holds the cell together and controls what goes in and out.

5) Ribosomes — these are where proteins are made in the cell.

Subcellular structures are all the different parts of a cell

Make sure you get to grips with the different subcellular structures that animal cells contain before you move on to the next page. There are more subcellular structures coming up that you need to know...

Cells

Plant Cells

Plant cells usually have <u>all the bits</u> that <u>animal</u> cells have, plus a few <u>extra</u> things that animal cells <u>don't</u> have:

> The cells of algae (e.g. seaweed) also have a rigid cell wall and chloroplasts.

1) Rigid <u>cell wall</u> — made of <u>cellulose</u>. It <u>supports</u> the cell and strengthens it.

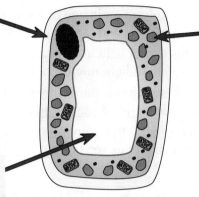

2) <u>Permanent vacuole</u> — contains <u>cell sap</u>, a weak solution of sugar and salts.

3) <u>Chloroplasts</u> — these are where <u>photosynthesis</u> occurs, which makes food for the plant (see page 101). They contain a <u>green</u> substance called <u>chlorophyll</u>, which absorbs the <u>light</u> needed for photosynthesis.

> You could get asked to estimate the area of a subcellular structure. If you do, treat it as a regular shape. For example, if it's close to a rectangle, use the area formula 'area = length × width'.

Bacterial Cells Are Much Smaller

1) Bacteria are <u>prokaryotes</u>.

2) Bacterial cells <u>don't</u> have a 'true' <u>nucleus</u> — instead they have a <u>single circular strand</u> of <u>DNA</u> that floats <u>freely</u> in the cytoplasm.

3) They may also contain one or more small rings of DNA called <u>plasmids</u>.

4) Bacteria <u>don't</u> have <u>chloroplasts</u> or <u>mitochondria</u>.

Here's what a bacterial cell might look like:

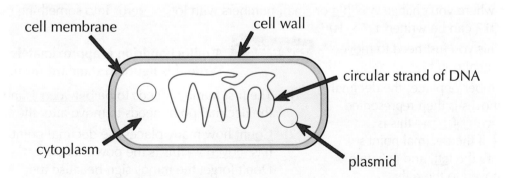

cell membrane

cell wall

circular strand of DNA

cytoplasm

plasmid

There's quite a bit to learn in biology — but that's life, I guess...

On these pages are a <u>typical animal cell</u>, <u>plant cell</u> and <u>bacterial cell</u>. Make sure you're familiar with all their <u>structures</u>. A good way to check that you know what all the bits and pieces are is to copy out the diagrams and see if you can remember all the labels. No cheating.

Microscopy

Microscopes are pretty important for biology. There's a lot you need to know about them...

Cells are **Studied** Using **Microscopes**

1) <u>Microscopes</u> let us see things that we <u>can't see</u> with the <u>naked eye</u>. The <u>microscopy techniques</u> we can use have <u>developed</u> over the years as technology and knowledge have improved.

2) <u>Light microscopes</u> use <u>light</u> and <u>lenses</u> to form an image of a specimen and <u>magnify</u> it (make it look bigger). They let us see <u>individual cells</u> and <u>large subcellular structures</u>, like <u>nuclei</u>.

3) <u>Electron microscopes</u> use <u>electrons</u> instead of light to form an image. They have a much <u>higher magnification</u> than light microscopes.

4) They also have a <u>higher resolution</u>. (Resolution is the ability to <u>distinguish</u> between <u>two points</u>, so a higher resolution gives a <u>sharper image</u>.)

See pages 19-20 for how to use a light microscope.

5) Electron microscopes let us see much <u>smaller things</u> in <u>more detail</u>, like the <u>internal structure</u> of <u>mitochondria</u> and <u>chloroplasts</u>. They even let us see <u>tinier</u> things like <u>ribosomes</u> and <u>plasmids</u>.

You Need to be Able to Use the **Formula** for **Magnification**

You can calculate the magnification of an image using this formula:

$$\text{magnification} = \frac{\text{image size}}{\text{real size}}$$

Both image size and real size should have the same units. If they don't, you'll need to convert them first (see page 12).

EXAMPLE

A specimen is 50 μm wide. Calculate the width of the image of the specimen under a magnification of × 100. Give your answer in mm.

1) <u>Rearrange</u> the formula.

2) Fill in the <u>values</u> you know.

3) Remember the <u>units</u> in your answer.

4) <u>Convert</u> the units.

image size = magnification × real size

image size = 100 × 50

= 5000 μm

= 5 mm

Remember, to convert from micrometres (μm) to millimetres (mm), you need to divide by 1000 (see p.12). E.g. 5000 μm ÷ 1000 = 5 mm

You Need to Know How to Work With Numbers in **Standard Form**

1) As microscopes can see such <u>tiny objects</u>, sometimes it's useful to write numbers in <u>standard form</u>.

2) This is where you change <u>very big</u> or <u>small</u> numbers with <u>lots of zeros</u> into something more manageable, e.g. 0.017 can be written 1.7×10^{-2}.

3) To do this you just need to <u>move</u> the <u>decimal point</u> left or right.

4) The number of places the decimal point moves is then represented by a <u>power of 10</u> — this is <u>positive</u> if the decimal point's moved to the <u>left</u>, and <u>negative</u> if it's moved to the <u>right</u>.

EXAMPLE

A mitochondrion is approximately 0.0025 mm long. Write this figure in standard form.

1) The first number needs to be <u>between 1 and 10</u> so the decimal point needs to move after the '2'.

0.0025

2) <u>Count</u> how many places the decimal point has <u>moved</u> — this is the power of 10. Don't forget the <u>minus</u> sign because the decimal point has moved <u>right</u>.

2.5×10^{-3}

Check the units used in that equation are both the same

Q1 A cheek cell is viewed under a microscope with × 40 magnification.
The image of the cell is 2.4 mm wide.
Calculate the real width of the cheek cell. Give your answer in μm. **[2 marks]**

Q1 Video Solution

Microscopy

*It's all very well knowing what microscopes **do** — you also have to know how to actually **use** one.*

You Need to **Prepare** Your **Slide**

If you want to look at a specimen (e.g. plant or animal cells) under a light microscope, you need to put it on a <u>microscope slide</u> first. A slide is a strip of clear <u>glass</u> or <u>plastic</u> onto which the specimen is <u>mounted</u>.

For example, here's how to prepare a slide to view onion cells:

1) Add a <u>drop of water</u> to the middle of a clean slide.

2) Cut up an onion and separate it out into <u>layers</u>. Use <u>tweezers</u> to peel off some <u>epidermal tissue</u> from the bottom of one of the layers.

3) Using the tweezers, place the epidermal tissue into the <u>water</u> on the slide.

4) Add a drop of <u>iodine solution</u>. Iodine solution is a <u>stain</u>. Stains are used to highlight objects in a cell by adding <u>colour</u> to them.

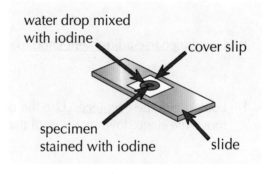

water drop mixed with iodine

cover slip

specimen stained with iodine

slide

5) Place a <u>cover slip</u> (a square of thin, transparent plastic or glass) on top. To do this, stand the cover slip <u>upright</u> on the slide, <u>next to</u> the water droplet. Then carefully <u>tilt</u> and <u>lower</u> it so it covers the specimen. Try <u>not</u> to get any <u>air bubbles</u> under there — they'll <u>obstruct</u> your view of the specimen.

Know the Parts of a **Light Microscope**

To look at your prepared slides, you need to know how to use a light microscope. Here are the main parts you'll use:

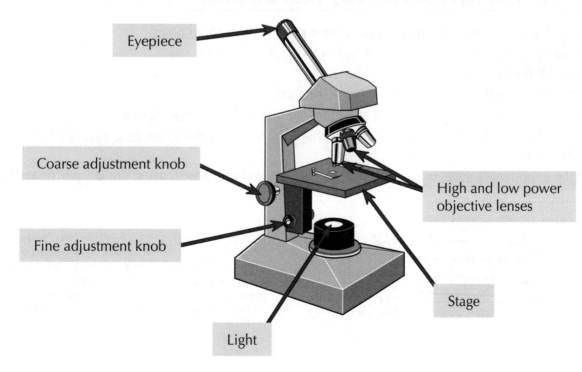

Eyepiece

Coarse adjustment knob

Fine adjustment knob

High and low power objective lenses

Stage

Light

Stains can make subcellular structures easier to see

Carry on to the next page for <u>how to use</u> the microscope above to view your specimen.

Microscopy

Use a **Light Microscope** to Look at Your **Slide**

1) Clip the <u>slide</u> you've prepared onto the <u>stage</u>.

> Have a look back at the previous page if you need a reminder of where these parts are on the microscope.

2) Select the <u>lowest-powered objective lens</u> (i.e. the one that produces the lowest magnification).

3) Use the <u>coarse adjustment knob</u> to move the stage up to just below the objective lens.

4) Look down the <u>eyepiece</u>. Use the coarse adjustment knob to move the stage downwards until the image is <u>roughly in focus</u>.

5) Adjust the <u>focus</u> with the <u>fine adjustment knob</u>, until you get a <u>clear image</u> of what's on the slide.

6) If you need to see the slide with <u>greater magnification</u>, swap to a <u>higher-powered objective lens</u> and refocus.

Draw Your Observations **Neatly** with a **Pencil**

1) Draw what you see under the microscope using a <u>pencil</u> with a <u>sharp point</u>.
2) Make sure your drawing takes up <u>at least half</u> of the space available and that it is drawn with <u>clear, unbroken lines</u>.
3) Your drawing should not include any <u>colouring</u> or <u>shading</u>.
4) If you are drawing <u>cells</u>, the <u>subcellular structures</u> should be drawn in <u>proportion</u>.
5) Remember to include a <u>title</u> of what you were observing and write down the <u>magnification</u> that it was observed under.
6) <u>Label</u> the <u>important features</u> of your drawing (e.g. nucleus, chloroplasts), using <u>straight, uncrossed lines</u>.

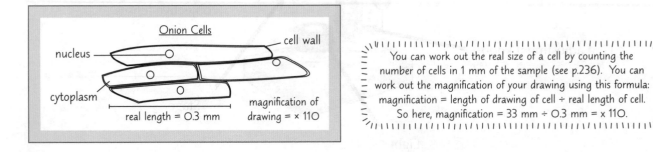

> You can work out the real size of a cell by counting the number of cells in 1 mm of the sample (see p.236). You can work out the magnification of your drawing using this formula: magnification = length of drawing of cell ÷ real length of cell. So here, magnification = 33 mm ÷ 0.3 mm = × 110.

Your microscope might look a bit different

PRACTICAL TIP

The appearance of light microscopes can <u>vary</u> (e.g. they might have two eyepieces rather than one) but they should have the <u>same basic features</u> shown on the previous page.

Warm-Up & Exam Questions

So, hopefully you've read the last five pages. But could you cope if a question on cells or microscopes came up in the exam? With amazing new technology we can simulate that very situation...

Warm-Up Questions

1) Name the subcellular structures where aerobic respiration takes place. *Mitochondria*
2) Give three ways in which animal cells are different from plant cells. *Chloroplast, cell wall*
3) Give two differences in structure between prokaryotic and eukaryotic cells. *nucleus,*
4) What type of microscope should be used to look at the internal structure of chloroplasts? *electron microscope*
5) Write the number 0.00045 µm in standard form. *4.5 × 10⁻⁴*

Exam Questions

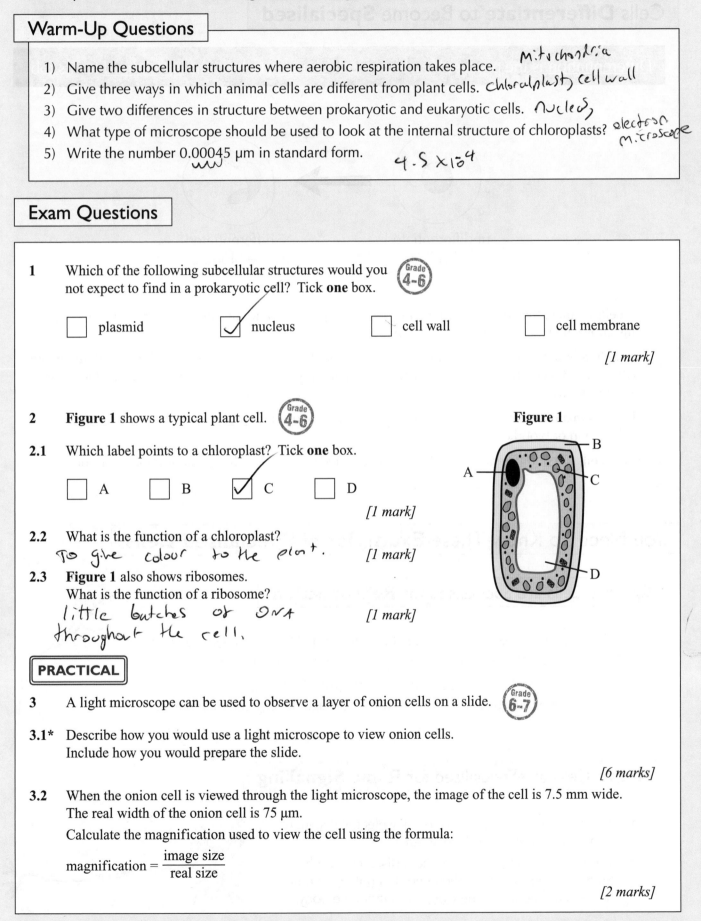

1 Which of the following subcellular structures would you not expect to find in a prokaryotic cell? Tick **one** box. *(Grade 4-6)*

☐ plasmid ☑ nucleus ☐ cell wall ☐ cell membrane

[1 mark]

2 **Figure 1** shows a typical plant cell. *(Grade 4-6)*

Figure 1

2.1 Which label points to a chloroplast? Tick **one** box.

☐ A ☐ B ☑ C ☐ D

[1 mark]

2.2 What is the function of a chloroplast? *To give colour to the plant.* *[1 mark]*

2.3 **Figure 1** also shows ribosomes.
What is the function of a ribosome? *little batches of DNA throughout the cell.* *[1 mark]*

PRACTICAL

3 A light microscope can be used to observe a layer of onion cells on a slide. *(Grade 6-7)*

3.1* Describe how you would use a light microscope to view onion cells.
Include how you would prepare the slide.

[6 marks]

3.2 When the onion cell is viewed through the light microscope, the image of the cell is 7.5 mm wide.
The real width of the onion cell is 75 µm.

Calculate the magnification used to view the cell using the formula:

$$\text{magnification} = \frac{\text{image size}}{\text{real size}}$$

[2 marks]

Cell Differentiation and Specialisation

*Cells **don't** all look the **same**. They have **different structures** to suit their **different functions**.*

Cells **Differentiate** to Become **Specialised**

Differentiation is the process by which a cell changes to become specialised for its job.

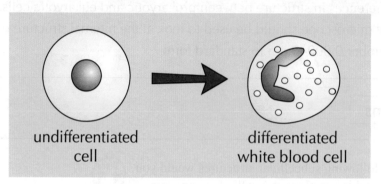

undifferentiated
cell

differentiated
white blood cell

1) As cells change, they develop different subcellular structures and turn into different types of cells. This allows them to carry out specific functions.

2) Most differentiation occurs as an organism develops. In most animal cells, the ability to differentiate is then lost at an early stage, after they become specialised. However, lots of plant cells don't ever lose this ability.

3) The cells that differentiate in mature animals are mainly used for repairing and replacing cells, such as skin or blood cells.

4) Some cells are undifferentiated cells — they're called stem cells. There's more about them on page 24.

You Need To Know These **Examples** of **Specialised Cells**

Sperm Cells are Specialised for **Reproduction**

1) The function of a sperm is basically to get the male DNA to the female DNA.
2) It has a long tail and a streamlined head to help it swim to the egg.
3) There are a lot of mitochondria in the cell to provide the energy needed.
4) It also carries enzymes in its head to digest through the egg cell membrane.

Nerve Cells are Specialised for **Rapid Signalling**

1) The function of nerve cells is to carry electrical signals from one part of the body to another.
2) These cells are long (to cover more distance) and have branched connections at their ends to connect to other nerve cells and form a network throughout the body.

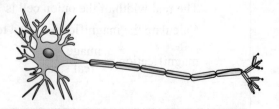

Cell Specialisation

Muscle Cells are Specialised for Contraction

1) The function of a <u>muscle cell</u> is to contract quickly.

2) These cells are <u>long</u> (so that they have space to <u>contract</u>) and contain <u>lots of mitochondria</u> to generate the <u>energy</u> needed for contraction.

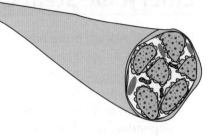

Root Hair Cells are Specialised for Absorbing Water and Minerals

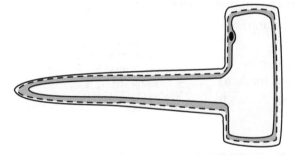

1) Root hair cells are cells on the surface of plant roots, which grow into long "<u>hairs</u>" that stick out into the soil.

2) This gives the plant a <u>big</u> <u>surface area</u> for absorbing <u>water</u> and <u>mineral ions</u> from the soil.

Phloem and Xylem Cells are Specialised for Transporting Substances

1) <u>Phloem</u> and <u>xylem cells</u> form phloem and xylem <u>tubes</u>, which <u>transport</u> substances such as <u>food</u> and <u>water</u> around plants.

2) To form the tubes, the cells are long and joined <u>end to end</u>.

3) Xylem cells are <u>hollow</u> in the centre and phloem cells have <u>very few subcellular structures</u>, so that stuff can <u>flow through</u> them.

phloem   xylem

There's more about phloem and xylem on page 74.

Cells have the same basic bits but are specialised for their function

Not all cells contain <u>all</u> of the bits shown on pages 16-17. This is because some specialised cells don't have a use for certain subcellular structures — it depends on their <u>function</u>. For example, root hair cells grow <u>underground</u> in the soil, so they <u>don't need chloroplasts</u> because they don't photosynthesise.

Stem Cells

*Stem cell research has exciting **possibilities**, but it's also pretty **controversial**.*

Embryonic Stem Cells Can Turn into ANY Type of Cell

1) <u>Differentiation</u> is the process by which a cell <u>changes</u> to become <u>specialised</u> for its job — see p.22.

2) <u>Undifferentiated</u> cells, called <u>stem cells</u>, can divide to produce lots <u>more</u> undifferentiated cells. They can differentiate into <u>different types of cell</u>, depending on what <u>instructions</u> they're given.

3) Stem cells are found in early <u>human embryos</u>. They're <u>exciting</u> to doctors and medical researchers because they have the potential to turn into <u>any</u> kind of cell at all. This makes sense if you think about it — <u>all</u> the <u>different types</u> of cell found in a human being have to come from those <u>few cells</u> in the early embryo.

4) Adults also have stem cells, but they're only found in certain places, like <u>bone marrow</u>.

5) Unlike embryonic stem cells, adult stem cells <u>can't</u> turn into <u>any</u> cell type at all — only certain ones, such as blood cells.

6) Stem cells from embryos and bone marrow can be grown in a lab to produce <u>clones</u> (<u>genetically identical cells</u>) and made to <u>differentiate</u> into specialised cells to use in <u>medicine</u> or <u>research</u>.

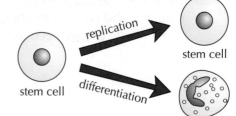

replication

stem cell

stem cell

differentiation

differentiated white blood cell

There's more about cloning animals on page 184.

Stem Cells May Be Able to Cure Many Diseases

1) Medicine already uses <u>adult stem cells</u> to cure <u>disease</u>. For example, <u>stem cells</u> transferred from the bone marrow of a <u>healthy person</u> can <u>replace faulty blood cells</u> in the patient who receives them.

2) <u>Embryonic stem cells</u> could also be used to <u>replace faulty cells</u> in sick people — you could make <u>insulin-producing cells</u> for people with <u>diabetes</u>, <u>nerve cells</u> for people <u>paralysed by spinal injuries</u>, and so on.

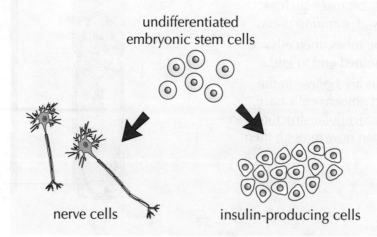

undifferentiated embryonic stem cells

nerve cells

insulin-producing cells

3) In a type of cloning, called <u>therapeutic cloning</u>, an embryo could be made to have the <u>same genetic information</u> as the patient. This means that the <u>stem cells</u> produced from it would also contain the <u>same genes</u> and so <u>wouldn't</u> be <u>rejected</u> by the patient's body if used to replace faulty cells.

4) However, there are <u>risks</u> involved in using stem cells in medicine. For example, stem cells grown in the lab may become <u>contaminated</u> with a <u>virus</u> which could be <u>passed on</u> to the patient and so make them <u>sicker</u>.

Stem Cells

Some People Are **Against Stem Cell Research**

1) Some people are <u>against</u> stem cell research because they feel that human embryos <u>shouldn't</u> be used for experiments since each one is a <u>potential human life</u>.

2) Others think that curing patients who <u>already exist</u> and who are <u>suffering</u> is more important than the rights of <u>embryos</u>.

3) They argue that the embryos used in the research are usually <u>unwanted ones</u> from <u>fertility clinics</u> which, if they weren't used for research, would probably just be <u>destroyed</u>.

4) However, campaigners for the rights of embryos feel that scientists should concentrate more on finding and developing <u>other sources</u> of stem cells, so people could be helped <u>without</u> having to use embryos.

5) In some countries stem cell research is <u>banned</u>, but it's allowed in the UK as long as it follows <u>strict guidelines</u>.

Stem Cells Can Produce **Identical Plants**

1) In plants, stem cells are found in the <u>meristems</u> (parts of the plant where <u>growth</u> occurs — see p.73).

2) Throughout the plant's <u>entire life</u>, cells in the meristem tissues can differentiate into <u>any type</u> of plant cell.

3) These stem cells can be used to produce <u>clones</u> (identical copies) of whole plants <u>quickly</u> and <u>cheaply</u>.

4) They can be used to grow more plants of <u>rare species</u> (to prevent them being wiped out).

5) Stem cells can also be used to grow crops of <u>identical</u> plants that have desired <u>features</u> for farmers, for example, <u>disease resistance</u>.

Some species of orchid are endangered in the UK. Many can be successfully reproduced by cloning using stem cells.

Alternative sources of stem cells would avoid the controversy

Research has been done into getting human stem cells from <u>other sources</u> — e.g. it may be possible to 'reprogramme' differentiated adult cells back to an undifferentiated stage. But whatever your opinion of stem cell research is, it's good to know what their <u>uses</u> are and the arguments <u>for</u> and <u>against</u> using them.

Chromosomes and Mitosis

*In order to survive and grow, our cells have got to be able to **divide**. And that means our DNA as well...*

Chromosomes Contain Genetic Information

1) Most cells in your body have a <u>nucleus</u>. The nucleus contains your <u>genetic material</u> in the form of <u>chromosomes</u>.

2) Chromosomes are <u>coiled up</u> lengths of <u>DNA molecules</u>.

3) Each chromosome carries a <u>large number</u> of genes. Different genes <u>control</u> the development of different <u>characteristics</u>, e.g. hair colour.

4) <u>Body cells</u> normally have <u>two copies</u> of each <u>chromosome</u> — one from the organism's 'mother', and one from its 'father'. So, humans have two copies of chromosome 1, two copies of chromosome 2, etc.

5) The diagram shows the <u>23 pairs of chromosomes</u> from a human cell.

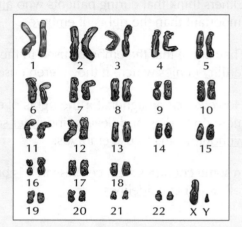

The Cell Cycle Makes Cells for Growth, Development and Repair

1) <u>Body cells</u> in <u>multicellular</u> organisms <u>divide</u> to produce new cells as part of a series of stages called the <u>cell cycle</u>.

2) The stage of the cell cycle when the cell divides is called <u>mitosis</u>.

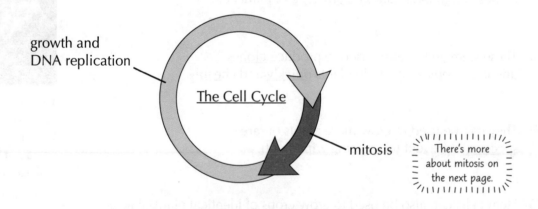

growth and DNA replication

The Cell Cycle

mitosis

There's more about mitosis on the next page.

3) Multicellular organisms use <u>mitosis</u> to <u>grow</u> or <u>replace cells</u> that have been <u>damaged</u>.

4) The end of the cell cycle results in two new cells <u>identical</u> to the <u>original</u> cell, with the <u>same number</u> of chromosomes.

The cell cycle is important for growth and repair

Not all cells are going through the cell cycle at the same time, but when a cell does go through these stages, you end up with <u>two cells</u> where you originally had just one. The body <u>closely controls</u> which cells divide and when — if this control <u>fails</u>, it can result in <u>cancer</u> (see page 71).

Chromosomes and Mitosis

*There are two main stages of the **cell cycle**...*

Growth and DNA Replication

In a cell that's not dividing, the DNA is all spread out in <u>long strings</u>.

Before it divides, the cell has to <u>grow</u> and <u>increase</u> the amount of <u>subcellular structures</u> such as <u>mitochondria</u> and <u>ribosomes</u>.

It then <u>duplicates</u> its DNA — so there's one copy for each new cell. The DNA is copied and forms <u>X-shaped</u> chromosomes. Each 'arm' of the chromosome is an <u>exact duplicate</u> of the other.

The left arm of the chromosome has the same DNA as the right arm.

Mitosis

Once its contents and DNA have been copied, the cell is ready for <u>mitosis</u>...

The chromosomes <u>line up</u> at the centre of the cell and <u>cell fibres</u> pull them apart. The <u>two arms</u> of each chromosome go to <u>opposite ends</u> of the cell.

<u>Membranes</u> form around each of the sets of chromosomes. These become the <u>nuclei</u> of the two new cells — the <u>nucleus</u> has <u>divided</u>.

Lastly, the <u>cytoplasm</u> and <u>cell membrane</u> divide.

The cell has now produced <u>two new daughter cells</u>.
The daughter cells contain exactly the <u>same DNA</u> — they're <u>identical</u>. Their DNA is also <u>identical</u> to the <u>parent cell</u>.

Mitosis produces two identical daughter cells

Mitosis can seem tricky at first. But don't worry — just go through it slowly, one step at a time.

Q1   A student looks at cells in the tip of a plant root under a microscope.
She counts 11 cells that are undergoing mitosis and 62 cells that are not.
a) Calculate the percentage of cells that are undergoing mitosis.   [1 mark]
b) Suggest how the student can tell whether a cell is undergoing mitosis or not.   [1 mark]

Q1 Video Solution

Binary Fission

*Prokaryotic cells can reproduce using a type of simple cell division called **binary fission**.*

Prokaryotic Cells Replicate by **Binary Fission**

In binary fission, the cell splits into two. There's a bit more to it than that though:

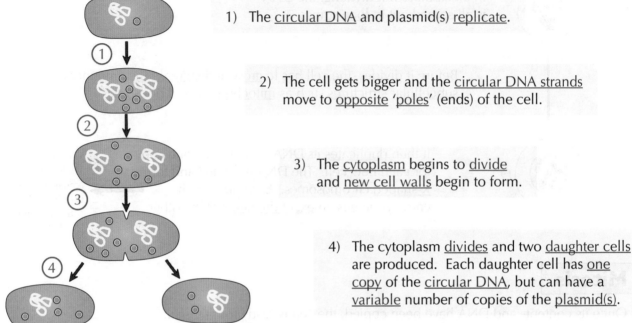

1) The circular DNA and plasmid(s) replicate.

2) The cell gets bigger and the circular DNA strands move to opposite 'poles' (ends) of the cell.

3) The cytoplasm begins to divide and new cell walls begin to form.

4) The cytoplasm divides and two daughter cells are produced. Each daughter cell has one copy of the circular DNA, but can have a variable number of copies of the plasmid(s).

Bacteria can divide very quickly if given the right conditions (e.g. a warm environment and lots of nutrients). Some bacteria, such as *E. coli*, can take as little as 20 minutes to replicate in the right environment. However, if conditions become unfavourable, the cells will stop dividing and eventually begin to die.

You can **Calculate** the **Number of Bacteria** in a **Population**

The mean division time is the average amount of time it takes for one bacterial cell to divide into two. If you know the mean division time of a cell, you can work out how many times it has divided in a certain amount of time, and so the number of cells it has produced in that time.

EXAMPLE **A bacterial cell has a mean division time of 30 minutes. How many cells will it have produced after 2.5 hours?**

1) Make sure both times are in the same units.

2.5 hours × 60 = 150 minutes.

2) Divide the total time that the bacteria are producing cells by the mean division time. This gives you the number of divisions.

150 minutes ÷ 30 minutes = 5 divisions

3) Multiply 2 by itself for the number of divisions to find the number of cells.

$2^5 = 2 × 2 × 2 × 2 × 2 = 32$ cells

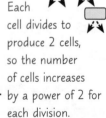

Each cell divides to produce 2 cells, so the number of cells increases by a power of 2 for each division.

Binary = two parts, fission = splitting

Q1   Give two things that help to maximise the rate of binary fission. [2 marks]

Q2   *E. coli* is a type of bacteria. The mean division time of an *E. coli* cell is 20 minutes. How many cells will a single *E. coli* cell produce in 2 hours and 40 minutes? [2 marks]

Q2 Video Solution

Warm-Up & Exam Questions

There's only one way to do well in the exam — learn the facts and then practise lots of exam questions to see what it'll be like on the big day. We couldn't have made it easier for you — so do it.

Warm-Up Questions

1) What does cell 'differentiation' mean?
2) Describe how a root hair cell is specialised for its function.
3) How can stem cells be used to preserve rare plant species?
4) Where in the cell are chromosomes found?
5) What type of cell replicates by binary fission — prokaryotic or eukaryotic?

Exam Questions

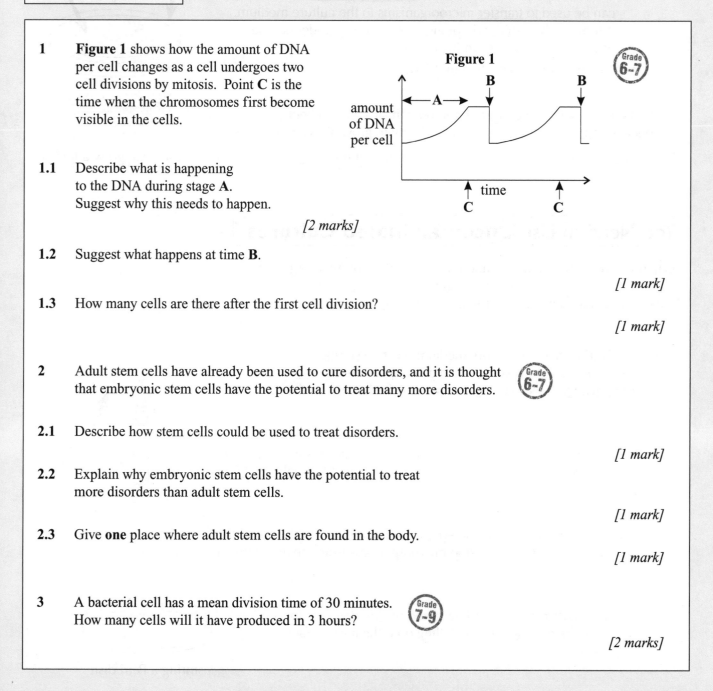

1 **Figure 1** shows how the amount of DNA per cell changes as a cell undergoes two cell divisions by mitosis. Point **C** is the time when the chromosomes first become visible in the cells.

Figure 1

Grade 6-7

amount of DNA per cell

time

1.1 Describe what is happening to the DNA during stage **A**. Suggest why this needs to happen.

[2 marks]

1.2 Suggest what happens at time **B**.

[1 mark]

1.3 How many cells are there after the first cell division?

[1 mark]

2 Adult stem cells have already been used to cure disorders, and it is thought that embryonic stem cells have the potential to treat many more disorders.

Grade 6-7

2.1 Describe how stem cells could be used to treat disorders.

[1 mark]

2.2 Explain why embryonic stem cells have the potential to treat more disorders than adult stem cells.

[1 mark]

2.3 Give **one** place where adult stem cells are found in the body.

[1 mark]

3 A bacterial cell has a mean division time of 30 minutes. How many cells will it have produced in 3 hours?

Grade 7-9

[2 marks]

PRACTICAL Culturing Microorganisms

*And now for some hands-on stuff. You can **grow your own** microorganisms and test how **effective** different **antibiotics**, **antiseptics** or **disinfectants** are at killing them...*

You Can **Grow Bacteria** in the Lab

1) Bacteria (and some other microorganisms) are grown (cultured) in a "<u>culture medium</u>", which contains the <u>carbohydrates</u>, <u>minerals</u>, <u>proteins</u> and <u>vitamins</u> they need to grow.

2) The culture medium used can be a <u>nutrient broth solution</u> or solid <u>agar jelly</u>.

3) Bacteria grown on agar 'plates' will form visible <u>colonies</u> on the <u>surface</u> of the jelly, or will <u>spread out</u> to give an even covering of bacteria.

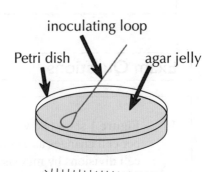

- To make an agar plate, <u>hot</u> agar jelly is poured into shallow round plastic dishes called <u>Petri dishes</u>.
- When the jelly's cooled and set, <u>inoculating loops</u> (wire loops) can be used to <u>transfer</u> microorganisms to the culture medium. Alternatively, a <u>sterile dropping pipette</u> and <u>spreader</u> can be used to get an <u>even covering</u> of bacteria.
- The microorganisms then <u>multiply</u>.

4) In the <u>lab at school</u>, cultures of microorganisms are not kept <u>above 25 °C</u>, because <u>harmful pathogens</u> are more likely to grow above this temperature.

Pathogens are microorganisms that cause disease (see p.81).

5) In <u>industrial conditions</u>, cultures are incubated at <u>higher temperatures</u> so that they can grow a lot faster.

You Need to Use **Uncontaminated Cultures**

When you're doing an investigation using a culture of microorganisms, <u>contamination</u> by <u>unwanted</u> microorganisms will <u>affect your results</u>. It can also potentially result in the growth of <u>pathogens</u>. To <u>avoid</u> this:

1) The Petri dishes and culture medium must be <u>sterilised</u> before use (e.g. by heating to a high temperature), to <u>kill</u> any <u>unwanted microorganisms</u> that may be lurking on them.

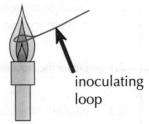

2) If an <u>inoculating loop</u> is used to transfer the bacteria to the culture medium, it should be <u>sterilised</u> first by <u>passing it through a hot flame</u>.

inoculating loop

3) After transferring the bacteria, the lid of the Petri dish should be <u>lightly taped on</u> — to stop microorganisms from the air getting in.

4) The Petri dish should be stored <u>upside down</u> — to <u>stop</u> drops of <u>condensation</u> falling onto the agar surface.

storing a Petri dish

Culturing Microorganisms

You Can Investigate the **Effect** of **Antibiotics** on **Bacterial Growth**

You can test the action of antibiotics (or antiseptics) on cultures of bacteria:

1) Place paper discs soaked in different types (or different concentrations) of antibiotics on an agar plate that has an even covering of bacteria. Leave some space between the discs.

2) The antibiotic should diffuse (soak) into the agar jelly. Antibiotic-resistant bacteria (i.e. bacteria that aren't affected by the antibiotic — see p.90) will continue to grow on the agar around the paper discs, but non-resistant strains will die. A clear area will be left where the bacteria have died — this is called an inhibition zone.

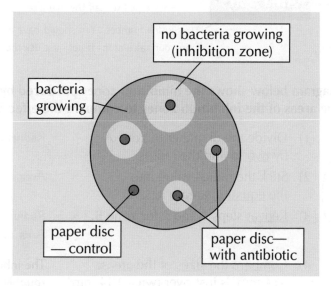

3) Make sure you use a control. This is a paper disc that has not been soaked in an antibiotic. Instead, soak it in sterile water. You can then be sure that any difference between the growth of the bacteria around the control disc and around one of the antibiotic discs is due to the effect of the antibiotic alone (and not something weird in the paper, for example).

4) Leave the plate for 48 hours at 25 °C.

5) The more effective the antibiotic is against the bacteria, the larger the inhibition zone will be — see next page.

The size of the inhibition zone shows how effective the antibiotic is

If you're comparing a few antibiotics, then the one with the largest clear zone is the most effective. Have a look at the next page to see how to work out the cross-sectional area of the clear zone.

PRACTICAL # Culturing Microorganisms

*Once you've got your **results**, you need to **analyse** them...*

Calculate the Sizes of the Inhibition Zones to Compare Results

You can <u>compare</u> the <u>effectiveness</u> of different antibiotics (or antiseptics) on bacteria by looking at the <u>relative sizes</u> of the <u>inhibition zones</u>. The <u>larger</u> the inhibition zone around a disc, the <u>more effective</u> the antibiotic is against the bacteria.

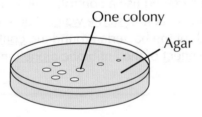

You can do this <u>by eye</u> if there are large differences in size. But to get more accurate results it's a good idea to calculate the <u>area</u> of the inhibition zones using their <u>diameter</u> (the distance <u>across</u>).

Don't open the Petri dish to measure the inhibition zones — they should be visible through the bottom of the dish.

To calculate the area of an inhibition zone, you need to use <u>this equation</u>:

This is the equation for the area of a circle. You're likely to use the units cm^2 or mm^2.

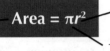

$$\text{Area} = \pi r^2$$

r is the radius of the inhibition zone — it's equal to half the diameter.

π is just a number. You should have a button for it on your calculator. If not, just use the value 3.14.

EXAMPLE

The diagram below shows the inhibition zones produced by antibiotics A and B. Use the areas of the inhibition zones to compare the effectiveness of the antibiotics.

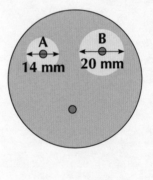

A B
14 mm 20 mm

1) Divide the diameter of zone A by <u>two</u> to find the <u>radius</u>.

2) Stick the radius value into the <u>equation</u> area = π*r*².

3) <u>Repeat</u> steps 1 and 2 for zone B.

4) <u>Compare</u> the <u>sizes</u> of the <u>areas</u>. 314 mm² is just over twice 154 mm², so you could say that:

Radius of A = 14 ÷ 2 = 7 mm

Area of A = π × 7² = 154 mm²

Radius of B = 20 ÷ 2 = 10 mm
Area of B = π × 10² = 314 mm²

The inhibition zone of antibiotic B is roughly twice the size of the inhibition zone of antibiotic A.

You Can Also Find the Area of a Colony

The equation above can also be used to calculate the <u>area</u> of a bacterial <u>colony</u>. You just need to measure the <u>diameter</u> of the colony you are interested in first.

One colony

Agar

The greater the area, the more effective the antibiotic

Q1 Helena investigated the effect of four different concentrations (A-D) of an antiseptic on the growth of bacteria. The diagram on the right shows the results.

a) Suggest which concentration of antiseptic was the strongest. [1 mark]

b) Calculate the size of the inhibition zone for Concentration C. Give your answer to the nearest mm². [2 marks]

c) Suggest what Helena used as a control in this investigation. [1 mark]

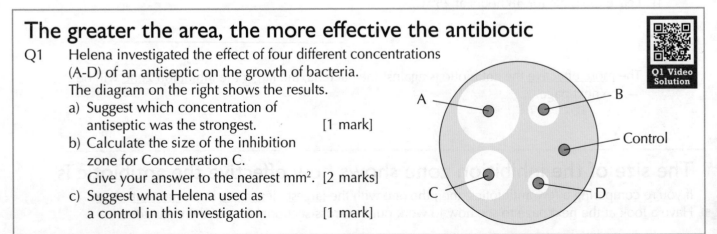

Q1 Video Solution

A
B
Control
C
D

Warm-Up & Exam Questions

Just like bacteria, this topic can grow on you. Here are some questions to enjoy now, you lucky thing...

Warm-Up Questions

1) What lab equipment can be used to transfer microorganisms to an agar jelly culture medium?
2) Why is it important to sterilise Petri dishes and culture medium before use?

Exam Questions

1   A researcher was investigating the effect of different antiseptics on the growth of bacteria. He soaked four paper discs in different antiseptics. **Figure 1** shows the results.

Grade 6-7

Figure 1

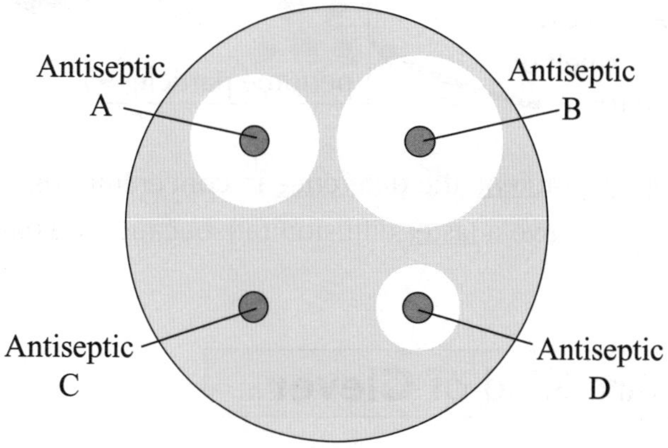

Antiseptic A

Antiseptic B

Antiseptic C

Antiseptic D

1.1   Which antiseptic was most effective against the bacteria?

[1 mark]

1.2   Explain why the researcher should have used a control.

[1 mark]

2   A student was investigating the effectiveness of different antibiotics on a strain of bacteria.

The student placed paper discs soaked in the different antibiotics on an agar plate that had an even covering of the bacteria. The results are shown in **Table 1**.

Grade 6-7

Table 1

Antibiotic	X	Y	Z
Diameter of inhibition zone (mm)	15	9	0

2.1   Calculate the area of the inhibition zone for antibiotic X. Give your answer in mm². Use the equation: area = πr^2

[2 marks]

2.2   No inhibition zone was formed around the disc soaked in antibiotic Z. Suggest a reason why.

[1 mark]

Diffusion

*Diffusion is **really important** in living organisms — it's how a lot of **substances** get **in** and **out** of cells.*

Don't be Put Off by the **Fancy Word**

1) Diffusion is simple. It's just the gradual movement of particles from places where there are lots of them to places where there are fewer of them.

2) That's all it is — just the natural tendency for stuff to spread out.

3) Unfortunately you also have to learn the fancy way of saying the same thing, which is this:

> Diffusion is the spreading out of particles from an area of higher concentration to an area of lower concentration.

4) Diffusion happens in both solutions and gases — that's because the particles in these substances are free to move about randomly.

5) The simplest type is when different gases diffuse through each other. This is what's happening when the smell of perfume diffuses through a room:

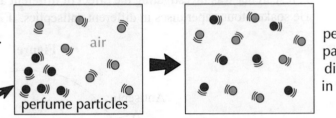

perfume particles

air

perfume particles diffused in the air

> The bigger the concentration gradient (the difference in concentration), the faster the diffusion rate.
> A higher temperature will also give a faster diffusion rate because the particles have more energy, so move around faster.

Cell Membranes Are Kind of **Clever**...

1) They're clever because they hold the cell together but they let stuff in and out as well.

2) Dissolved substances can move in and out of cells by diffusion.

3) Only very small molecules can diffuse through cell membranes though — things like oxygen (needed for respiration — see page 112), glucose, amino acids and water.

4) Big molecules like starch and proteins can't fit through the membrane:

5) Just like with diffusion in air, particles flow through the cell membrane from where there's a higher concentration (a lot of them) to where there's a lower concentration (not such a lot of them).

protein

starch

glucose

amino acid

6) They're only moving about randomly of course, so they go both ways — but if there are a lot more particles on one side of the membrane, there's a net (overall) movement from that side.

> The larger the surface area of the membrane, the faster the diffusion rate because more particles can pass through at once — see page 39.

Diffusion is just particles spreading out

Really tiny particles can go through cell membranes to even up the concentration on either side.

Q1 A student adds a drop of ink to a glass of cold water.
a) What will the student observe to happen to the drop of ink. Explain your answer. [2 marks]
b) How might the observation differ if the ink was added to a glass of warm water?   [1 mark]

Q1 Video Solution

Osmosis

*If you've got your head round **diffusion**, osmosis will be a **breeze**.*
If not, have another look at the previous page...

Osmosis is a **Special Case** of **Diffusion**, That's All

Learn this definition of osmosis:

> Osmosis is the <u>movement of water molecules</u> across a
> <u>partially permeable membrane</u> from a region of <u>higher water
> concentration</u> to a region of <u>lower water concentration</u>.

1) A <u>partially permeable</u> membrane is just one with very small holes in it.
   So small, in fact, only tiny <u>molecules</u> (like water) can pass through them,
   and bigger molecules (e.g. <u>sucrose</u>) can't.

2) The water molecules actually pass <u>both ways</u> through the membrane during osmosis.
   This happens because water molecules <u>move about randomly</u> all the time.

3) But because there are <u>more</u> water molecules on one side than on the other,
   there's a steady <u>net flow</u> of water into the region with <u>fewer</u> water molecules,
   i.e. into the <u>stronger</u> sugar solution.

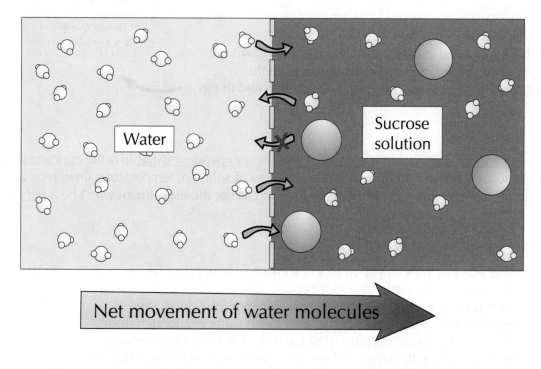

Net movement of water molecules

4) This means the <u>strong sugar</u> solution gets more <u>dilute</u>. The water acts like
   it's trying to "<u>even up</u>" the concentration either side of the membrane.

5) Osmosis is a type of <u>diffusion</u> — passive movement of <u>water particles</u> from
   an area of <u>higher water concentration</u> to an area of <u>lower water concentration</u>.

Diffusion is movement from where there's lots to where there's few...

...so osmosis is really just a fancy word for the <u>diffusion of water molecules</u>. It's simple really.

Osmosis

*There's an **experiment** you can do to show osmosis at work.*

You can **Observe** the Effect of **Sugar Solutions** on **Plant Tissue**

1) Cut up a <u>potato</u> into identical cylinders, and get some beakers with <u>different sugar solutions</u> in them. One should be <u>pure water</u> and another should be a <u>very concentrated sugar solution</u> (e.g. 1 mol/dm³). Then you can have a few others with concentrations <u>in between</u> (e.g. 0.2 mol/dm³, 0.4 mol/dm³, 0.6 mol/dm³, etc.)

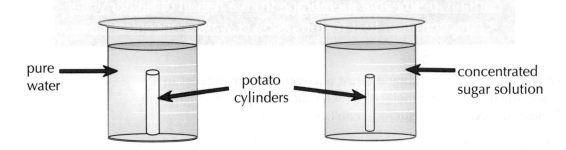

pure water →   potato cylinders   ← concentrated sugar solution

2) You measure the <u>mass</u> of the cylinders, then leave one cylinder in each beaker for twenty four hours or so.

3) Then you take them out, <u>dry</u> them with a paper towel and measure their masses <u>again</u>.

> By calculating the percentage change (see p.237), you can compare the effect of sugar concentration on cylinders that didn't have the same initial mass. An increase in mass will give a positive percentage change and a decrease will give a negative percentage change.

4) If the cylinders have drawn in water by osmosis, they'll have <u>increased in mass</u>. If water has been drawn out, they'll have <u>decreased in mass</u>. You can calculate the <u>percentage change in mass</u>, then plot a few <u>graphs</u> and things.

The <u>dependent variable</u> is the <u>chip mass</u> and the <u>independent variable</u> is the <u>concentration</u> of the sugar solution. All <u>other</u> variables (volume of solution, temperature, time, type of sugar used, etc.) must be kept the <u>same</u> in each case or the experiment won't be a <u>fair test</u>.

Like any experiment, you need to be aware of how <u>errors</u> (see p.7) may arise. Sometimes they may occur when <u>carrying out the method</u>, e.g. if some potato cylinders were not <u>fully dried</u>, the excess water would give a <u>higher mass</u>, or if water <u>evaporated</u> from the beakers, the <u>concentrations</u> of the sugar solutions would change. You can <u>reduce the effect</u> of these errors by <u>repeating</u> the experiment and calculating a <u>mean percentage change</u> at each concentration.

> You could also carry out this experiment using different salt solutions and see what effect they have on potato chip mass.

Osmosis is the reason why it's bad to drink sea-water...

The high <u>salt</u> content means you end up with a much <u>lower water concentration</u> in your blood and tissue fluid than in your cells. All the water is sucked out of your cells and they <u>shrivel and die</u>.

Q1   Explain what will happen to the mass of a piece of potato added to a concentrated salt solution.   [2 marks]

Q1 Video Solution

Active Transport

*Sometimes substances need to be absorbed against a concentration gradient, i.e. from a lower to a higher concentration. This process is referred to as **active transport**.*

Root Hairs Take In **Minerals** and **Water**

<u>Root Hair Cell</u>

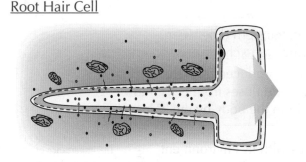

1) As you saw on page 23, the cells on plant roots grow into "<u>hairs</u>" which stick out into the soil.

2) Each branch of a root will be covered in <u>millions</u> of these microscopic hairs.

3) This gives the plant a <u>large surface area</u> for absorbing <u>water</u> and <u>mineral ions</u> from the soil.

4) Plants <u>need</u> these mineral ions for <u>healthy growth</u>.

5) The concentration of minerals is usually <u>higher</u> in the <u>root hair</u> cells than in the <u>soil</u> around them.

6) So the root hair cells <u>can't</u> use <u>diffusion</u> to take up minerals from the soil.

Root Hairs Take in Minerals Using **Active Transport**

1) Minerals should move <u>out</u> of the root hairs if they followed the rules of diffusion. The cells must use another method to draw them in.

2) That method is a process called "<u>active transport</u>".

3) Active transport allows the plant to absorb minerals from a very <u>dilute</u> solution, <u>against</u> a concentration gradient. This is essential for its growth. But active transport needs <u>energy</u> from <u>respiration</u> to make it work.

4) Active transport also happens in <u>humans</u>, for example in taking <u>glucose</u> from the <u>gut</u> (see below), and from the <u>kidney tubules</u>.

> Water is taken into root hair cells by osmosis (see page 35).

We Need **Active Transport** to Stop Us Starving

<u>Active transport</u> is used in the gut when there is a <u>lower concentration</u> of nutrients in the <u>gut</u>, but a <u>higher concentration</u> of nutrients in the <u>blood</u>.

1) When there's <u>a higher concentration</u> of glucose and amino acids in the gut they <u>diffuse naturally</u> into the blood.

2) <u>BUT</u> — sometimes there's a <u>lower concentration</u> of nutrients in the gut than there is in the blood.

3) This means that the <u>concentration gradient</u> is the wrong way.

4) The same process used in plant roots is used here — <u>active transport</u>.

5) Active transport allows nutrients to be taken into the blood, despite the fact that the <u>concentration gradient</u> is the wrong way.

Inside the gut

Inside the blood

This means that <u>glucose</u> can be taken into the bloodstream when its concentration in the blood is already <u>higher</u> than in the gut. It can then be transported to cells, where it's used for <u>respiration</u> (see p.110).

Active transport uses energy

An important difference between <u>active transport</u> and <u>diffusion</u> is that active transport uses <u>energy</u>.

Exchanging Substances

*How easily stuff **moves** between an **organism** and its **environment** depends on its **surface area to volume ratio**.*

Organisms **Exchange Substances** with their **Environment**

1) Cells can use diffusion to take in substances they need and get rid of waste products.
   For example:

   > • Oxygen and carbon dioxide are transferred between cells and the environment during gas exchange.
   >
   > • In humans, urea (a waste product produced from the breakdown of proteins, see p.135) diffuses from cells into the blood plasma for removal from the body by the kidneys.

2) How easy it is for an organism to exchange substances with its environment depends on the organism's surface area to volume ratio (SA : V).

The importance of an organism's SA : V is explained on the next page.

You Can Compare **Surface Area to Volume Ratios**

A ratio shows how big one value is compared to another. The larger an organism is, the smaller its surface area is compared to its volume. You can show this by calculating surface area to volume ratios:

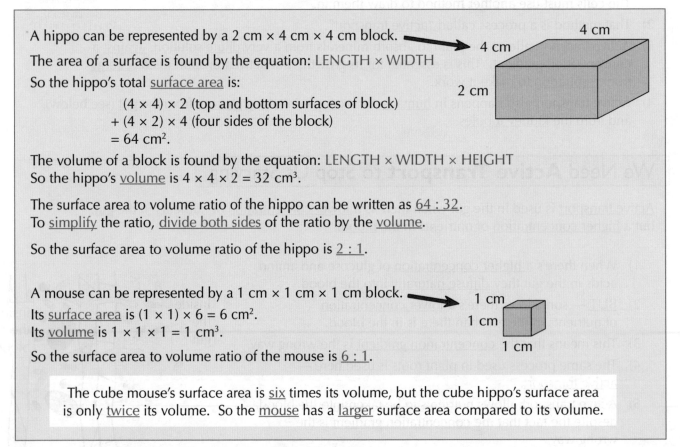

A hippo can be represented by a 2 cm × 4 cm × 4 cm block.

The area of a surface is found by the equation: LENGTH × WIDTH

So the hippo's total surface area is:

$(4 \times 4) \times 2$ (top and bottom surfaces of block)
$+ (4 \times 2) \times 4$ (four sides of the block)
$= 64 \text{ cm}^2$.

The volume of a block is found by the equation: LENGTH × WIDTH × HEIGHT
So the hippo's volume is $4 \times 4 \times 2 = 32 \text{ cm}^3$.

The surface area to volume ratio of the hippo can be written as 64 : 32.
To simplify the ratio, divide both sides of the ratio by the volume.

So the surface area to volume ratio of the hippo is 2 : 1.

A mouse can be represented by a 1 cm × 1 cm × 1 cm block.
Its surface area is $(1 \times 1) \times 6 = 6 \text{ cm}^2$.
Its volume is $1 \times 1 \times 1 = 1 \text{ cm}^3$.

So the surface area to volume ratio of the mouse is 6 : 1.

> The cube mouse's surface area is six times its volume, but the cube hippo's surface area is only twice its volume. So the mouse has a larger surface area compared to its volume.

Surface area to volume ratios crop up a lot in biology...

...so it's a good idea to try to understand them now. Remember that, generally speaking, a smaller object has a larger surface area to volume ratio than a bigger object.

Q1 A bacterial cell can be represented by a 2 μm × 2 μm × 1 μm block.
Calculate the cell's surface area to volume ratio. [3 marks]

Q1 Video Solution

Exchanging Substances

Multicellular Organisms Need Exchange Surfaces

1) In single-celled organisms, gases and dissolved substances can diffuse directly into (or out of) the cell across the cell membrane. It's because they have a large surface area compared to their volume, so enough substances can be exchanged across the membrane to supply the volume of the cell.

2) Multicellular organisms have a smaller surface area compared to their volume — not enough substances can diffuse from their outside surface to supply their entire volume. This means they need some sort of exchange surface for efficient diffusion (see below and pages 40-41 for some examples). The exchange surface structures have to allow enough of the necessary substances to pass through.

3) Exchange surfaces are adapted to maximise effectiveness:

   • They have a thin membrane, so substances only have a short distance to diffuse.
   • They have a large surface area so lots of a substance can diffuse at once.
   • Exchange surfaces in animals have lots of blood vessels, to get stuff into and out of the blood quickly.
   • Gas exchange surfaces in animals (e.g. alveoli) are often ventilated too — air moves in and out.

Gas Exchange Happens in the Lungs

1) The job of the lungs is to transfer oxygen to the blood and to remove waste carbon dioxide from it.

2) To do this the lungs contain millions of little air sacs called alveoli where gas exchange takes place.

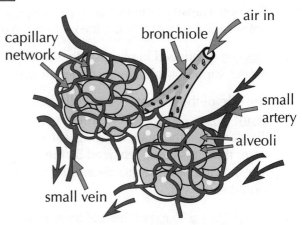

Blue = blood with carbon dioxide.
Red = blood with oxygen.

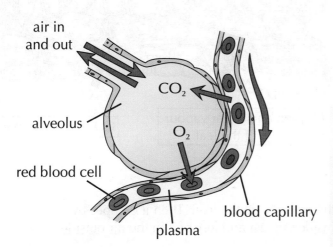

3) The alveoli are specialised to maximise the diffusion of oxygen and CO_2. They have:
   • An enormous surface area (about 75 m² in humans).
   • A moist lining for dissolving gases.
   • Very thin walls.
   • A good blood supply.

Humans need alveoli for gas exchange

You might well get asked to explain how the adaptations of the alveoli help gas exchange, so make sure you know what those adaptations are and why they affect the rate of diffusion. There are some more structures you need to know about coming up on the next couple of pages...

More on Exchanging Substances

The Villi Provide a Really Big Surface Area

1) The inside of the <u>small intestine</u> is covered in millions and millions of these tiny little projections called <u>villi</u>.

2) They increase the surface area in a big way so that digested food is <u>absorbed</u> much more quickly into the <u>blood</u>.

3) Notice they have:

- a <u>single</u> layer of surface cells
- a very good <u>blood supply</u> to assist <u>quick absorption</u>.

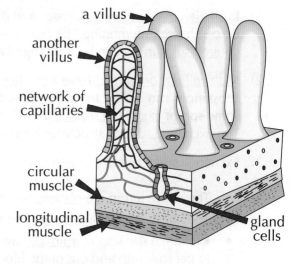

> The digested food moves into the blood by diffusion and by active transport (see page 37).

The Structure of Leaves Lets Gases Diffuse In and Out of Cells

Carbon dioxide <u>diffuses into the air spaces</u> within the leaf, then it <u>diffuses into the cells</u> where photosynthesis happens. The leaf's structure is <u>adapted</u> so that this can happen easily:

1) The underneath of the leaf is an <u>exchange surface</u>. It's covered in little holes called <u>stomata</u> which the carbon dioxide diffuses in through.

2) <u>Oxygen</u> (produced in photosynthesis) and <u>water vapour</u> also diffuse <u>out</u> through the stomata. (Water vapour is actually lost from all over the leaf surface, but most of it is lost through the stomata.)

3) The size of the stomata is controlled by <u>guard cells</u> — see page 77. These <u>close</u> the stomata if the plant is losing water faster than it is being replaced by the roots. Without these guard cells the plant would soon <u>wilt</u>.

4) The <u>flattened shape</u> of the leaf increases the <u>area</u> of this exchange surface so that it's more effective.

5) The <u>walls of the cells</u> inside the leaf form another exchange surface. The <u>air spaces</u> inside the leaf increase the <u>area</u> of this surface so there's more chance for carbon dioxide to get into the cells.

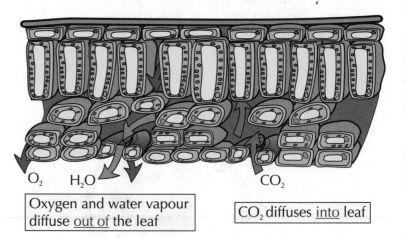

O_2 H_2O CO_2

| Oxygen and water vapour diffuse <u>out of</u> the leaf | CO_2 diffuses <u>into</u> leaf |

> The water vapour <u>evaporates</u> from the cells inside the leaf. Then it escapes by <u>diffusion</u> because there's a lot of it <u>inside</u> the leaf and less of it in the <u>air outside</u>.

Big surface areas mean substances can diffuse through quickly

Q1 In terms of gas exchange, explain why the flat shape of a leaf increases the rate at which a plant can photosynthesise. [2 marks]

Q2 Coeliac disease causes inflammation of the small intestine, which can damage the villi. Suggest why a person with coeliac disease might have low levels of iron in their blood. [2 marks]

Q2 Video Solution

More on Exchanging Substances

*It's not just **humans** and **plants** that need specialised surfaces for gas exchange.*
***Fish** need an exchange surface that allows them to **efficiently** exchange gases **underwater**.*

Gills Have a **Large Surface Area** for **Gas Exchange**

1) The gills are the gas exchange surface in fish.

2) Water (containing oxygen) enters the fish through its mouth and passes out through the gills. As this happens, oxygen diffuses from the water into the blood in the gills and carbon dioxide diffuses from the blood into the water.

3) Each gill is made of lots of thin plates called gill filaments, which give a big surface area for exchange of gases.

4) The gill filaments are covered in lots of tiny structures called lamellae, which increase the surface area even more.

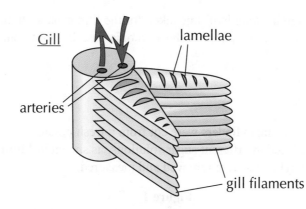

5) The lamellae have lots of blood capillaries to speed up diffusion.

6) They also have a thin surface layer of cells to minimise the distance that the gases have to diffuse.

7) Blood flows through the lamellae in one direction and water flows over in the opposite direction. This maintains a large concentration gradient between the water and the blood.

8) The concentration of oxygen in the water is always higher than that in the blood, so as much oxygen as possible diffuses from the water into the blood.

Exchange surfaces are specialised for efficient diffusion

Multicellular organisms are really well adapted for getting the substances they need to their cells. It makes sense — if they couldn't do this well, they'd die out. A large surface area is a key way that organisms' exchange surfaces are made more effective — molecules can only diffuse through a membrane when they're right next to it, and a large surface area means that a lot more molecules are close to the membrane.

Warm-Up & Exam Questions

Question time again — Warm-Up first, then Exam (or the other way round if you want to be different).

Warm-Up Questions

1) Explain why temperature affects the rate of diffusion.
2) Explain what is meant by a partially permeable membrane.
3) Other than diffusion, by what two processes do substances move across exchange surfaces?
4) Give four ways in which exchange surfaces in animals are adapted to maximise their effectiveness.
5) Name two exchange surfaces in humans.
6) Give two ways in which the structure of a gill is adapted for effective gas exchange.

Exam Questions

1   In a fume cupboard, a student injects a sample of ammonia gas into one end of a glass tube. A piece of damp litmus paper in the opposite end of the tube turns blue when the ammonia gas reaches it. It takes 35 seconds for the litmus paper to turn completely blue. *(Grade 6-7)*

Suggest what will happen to the length of time taken for the litmus paper to turn completely blue if the student injects a greater amount of the ammonia gas. Explain your answer.

[3 marks]

PRACTICAL

2   In an experiment, four 5 cm long cylinders were cut from a fresh potato. The cylinders were then placed in different sugar solutions, as shown in **Figure 1**. After 24 hours the potato cylinders were removed and measured.

Figure 1

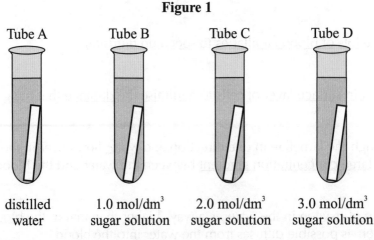

| Tube A | Tube B | Tube C | Tube D |

| distilled water | 1.0 mol/dm³ sugar solution | 2.0 mol/dm³ sugar solution | 3.0 mol/dm³ sugar solution |

2.1   Which potato cylinder would you expect to be shortest after 24 hours? Explain your answer.

[2 marks]

2.2   The potato cylinder in tube A increased in length during the 24 hours. Explain why this happened.

[2 marks]

Exam Questions

3 **Figure 2** shows a villus from the small intestine.
Glucose and other products of digestion are absorbed into the blood through the villi.

Figure 2

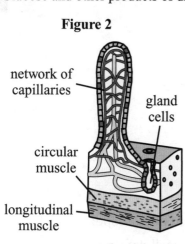

network of capillaries

gland cells

circular muscle

longitudinal muscle

3.1 Suggest how the products of digestion move into the blood.

[2 marks]

3.2 Explain how the structure of villi is related to their function.

[3 marks]

4 A student made up some gelatine with cresol red solution and ammonium hydroxide.
Cresol red solution is a pH indicator that is red in alkaline solutions and yellow in acidic solutions. The student cut the gelatine into cubes of different sizes, and placed the cubes in a beaker of dilute hydrochloric acid. He measured how long it took for the cubes to change from red to yellow as the acid moved into the gelatine and neutralised the ammonium hydroxide.
His results are shown in **Table 1**.

Table 1

Size of cube (mm)	Time taken for cube to become yellow (s)			
	Trial 1	Trial 2	Trial 3	Trial 4
$5 \times 5 \times 5$	174	167	177	182
$7 \times 7 \times 7$	274	290	284	292
$10 \times 10 \times 10$	835	825	842	838

4.1 Name the process by which hydrochloric acid moves into the gelatine cubes in this experiment.

[1 mark]

4.2 Calculate the mean time for a $10 \times 10 \times 10$ mm gelatine cube to become yellow in this experiment.

[2 marks]

4.3 Calculate the surface area to volume ratio of a $10 \times 10 \times 10$ mm cube.
Give the ratio in its simplest form.

[3 marks]

4.4 Describe and explain the relationship between the size of the gelatine cube and the time taken for the cube to become yellow.

[3 marks]

Revision Summary for Topic 1

Well, that's <u>Topic 1</u> done. Now there's only one way to find out whether you've learnt anything from it. And you know what that is. It's obvious... there's a load of questions staring you in the face.

For even more practice, try the Retrieval Quiz for Topic 1 — just scan this QR code!

Topic 1 Quiz

- Try these questions and <u>tick off each one</u> when you <u>get it right</u>.
- When you're <u>completely happy</u> with a sub-topic, tick it off.

Cells and Microscopy (p.16-20) ☑

1) Name five subcellular structures that both plant and animal cells have. ☑
2) What three things do plant cells have that animal cells don't? ☑
3) Where is the genetic material found in:
   a) animal cells,
   b) bacterial cells? ☑
4) What type of organisms are bacteria — prokaryotes or eukaryotes? ☑
5) Which gives a higher resolution — a light microscope or an electron microscope? ☑
6) How have electron microscopes increased our understanding of subcellular structures? ☑

Differentiation (p.22-23) ☑

7) Why do cells differentiate? ☑
8) Give three ways that a sperm cell is adapted for swimming to an egg cell. ☑
9) Draw a diagram of a nerve cell. Why is it this shape? ☑

Stem Cells (p.24-25) ☑

10) Give two ways that embryonic stem cells could be used to cure diseases. ☑
11) Why might some people be opposed to the use of human embryos in stem cell research? ☑

Cell Division (p.26-28) ☑

12) What are chromosomes? ☑
13) What is the cell cycle? ☑
14) What is mitosis used for by multicellular organisms? ☑
15) What is the name of the process by which bacteria divide? ☑

Culturing Microorganisms (p.30-32) ☑

16) What is the maximum temperature at which microorganisms in a school lab should be grown? ☑
17) There are ways in which you can make sure an experiment testing the effect of antibiotics on bacteria has not been contaminated. Give three of these ways. ☑

Exchanging Substances (p.34-41) ☑

18) What is diffusion? ☑
19) Name three substances that can diffuse through cell membranes, and two that can't. ☑
20) What type of molecules move by osmosis? ☑
21) Give the two main differences between active transport and diffusion. ☑
22) Give one way in which alveoli are adapted for gas exchange. ☑
23) Give two ways that the villi in the small intestine are adapted for absorbing digested food. ☑
24) Explain how leaves are adapted to maximise the amount of carbon dioxide that gets to their cells. ☑

Cell Organisation

*Some organisms contain loads of **cells**, but how, you might wonder, do all these cells mean you end up with a working human... the answer's **organisation**.*

Large Multicellular Organisms are Made Up of Organ Systems

1) <u>Cells</u> are the <u>basic building blocks</u> that make up <u>all living organisms</u>.
2) As you know from page 22, <u>specialised cells</u> carry out a <u>particular function</u>.
3) The <u>process</u> by which cells become specialised for a particular job is called <u>differentiation</u>.

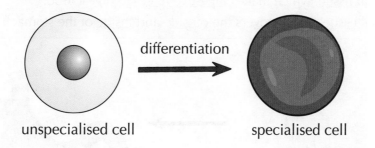

unspecialised cell   specialised cell

4) Differentiation occurs during the <u>development</u> of a multicellular organism.
5) These specialised cells form <u>tissues</u>, which form <u>organs</u>, which form <u>organ systems</u> (see below and next page).
6) <u>Large multicellular organisms</u> (e.g. humans) have different <u>systems</u> inside them for <u>exchanging</u> and <u>transporting</u> materials.

Similar Cells are Organised into Tissues

1) A <u>tissue</u> is a <u>group</u> of <u>similar cells</u> that work together to carry out a particular <u>function</u>.
2) It can include <u>more than one type</u> of cell.
3) In <u>mammals</u> (like humans), examples of tissues include:

> • <u>Muscular tissue</u>, which <u>contracts</u> (shortens) to <u>move</u> whatever it's attached to.
> • <u>Glandular tissue</u>, which <u>makes</u> and <u>secretes</u> chemicals like <u>enzymes</u> and <u>hormones</u>.
> • <u>Epithelial tissue</u>, which <u>covers</u> some parts of the body, e.g. the <u>inside</u> of the <u>gut</u>.

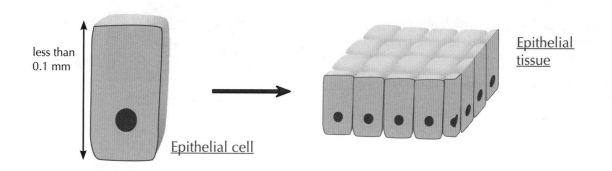

less than 0.1 mm

<u>Epithelial cell</u>

<u>Epithelial tissue</u>

Cell Organisation

*We left off at **tissues** on the previous page — now you need to know how they're organised...*

Tissues are Organised into Organs

An <u>organ</u> is a group of <u>different tissues</u> that work together to perform a certain <u>function</u>.

> For example, the <u>stomach</u> is an organ made of these tissues:
> - <u>Muscular tissue</u>, which moves the stomach wall to <u>churn up the food</u>.
> - <u>Glandular tissue</u>, which makes <u>digestive juices</u> to digest food.
> - <u>Epithelial tissue</u>, which covers the <u>outside</u> and <u>inside</u> of the stomach.

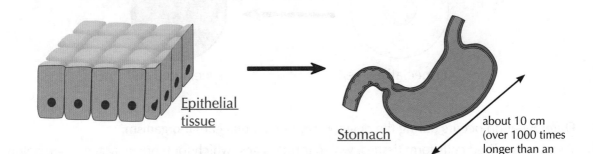

<u>Epithelial tissue</u>

<u>Stomach</u>

about 10 cm (over 1000 times longer than an epithelial cell)

Organs are Organised into Organ Systems

An <u>organ system</u> is a <u>group of organs</u> working together to perform a particular <u>function</u>.

> For example, the <u>digestive system</u> (found in humans and other mammals) <u>breaks down</u> and <u>absorbs food</u>. It is made up of these organs:
> 1) <u>Glands</u> (e.g. the <u>pancreas</u> and <u>salivary glands</u>), which produce <u>digestive juices</u>.
> 2) The <u>stomach</u> and <u>small intestine</u>, which <u>digest</u> food.
> 3) The <u>liver</u>, which produces <u>bile</u>.
> 4) The <u>small intestine</u>, which <u>absorbs</u> soluble <u>food</u> molecules.
> 5) The <u>large intestine</u>, which <u>absorbs water</u> from undigested food, leaving <u>faeces</u>.

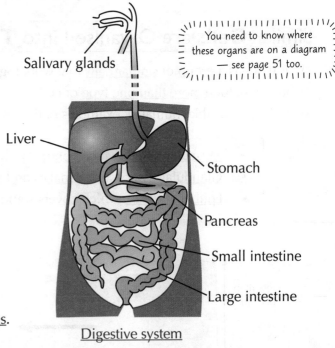

Salivary glands

You need to know where these organs are on a diagram — see page 51 too.

Liver

Stomach

Pancreas

Small intestine

Large intestine

Digestive system

Organ systems work together to make entire <u>organisms</u>.

Remember — cells, tissues, organs, organ systems

OK, so from the last couple of pages you know that <u>cells</u> are organised into <u>tissues</u>, the tissues into <u>organs</u>, the organs into <u>organ systems</u> and the organ systems into a whole <u>organism</u>.

Enzymes

Chemical reactions are what make you work. And *enzymes* are what make them work.

Enzymes Are Catalysts Produced by Living Things

1) Living things have thousands of different chemical reactions going on inside them all the time. These reactions need to be carefully controlled — to get the right amounts of substances.

2) You can usually make a reaction happen more quickly by raising the temperature. This would speed up the useful reactions but also the unwanted ones too... not good. There's also a limit to how far you can raise the temperature inside a living creature before its cells start getting damaged.

3) So... living things produce enzymes that act as biological catalysts. Enzymes reduce the need for high temperatures and we only have enzymes to speed up the useful chemical reactions in the body.

> A CATALYST is a substance which INCREASES the speed of a reaction, without being CHANGED or USED UP in the reaction.

4) Enzymes are all large proteins and all proteins are made up of chains of amino acids. These chains are folded into unique shapes, which enzymes need to do their jobs (see below).

Enzymes Have Special Shapes So They Can Catalyse Reactions

1) Chemical reactions usually involve things either being split apart or joined together.

2) Every enzyme has an active site with a unique shape that fits onto the substance involved in a reaction.

3) Enzymes are really picky — they usually only catalyse one specific reaction.

4) This is because, for the enzyme to work, the substrate has to fit into its active site. If the substrate doesn't match the enzyme's active site, then the reaction won't be catalysed.

The substance that an enzyme acts on is called the substrate.

5) This diagram shows the 'lock and key' model of enzyme action.

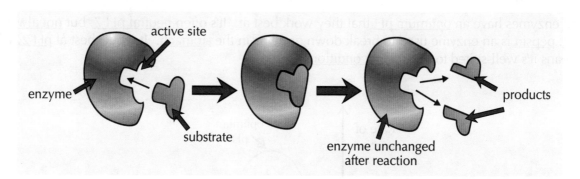

active site

enzyme

substrate

enzyme unchanged after reaction

products

6) This is simpler than how enzymes actually work. In reality, the active site changes shape a little as the substrate binds to it to get a tighter fit. This is called the 'induced fit' model of enzyme action.

Enzymes speed up chemical reactions

Just like you've got to have the correct key for a lock, you've got to have the right substance for an enzyme. As you can see in the diagram above, if the substance doesn't fit, the enzyme won't catalyse the reaction...

Enzymes

*Enzymes are clearly very clever, but they're **not** very versatile. They need just the right **conditions** if they're going to work properly.*

Enzymes Need the **Right Temperature**...

1) Changing the temperature changes the rate of an enzyme-catalysed reaction.

2) Like with any reaction, a higher temperature increases the rate at first.

3) But if it gets too hot, some of the bonds holding the enzyme together break. This changes the shape of the enzyme's active site, so the substrate won't fit any more. The enzyme is said to be denatured.

4) All enzymes have an optimum temperature that they work best at.

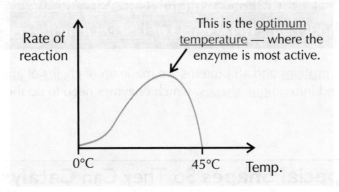

This is the optimum temperature — where the enzyme is most active.

... and the **Right pH**

1) The pH also affects enzymes. If it's too high or too low, the pH interferes with the bonds holding the enzyme together.

2) This changes the shape of the active site and denatures the enzyme.

3) All enzymes have an optimum pH that they work best at. It's often neutral pH 7, but not always — e.g. pepsin is an enzyme used to break down proteins in the stomach. It works best at pH 2, which means it's well-suited to the acidic conditions there.

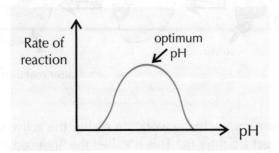

Most enzymes catalyse just one reaction

The optimum temperature for most human enzymes is around normal body temperature.
And stomach enzymes work best at low pH, but the enzymes in your small intestine like a higher pH.

Investigating Enzymatic Reactions

You Can **Investigate** the Effect of **pH** on **Enzyme Activity** | PRACTICAL

The enzyme <u>amylase</u> catalyses the breakdown of <u>starch</u> to <u>maltose</u>. It's easy to <u>detect starch</u> using <u>iodine solution</u> — if starch is present, the iodine solution will change from <u>browny-orange</u> to <u>blue-black</u>. This is how you can <u>investigate</u> how pH affects <u>amylase activity</u>:

1) Put a <u>drop</u> of iodine solution into every well of a <u>spotting tile</u>.

2) Place a <u>Bunsen burner</u> on a <u>heat-proof mat</u>, and a <u>tripod</u> and <u>gauze</u> over the Bunsen burner. Put a beaker of <u>water</u> on top of the tripod and <u>heat</u> the water until it is <u>35 °C</u> (use a <u>thermometer</u> to measure the temperature). Try to keep the temperature of the water <u>constant</u> throughout the experiment.

You could use an electric water bath, instead of a Bunsen and a beaker of water, to control the temperature.

3) Use a <u>syringe</u> to add 1 cm³ of <u>amylase solution</u> and 1 cm³ of a <u>buffer solution</u> with a pH of 5 to a boiling tube. Using <u>test tube holders</u>, put the tube into the beaker of water and wait for five minutes.

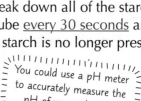

mixture sampled every 30 seconds

amylase, starch and buffer solution

dropping pipette

drop of iodine solution

spotting tile

4) Next, use a <u>different syringe</u> to add 5 cm³ of a <u>starch solution</u> to the boiling tube.

5) Immediately <u>mix the contents</u> of the boiling tube and start a <u>stop clock</u>.

6) Use <u>continuous sampling</u> to record <u>how long</u> it takes for the amylase to break down all of the starch. To do this, use a dropping pipette to take a <u>fresh sample</u> from the boiling tube <u>every 30 seconds</u> and put a <u>drop</u> into a <u>well</u>. When the iodine solution <u>remains browny-orange</u>, starch is no longer present.

7) <u>Repeat</u> the whole experiment with buffer solutions of different <u>pH values</u> to see how pH <u>affects</u> the time taken for the starch to be broken down.

You could use a pH meter to accurately measure the pH of your solutions.

8) Remember to <u>control any variables</u> each time (e.g. concentration and volume of amylase solution) to make it a <u>fair test</u>.

Here's How to **Calculate** the **Rate of Reaction**

1) It's often useful to calculate the <u>rate of reaction</u> after an experiment. Rate is a measure of how much something changes over time.

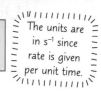

$$\text{Rate} = \frac{1000}{\text{time}}$$

2) For the <u>experiment above</u>, you can calculate the rate of reaction using <u>this formula</u>:
E.g.

> At <u>pH 6</u>, the <u>time taken</u> for amylase to break down all of the starch in a solution was <u>90 seconds</u>. So the <u>rate</u> of the reaction = <u>1000 ÷ 90 = 11 s⁻¹</u> (2 s.f.)

The units are in s^{-1} since rate is given per unit time.

3) If an experiment measures <u>how much something changes</u> over time, you calculate the rate of reaction by <u>dividing</u> the <u>amount</u> that it has <u>changed</u> by the <u>time taken</u>.

EXAMPLE **The enzyme catalase catalyses the breakdown of hydrogen peroxide into water and oxygen. During an investigation into the activity of catalase, 24 cm³ of oxygen was released in 50 seconds (s). Calculate the rate of the reaction. Write your answer in cm³ s⁻¹.**

Amount of product formed = change = 24 cm³

Rate of reaction = change ÷ time = 24 cm³ ÷ 50 s = 0.48 cm³ s⁻¹

cm^3 s^{-1} is another way of writing cm^3/s.

You can investigate other factors too...

You could easily <u>adapt</u> this experiment to investigate how factors <u>other than pH</u> affect the rate of amylase activity. For example, you could use a <u>water bath</u> to investigate the effect of <u>temperature</u>.

Q1 Video Solution

Q1 An enzyme-controlled reaction was carried out at pH 4. After 2 minutes, 36 cm³ of product had been released. Calculate the rate of reaction in cm³/s. [1 mark]

Enzymes and Digestion

*The **enzymes** used in **digestion** are produced by **cells** and then released into the **gut** to mix with food.*

Digestive Enzymes Break Down Big Molecules

1) <u>Starch</u>, <u>proteins</u> and <u>fats</u> are <u>big</u> molecules. They're too big to pass through the walls of the digestive system, so <u>digestive enzymes</u> break these <u>big</u> molecules down into <u>smaller</u> ones like <u>sugars</u> (e.g. glucose and maltose), <u>amino acids</u>, <u>glycerol</u> and <u>fatty acids</u>. These <u>smaller</u>, <u>soluble</u> molecules can <u>pass easily</u> through the walls of the digestive system, allowing them to be <u>absorbed</u> into the <u>bloodstream</u>.

Carbohydrases Convert Carbohydrates into Simple Sugars

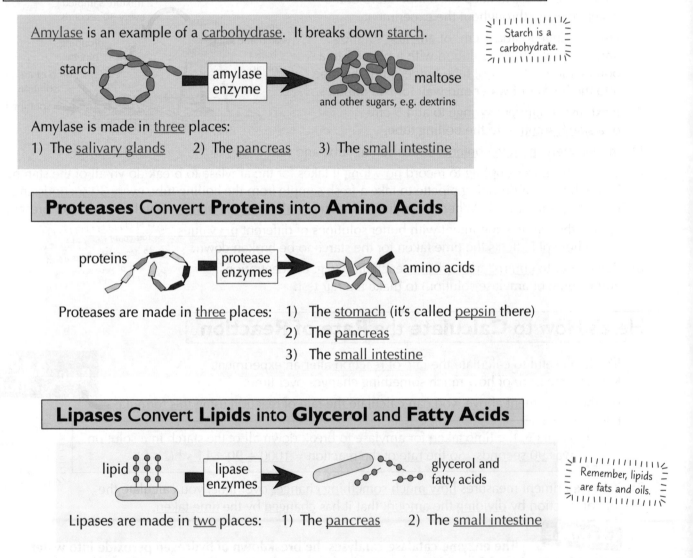

Amylase is an example of a <u>carbohydrase</u>. It breaks down <u>starch</u>.

starch → amylase enzyme → maltose
and other sugars, e.g. dextrins

Starch is a carbohydrate.

Amylase is made in <u>three</u> places:
1) The <u>salivary glands</u>   2) The <u>pancreas</u>   3) The <u>small intestine</u>

Proteases Convert Proteins into Amino Acids

proteins → protease enzymes → amino acids

Proteases are made in <u>three</u> places:
1) The <u>stomach</u> (it's called <u>pepsin</u> there)
2) The <u>pancreas</u>
3) The <u>small intestine</u>

Lipases Convert Lipids into Glycerol and Fatty Acids

lipid → lipase enzymes → glycerol and fatty acids

Remember, lipids are fats and oils.

Lipases are made in <u>two</u> places: 1) The <u>pancreas</u>   2) The <u>small intestine</u>

2) The body makes good use of the <u>products</u> of digestion. They can be used to make <u>new carbohydrates</u>, <u>proteins</u> and <u>lipids</u>. Some of the <u>glucose</u> (a carbohydrate) that's made is used in <u>respiration</u> (see p.110).

Bile Neutralises the Stomach Acid and Emulsifies Fats

1) Bile is <u>produced</u> in the <u>liver</u>. It's <u>stored</u> in the <u>gall bladder</u> before it's released into the <u>small intestine</u>.
2) The <u>hydrochloric acid</u> in the stomach makes the pH <u>too acidic</u> for enzymes in the small intestine to work properly. Bile is <u>alkaline</u> — it <u>neutralises</u> the acid and makes conditions <u>alkaline</u>. The enzymes in the small intestine <u>work best</u> in these alkaline conditions.
3) It <u>emulsifies</u> fats. In other words it breaks the fat into <u>tiny droplets</u>. This gives a much <u>bigger surface area</u> of fat for the enzyme lipase to work on — which makes its digestion <u>faster</u>.

More on Enzymes and Digestion

*So now you know what the enzymes do, here's a nice **big picture** of the **whole** of the digestive system.*

The **Breakdown** of Food is Catalysed by **Enzymes**

1) Enzymes used in the digestive system are produced by specialised cells in <u>glands</u> and in the <u>gut lining</u>.

2) Different enzymes catalyse the <u>breakdown</u> of different food molecules.

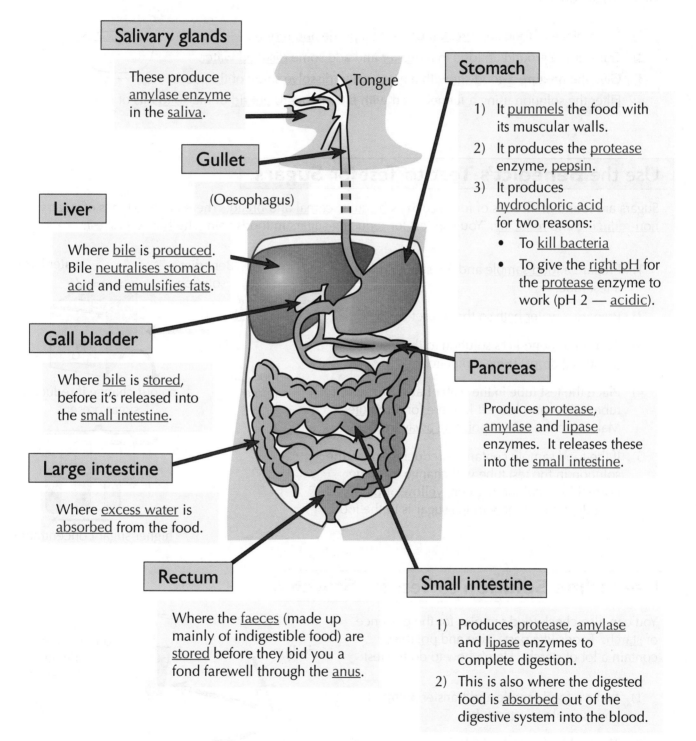

Salivary glands

These produce <u>amylase enzyme</u> in the <u>saliva</u>.

Tongue

Gullet

(Oesophagus)

Liver

Where <u>bile</u> is <u>produced</u>. Bile <u>neutralises stomach acid</u> and <u>emulsifies fats</u>.

Gall bladder

Where <u>bile</u> is <u>stored</u>, before it's released into the <u>small intestine</u>.

Large intestine

Where <u>excess water</u> is <u>absorbed</u> from the food.

Rectum

Where the <u>faeces</u> (made up mainly of indigestible food) are <u>stored</u> before they bid you a fond farewell through the <u>anus</u>.

Stomach

1) It <u>pummels</u> the food with its muscular walls.

2) It produces the <u>protease</u> enzyme, <u>pepsin</u>.

3) It produces <u>hydrochloric acid</u> for two reasons:
   • To <u>kill bacteria</u>
   • To give the <u>right pH</u> for the <u>protease</u> enzyme to work (pH 2 — <u>acidic</u>).

Pancreas

Produces <u>protease</u>, <u>amylase</u> and <u>lipase</u> enzymes. It releases these into the <u>small intestine</u>.

Small intestine

1) Produces <u>protease</u>, <u>amylase</u> and <u>lipase</u> enzymes to complete digestion.

2) This is also where the digested food is <u>absorbed</u> out of the digestive system into the blood.

That's nine different bits of the digestive system with different jobs

Did you know that the whole of your digestive system is actually <u>a big hole</u> that goes right through your body? It just gets loads of <u>food</u>, <u>digestive juices</u> and <u>enzymes</u> piled into it...

PRACTICAL

Food Tests

*There are some clever ways to **identify** what type of **food molecule** a sample contains.*
*For each of the tests, you need to prepare a **food sample** first. It's the same each time though.*

Prepare Your Food Sample First

Before you can carry out any of the food tests on these pages, you need to prepare a food sample.
Here's what you'd do:

1) Get a piece of food and break it up using a pestle and mortar.
2) Transfer the ground up food to a beaker and add some distilled water.
3) Give the mixture a good stir with a glass rod to dissolve some of the food.
4) Filter the solution using a funnel lined with filter paper to get rid of the solid bits of food.

Use the Benedict's Test to Test for Sugars

Sugars are found in all sorts of foods such as biscuits, cereal and bread. There are two types of sugars —
non-reducing and reducing. You can test for reducing sugars in foods using the Benedict's test:

1) Prepare a food sample and transfer 5 cm³ to a test tube.

2) Prepare a water bath so that it's set to 75 °C.

3) Add some Benedict's solution to the test tube (about 10 drops) using a pipette.

4) Place the test tube in the water bath using a test tube holder and leave it in there for 5 minutes. Make sure the tube is pointing away from you.

5) If the food sample contains a reducing sugar, the solution in the test tube will change from the normal blue colour to green, yellow or brick-red — it depends on how much sugar is in the food.

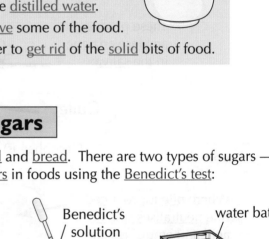

Benedict's solution · water bath · food sample · colour change if reducing sugar present

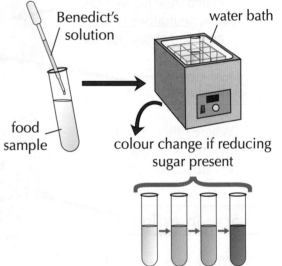

higher sugar concentration

Use Iodine Solution to Test for Starch

You can also check food samples for the presence of starch. Foods like pasta, rice and potatoes contain a lot of starch. Here's how to do the test:

1) Make a food sample and transfer 5 cm³ of your sample to a test tube.

2) Then add a few drops of iodine solution and gently shake the tube to mix the contents. If the sample contains starch, the colour of the solution will change from browny-orange to black or blue-black.

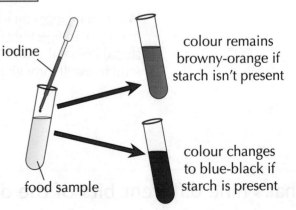

iodine · colour remains browny-orange if starch isn't present · food sample · colour changes to blue-black if starch is present

Food Tests

*There are a couple more **food tests** coming up on this page — for proteins and for lipids. As with the other tests, you need to use the method on the previous page to prepare a **sample** of your food first.*

Use the **Biuret Test** to Test for **Proteins**

You can use the <u>biuret test</u> to see if a type of food contains <u>protein</u>.
<u>Meat</u> and <u>cheese</u> are protein rich and good foods to use in this test. Here's how it's done:

1) Prepare a <u>sample</u> of your food and transfer <u>2 cm³</u> of your sample to a test tube.

2) Add 2 cm³ of <u>biuret solution</u> to the sample and mix the contents of the tube by <u>gently shaking</u> it.

3) If the food sample contains protein, the solution will change from <u>blue</u> to <u>purple</u>.
   If no protein is present, the solution will stay blue.

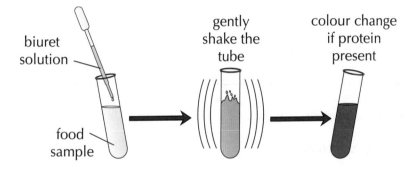

biuret solution

food sample

gently shake the tube

colour change if protein present

Use the **Sudan III Test** to Test for **Lipids**

<u>Lipids</u> are found in foods such as <u>olive oil</u>, <u>margarine</u> and <u>milk</u>.
You can test for the presence of lipids in a food using <u>Sudan III stain solution</u>.

1) Prepare a <u>sample</u> of the food you're testing (but you don't need to filter it). Transfer about <u>5 cm³</u> into a test tube.

2) Use a pipette to add <u>3 drops</u> of <u>Sudan III stain solution</u> to the test tube and <u>gently shake</u> the tube.

3) Sudan III stain solution <u>stains</u> lipids. If the sample contains lipids, the mixture will separate out into <u>two layers</u>. The top layer will be <u>bright red</u>. If no lipids are present, no separate red layer will form at the top of the liquid.

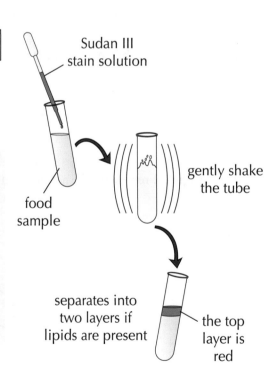

Sudan III stain solution

food sample

gently shake the tube

separates into two layers if lipids are present

the top layer is red

Make sure you think about all of the hazards...

<u>Iodine</u> is an <u>irritant</u> to the <u>eyes</u>, and the chemicals in the <u>biuret solution</u> are <u>dangerous</u>, so wear <u>safety goggles</u> for food tests. If you <u>spill</u> any of the chemicals on your <u>skin</u>, wash it off <u>straight away</u>. Be careful around the <u>water bath</u> in the <u>Benedict's test</u>, too. And if that's not enough to be cautious about, <u>Sudan III stain solution</u> is <u>flammable</u>, so keep it away from any <u>lit Bunsen burners</u>.

Warm-Up & Exam Questions

Doing well in exams isn't just about remembering all the facts, although that's important. You have to get used to the way the exams are phrased and make sure you always read the question carefully.

Warm-Up Questions

1) What is an organ system?
2) What is meant by the optimum pH of an enzyme?
3) Which enzyme digests: (a) starch   (b) protein   (c) lipids?
4) What are the products of the digestion of: (a) starch   (b) protein   (c) lipids?
5) Name the three parts of the digestive system that produce protease enzymes.
6) Describe how you would prepare a food sample before testing it for the presence of different food molecules.

Exam Questions

1   **Figure 1** shows the human digestive system.

Figure 1

1.1   Label the place where bile is produced.

[1 mark]

1.2   Describe why bile needs to have an alkaline pH.

[1 mark]

1.3   Outline how bile helps with the digestion of fats.

[2 marks]

2   **Figure 2** represents the action of an enzyme in catalysing a biological reaction.   Grade 4-6

Figure 2

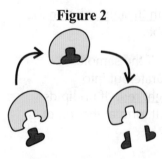

2.1   In terms of the enzyme's shape, explain why an enzyme only catalyses one reaction.

[1 mark]

2.2   The optimum pH of the enzyme is pH 7.
         Explain what effect a very low pH would have on the activity of the enzyme.

[2 marks]

Exam Questions

3   **Figure 3** shows the effect of temperature on the action of two different enzymes.   Grade 6~7

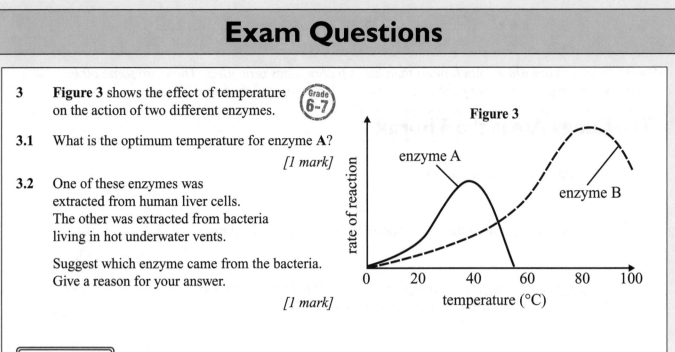

Figure 3

3.1   What is the optimum temperature for enzyme **A**?

[1 mark]

3.2   One of these enzymes was extracted from human liver cells. The other was extracted from bacteria living in hot underwater vents.

Suggest which enzyme came from the bacteria. Give a reason for your answer.

[1 mark]

PRACTICAL

4   A student wanted to know which substances were present in a food sample. She prepared a solution containing the food, and added some of the solution to each of three test tubes. She then added iodine solution to test tube **A**, biuret solution to test tube **B** and Sudan III stain solution to test tube **C**. Her results are shown in **Table 1**.   Grade 6~7

Table 1

Test tube	Description of solution in test tube
A	Blue-black
B	Blue
C	In two layers. Top layer red.

Describe what the student's results show about which substances are present in the food sample.

[3 marks]

PRACTICAL

5   A student was investigating the effect of pH on the rate of amylase activity. He used a syringe to put amylase solution and a buffer solution with a pH of 6 into a test tube. He then used a different syringe to add a starch solution to the boiling tube. He mixed the contents and then started a stop clock. Every 30 seconds he took a sample from the boiling tube and tested it for the presence of starch. When there was no starch present he stopped the stop clock. He repeated the experiment three times.   Grade 6~7

5.1   Suggest why he used two different syringes when adding substances to the boiling tube.

[1 mark]

5.2   His experiment showed that the average time taken for the starch in the boiling tube to be broken down was 60 seconds. Calculate the rate of the reaction. Give your answer in s^{-1} to 2 significant figures. Use the formula: $rate = \dfrac{1000}{time}$

[1 mark]

5.3   Describe what the student needs to do next in his investigation to determine the effect of pH on the rate of amylase activity.

[1 mark]

The Lungs

*When it comes to **breathing**, much more than just a pair of lungs is needed. There are some other vital parts that help to get the **oxygen** you need in, and the waste **carbon dioxide** out...*

The **Lungs** Are in the **Thorax**

1) The thorax is the top part of your body.

2) It's separated from the lower part of the body by the diaphragm.

3) The lungs are like big pink sponges and are protected by the ribcage. They're surrounded by the pleural membranes.

4) The air that you breathe in goes through the trachea. This splits into two tubes called bronchi (each one is a bronchus), one going to each lung.

5) The bronchi split into progressively smaller tubes called bronchioles.

6) The bronchioles finally end at small bags called alveoli where the gas exchange takes place (see next page).

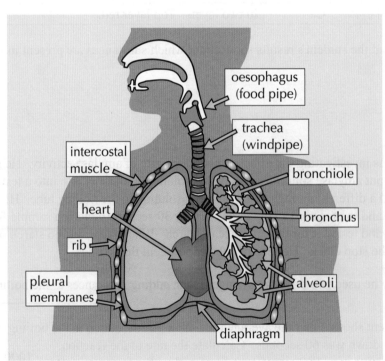

Take a deep breath...

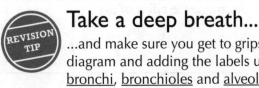

...and make sure you get to grips with the layout of the innards of your chest. Try sketching the diagram and adding the labels until you think you've got it sussed. If you know where the trachea, bronchi, bronchioles and alveoli are, then you're making a pretty good start.

The Lungs

Now that you know where the alveoli are, it's time to find out what they do.

Alveoli Carry Out Gas Exchange in the Body

1) The lungs contain millions and millions of little air sacs called alveoli, surrounded by a network of blood capillaries. This is where gas exchange happens.

2) The blood passing next to the alveoli has just returned to the lungs from the rest of the body, so it contains lots of carbon dioxide and very little oxygen. Oxygen diffuses out of the alveolus (high concentration) into the blood (low concentration). Carbon dioxide diffuses out of the blood (high concentration) into the alveolus (low concentration) to be breathed out.

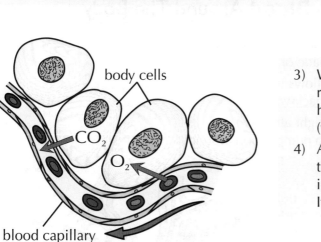

air in and out

CO_2

alveolus

O_2

blood capillary

body cells

CO_2

O_2

blood capillary

3) When the blood reaches body cells oxygen is released from the red blood cells (where there's a high concentration) and diffuses into the body cells (where the concentration is low).

4) At the same time, carbon dioxide diffuses out of the body cells (where there's a high concentration) into the blood (where there's a low concentration). It's then carried back to the lungs.

You Can Calculate the Breathing Rate in Breaths Per Minute

Rate calculations pop up all the time in biology, and you're expected to know how to do them — thankfully they're pretty easy. Breathing rate is the sort of thing that you could get asked to work out in your exam.

EXAMPLE

Bob takes 91 breaths in 7 minutes.
Calculate his average breathing rate in breaths per minute.

breaths per minute = number of breaths ÷ number of minutes

= 91 ÷ 7

= 13 breaths per minute

Alveoli are exchange surfaces

Back on page 39, you read about how exchange surfaces can be adapted to maximise their effectiveness. Alveoli have all of these adaptations to speed up the process of getting oxygen into the blood and getting the waste carbon dioxide out of the body — flick back to page 39 for a reminder.

Circulatory System — The Heart

*The circulatory system carries **food** and **oxygen** to every cell in the body. As well as being a delivery service, it's also a waste collection service — it carries **waste products** to where they can be removed from the body.*

It's a DOUBLE Circulatory System

The circulatory system is made up of the <u>heart</u>, <u>blood vessels</u> and <u>blood</u>.
Humans have a <u>double circulatory system</u> — <u>two circuits</u> joined together:

1) In the first one, the <u>right ventricle</u> (see below) pumps <u>deoxygenated</u> blood (blood without oxygen) to the <u>lungs</u> to take in <u>oxygen</u>. The blood then <u>returns</u> to the heart.

2) In the second one, the <u>left ventricle</u> (see below) pumps <u>oxygenated</u> blood around all the <u>other organs</u> of the <u>body</u>. The blood <u>gives up</u> its oxygen at the body cells and the <u>deoxygenated</u> blood <u>returns</u> to the heart to be pumped out to the <u>lungs</u> again.

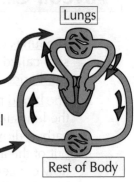

The Heart Contracts to Pump Blood Around The Body

1) The <u>heart</u> is a pumping <u>organ</u> that keeps the blood flowing around the body. The walls of the heart are mostly made of <u>muscle tissue</u>.

2) The heart has <u>valves</u> to make sure that blood flows in the right direction — they prevent it flowing <u>backwards</u>.

3) This is how the <u>heart</u> uses its <u>four chambers</u> (right atrium, right ventricle, left atrium and left ventricle) to pump blood around:

Atrium is when there is just one. Atria is plural.

1) <u>Blood flows into</u> the two <u>atria</u> from the <u>vena cava</u> and the <u>pulmonary vein</u>.

2) The <u>atria contract</u>, pushing the blood into the <u>ventricles</u>.

3) The <u>ventricles contract</u>, forcing the blood into the <u>pulmonary artery</u> and the <u>aorta</u>, and <u>out</u> of the <u>heart</u>.

4) The blood then flows to the <u>organs</u> through <u>arteries</u>, and <u>returns</u> through <u>veins</u> (see next page).

5) The atria fill again and the whole cycle <u>starts over</u>.

The heart also needs its <u>own</u> supply of <u>oxygenated</u> blood. Arteries called <u>coronary arteries</u> branch off the aorta and surround the heart, making sure that it gets all the <u>oxygenated</u> blood it needs.

Right Side   Left Side

pulmonary artery

vena cava

aorta

pulmonary vein

right atrium

left atrium

valve   valve   valve   valve

right ventricle   left ventricle

(No, we haven't made a mistake — this is the right and left side of the person whose heart it is.)

The Heart Has a Pacemaker

1) Your resting heart rate is <u>controlled</u> by a group of cells in the right atrium wall that act as a <u>pacemaker</u>.

2) These cells produce a small <u>electric impulse</u> which spreads to the surrounding muscle cells, causing them to <u>contract</u>.

3) An <u>artificial pacemaker</u> is often used to control heartbeat if the natural pacemaker cells don't work properly (e.g. if the patient has an <u>irregular heartbeat</u>). It's a little device that's implanted under the skin and has a wire going to the heart. It produces an <u>electric current</u> to keep the heart <u>beating regularly</u>.

Circulatory System — Blood Vessels

Blood needs a good set of 'tubes' to carry it round the body. Here's a page on the different types:

Blood Vessels are Designed for Their Function

There are <u>three</u> different types of <u>blood vessel</u>:

1) <u>ARTERIES</u> — these carry the blood <u>away</u> from the heart.
2) <u>CAPILLARIES</u> — these are involved in the <u>exchange of materials</u> at the tissues.
3) <u>VEINS</u> — these carry the blood <u>to</u> the heart.

Arteries Carry Blood Under Pressure

1) The heart pumps the blood out at <u>high pressure</u> so the artery walls are <u>strong</u> and <u>elastic</u>.
2) The walls are <u>thick</u> compared to the size of the hole down the middle (the "<u>lumen</u>").
3) They contain thick layers of <u>muscle</u> to make them <u>strong</u>, and <u>elastic fibres</u> to allow them to stretch and <u>spring back</u>.

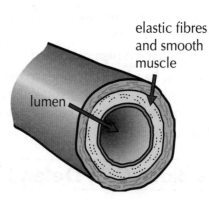

elastic fibres and smooth muscle

lumen

Capillaries are Really Small

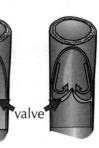

thin wall — only one cell thick

very small lumen

nucleus of cell

1) Arteries branch into <u>capillaries</u>.
2) Capillaries are really <u>tiny</u> — too small to see.
3) They carry the blood <u>really close</u> to <u>every cell</u> in the body to <u>exchange substances</u> with them.
4) They have <u>permeable</u> walls, so substances can <u>diffuse</u> in and out.
5) They supply <u>food</u> and <u>oxygen</u>, and take away <u>wastes</u> like CO_2.
6) Their walls are usually <u>only one cell thick</u>. This <u>increases</u> the rate of diffusion by <u>decreasing</u> the <u>distance</u> over which it occurs.

Veins Take Blood Back to the Heart

1) Capillaries eventually <u>join up</u> to form <u>veins</u>.
2) The blood is at <u>lower pressure</u> in the veins so the walls don't need to be as <u>thick</u> as artery walls.
3) They have a <u>bigger lumen</u> than arteries to help the blood <u>flow</u> despite the lower pressure.
4) They also have <u>valves</u> to help keep the blood flowing in the <u>right direction</u>.

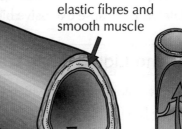

elastic fibres and smooth muscle

valve

large lumen

You Can Calculate the Rate of Blood Flow

You might get asked to calculate the <u>rate of blood flow</u> in your exam. Thankfully, it's not too tricky. Take a look at this example:

EXAMPLE

1464 ml of blood passed through an artery in 4.5 minutes. Calculate the rate of blood flow through the artery in ml/min.

rate of blood flow = volume of blood ÷ number of minutes
= 1464 ÷ 4.5 = 325 ml/min

<u>V</u>eins have <u>v</u>alves — <u>a</u>rteries carry blood <u>a</u>way from the heart

Q1   2.175 litres of blood passed through a vein in 8.7 minutes.
Calculate the rate of blood flow through the vein in ml/min.   [2 marks]

Q1 Video Solution

Circulatory System — Blood

*Blood is a **tissue**. It's part of a huge **transport system**. There are four main things in blood...*

Red Blood Cells Carry Oxygen

1) The job of red blood cells is to carry <u>oxygen</u> from the lungs to all the cells in the body.

2) Their shape is a <u>biconcave disc</u> (like a doughnut) — this gives a <u>large surface area</u> for absorbing <u>oxygen</u>.

3) They <u>don't</u> have a nucleus — this allows more room to carry oxygen.

4) They contain a red pigment called <u>haemoglobin</u>.

5) In the <u>lungs</u>, haemoglobin binds to <u>oxygen</u> to become <u>oxyhaemoglobin</u>. In body tissues, the reverse happens — oxyhaemoglobin splits up into haemoglobin and oxygen, to <u>release oxygen</u> to the <u>cells</u>.

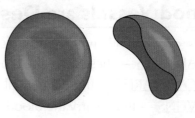

The more red blood cells you've got, the more oxygen can get to your cells. At high altitudes there's less oxygen in the air — so people who live there produce more red blood cells to compensate.

White Blood Cells Defend Against Infection

1) Some can change shape to engulf unwelcome <u>microorganisms</u>, in a process called <u>phagocytosis</u>.

2) Others produce <u>antibodies</u> to fight microorganisms, as well as <u>antitoxins</u> to neutralise any toxins produced by the microorganisms.

3) Unlike red blood cells, they <u>do</u> have a <u>nucleus</u>.

Platelets Help Blood Clot

1) These are <u>small fragments</u> of <u>cells</u>. They have <u>no nucleus</u>.

2) They help the blood to <u>clot</u> at a wound — to stop all your <u>blood pouring out</u> and to stop <u>microorganisms</u> getting in.

3) <u>Lack</u> of platelets can cause excessive bleeding and bruising.

Plasma is the Liquid That Carries Everything in Blood

This is a pale straw-coloured liquid which <u>carries just about everything</u>:

1) <u>Red</u> and <u>white blood cells</u> and <u>platelets</u>.

2) Nutrients like <u>glucose</u> and <u>amino acids</u>. These are the soluble products of digestion which are absorbed from the gut and taken to the cells of the body.

3) <u>Carbon dioxide</u> from the organs to the lungs.

4) <u>Urea</u> from the liver to the kidneys.

5) <u>Hormones</u>.

6) <u>Proteins</u>.

7) <u>Antibodies</u> and <u>antitoxins</u> produced by the white blood cells.

Blood — red blood cells, white blood cells, platelets and plasma

<u>Blood tests</u> can be used to diagnose loads of things — not just disorders of the blood. This is because the blood transports <u>so many chemicals</u> produced by <u>so many organs</u>.

Q1 Describe the purpose of platelets in blood. [1 mark]

Q2 State the function of the cell labelled X in the image on the right. [1 mark]

Q2 Video Solution

Warm-Up & Exam Questions

There are some nice diagrams to learn on the previous few pages. If you don't bother, you'll feel pretty silly if you turn over the exam paper and the first question asks you to label a diagram of the heart. Just saying... Anyway, let's see if these questions get your blood pumping...

Warm-Up Questions

1) What is the name of the tubes that the trachea splits into?
2) What is the function of the coronary arteries?
3) What is an artificial pacemaker?
4) What do veins do?
5) Which component of blood is made from small fragments of cells?

Exam Questions

1 A student ran for 12 minutes.

1.1 During this 12 minute run, the student took 495 breaths.
Calculate his average breathing rate in breaths per minute.

[1 mark]

1.2 The student also measured his heart rate before and during his run.
Before his run, the student's heart rate was at its natural resting rate.
Outline how natural resting heart rate is controlled.

[1 mark]

2 The cell shown in **Figure 1** transports oxygen around the body. ⟨Grade 6-7⟩

2.1 Explain how this cell's shape is adapted for transporting oxygen.

[1 mark]

Figure 1

View from above   Cut through view

2.2 Describe and explain **one** other way in which this cell is adapted for carrying oxygen.

[2 marks]

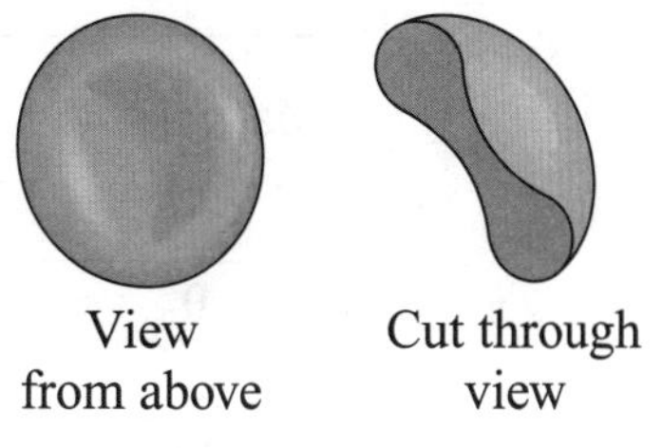

2.3 Name the other main type of blood cell, and state its function.

[2 marks]

Blood cells are carried in the bloodstream inside blood vessels.

2.4 Capillaries are one type of blood vessel.
Outline how the structure of a capillary enables it to carry out its function.

[4 marks]

2.5 Blood flows through different types of blood vessels at different rates.
The volume of blood that passed through an artery in 150 seconds was 1155 ml.
Calculate the rate of blood flow through the artery in ml/min.

[2 marks]

Exam Questions

3   **Figure 2** shows the human heart and four blood vessels, as seen from the front.
    The left ventricle has been labelled.

Figure 2

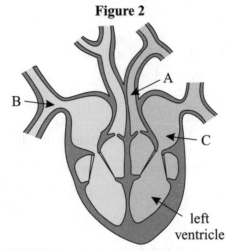

3.1   Name the parts labelled **A**, **B** and **C**.

[1 mark]

3.2   Describe the function of the left ventricle.

[1 mark]

3.3   What is the function of the valves in the heart?

[1 mark]

3.4* Describe how deoxygenated blood from the body passes through the heart to reach the lungs.

[4 marks]

4   A student did an experiment to compare the elasticity of arteries and veins. He dissected out
    an artery and a vein from a piece of fresh meat. He then took a 5 cm length of each vessel,
    hung different masses on it, and measured how much it stretched.
    His results are shown in **Table 1**.

Table 1

Mass added (g)	Length of blood vessel (mm)	
	Artery	Vein
0	50	50
5	51	53
10	53	56
15	55	59
20	56	-

4.1   Suggest **one** way in which the student could tell which was the artery and which was the vein
      when he was dissecting the meat.

[1 mark]

4.2   Which vessel stretched more easily?
      Suggest why this was.

[1 mark]

Cardiovascular Disease

*Cardiovascular disease is a term used to describe diseases of the heart or blood vessels, for example coronary heart disease. This page tells you all about how **stents** are used to combat coronary heart disease.*

Coronary Heart Disease is Life-Threatening

Coronary heart disease is when the coronary arteries that supply the blood to the muscle of the heart get blocked by layers of fatty material building up.

This causes the arteries to become narrow, so blood flow is restricted and there's a lack of oxygen to the heart muscle — this can result in a heart attack.

outside of heart

coronary artery

Stents Keep Arteries Open

1) Stents are tubes that are inserted inside arteries. They keep them open, making sure blood can pass through to the heart muscles. This keeps the person's heart beating (and the person alive).

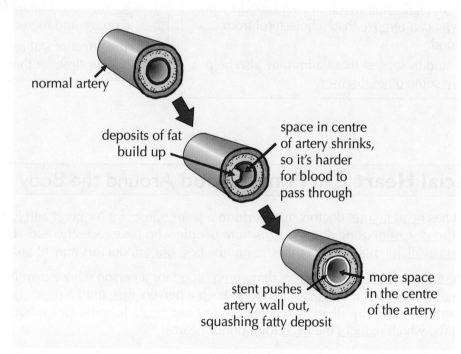

normal artery

deposits of fat build up

space in centre of artery shrinks, so it's harder for blood to pass through

stent pushes artery wall out, squashing fatty deposit

more space in the centre of the artery

2) Stents are a way of lowering the risk of a heart attack in people with coronary heart disease. They are effective for a long time and the recovery time from the surgery is relatively quick.

3) On the down side, there is a risk of complications during the operation (e.g. heart attack) and a risk of infection from surgery. There is also the risk of patients developing a blood clot near the stent — this is called thrombosis.

Coronary heart disease is a type of cardiovascular disease

Coronary heart disease is caused by the arteries being blocked by fatty material — if the heart muscle can't get enough oxygen, then it can't work properly. And if the heart can't work properly, well, you're in trouble.

Cardiovascular Disease

*You've read about stents, so now it's time for a second treatment for coronary heart disease — **statins**.*

Statins Reduce Cholesterol in the Blood

1) Cholesterol is an essential lipid that your body produces and needs to function properly. However, too much of a certain type of cholesterol (known as 'bad' or LDL cholesterol) can cause health problems.

2) Having too much of this 'bad' cholesterol in the bloodstream can cause fatty deposits to form inside arteries, which can lead to coronary heart disease.

3) Statins are drugs that can reduce the amount of 'bad' cholesterol present in the bloodstream. This slows down the rate of fatty deposits forming.

Statins Have Advantages and Disadvantages

Advantages

1) By reducing the amount of 'bad' cholesterol in the blood, statins can reduce the risk of strokes, coronary heart disease and heart attacks.

2) As well as reducing the amount of 'bad' cholesterol, statins can increase the amount of a beneficial type of cholesterol (known as 'good' or HDL cholesterol) in your bloodstream. This type can remove 'bad' cholesterol from the blood.

3) Some studies suggest that statins may also help prevent some other diseases.

Disadvantages

1) Statins are a long-term drug that must be taken regularly. There's the risk that someone could forget to take them.

2) Statins can sometimes cause negative side effects, e.g. headaches. Some of these side effects can be serious, e.g. kidney failure, liver damage and memory loss.

3) The effect of statins isn't instant. It takes time for their effect to kick in.

An Artificial Heart Can Pump Blood Around the Body

1) If a patient has heart failure, doctors may perform a heart transplant (or heart and lungs transplant if the lungs are also diseased) using donor organs from people who have recently died. However, if donor organs aren't available right away or they're not the best option, doctors may fit an artificial heart.

2) Artificial hearts are mechanical devices that pump blood for a person whose own heart has failed. They're usually only used as a temporary fix, to keep a person alive until a donor heart can be found or to help a person recover by allowing the heart to rest and heal. In some cases though they're used as a permanent fix, which reduces the need for a donor heart.

3) The main advantage of artificial hearts is that they're less likely to be rejected by the body's immune system than a donor heart. This is because they're made from metals or plastics, so the body doesn't recognise them as 'foreign' and attack in the same way as it does with living tissue.

4) But surgery to fit an artificial heart (as with transplant surgery) can lead to bleeding and infection. Also, artificial hearts don't work as well as healthy natural ones — parts of the heart could wear out or the electrical motor could fail. Blood doesn't flow through artificial hearts as smoothly, which can cause blood clots and lead to strokes. The patient has to take drugs to thin their blood and make sure this doesn't happen, which can cause problems with bleeding if they're hurt in an accident.

Replacing a person's heart is major surgery, which has risks.

Cardiovascular Disease

*One final page on cardiovascular disease. Having a heart transplant or getting an artificial heart fitted aren't the only surgeries for cardiovascular disease. Surgeons can do things like **replacing** just the **valves** in a heart.*

Faulty Heart Valves Can Be Replaced

1) The <u>valves</u> in the heart can be damaged or weakened by <u>heart attacks</u>, <u>infection</u> or <u>old age</u>.

2) The damage may cause the <u>valve tissue</u> to <u>stiffen</u>, so it <u>won't open properly</u>. Or a valve may become <u>leaky</u>, allowing blood to flow in <u>both directions</u> rather than just forward. This means that blood <u>doesn't circulate</u> as <u>effectively</u> as normal.

3) Severe valve damage can be treated by <u>replacing</u> the valve.

4) Replacement valves can be ones taken from <u>humans</u> or <u>other mammals</u> (e.g. cows or pigs) — these are <u>biological valves</u>. Or they can be <u>man-made</u> — these are <u>mechanical valves</u>.

5) Replacing a <u>valve</u> is a much <u>less drastic</u> procedure than a whole heart transplant. But fitting artificial valves is still <u>major surgery</u> and there can still be problems with <u>blood clots</u>.

Artificial Blood Can Keep You Alive In An Emergency

1) When someone <u>loses a lot of blood</u>, e.g. in an accident, their heart can still <u>pump</u> the remaining <u>red blood cells</u> around (to get <u>oxygen</u> to their <u>organs</u>), as long as the <u>volume</u> of their blood can be <u>topped up</u>.

2) <u>Artificial blood</u> is a <u>blood substitute</u>, e.g. a salt solution ("<u>saline</u>"), which is used to <u>replace</u> the <u>lost volume</u> of blood. It's <u>safe</u> (if no <u>air bubbles</u> get into the blood) and can keep people <u>alive</u> even if they lose $\frac{2}{3}$ of their red blood cells. This may give the patient enough <u>time</u> to produce <u>new</u> blood cells. If not, the patient will need a <u>blood transfusion</u>.

3) Ideally, an artificial blood product would <u>replace</u> the function of the <u>red blood cells</u>, so that there's <u>no need</u> for a blood transfusion. Scientists are currently working on products that can do this.

An artificial blood product that carries oxygen would replace the need for a blood transfusion from another person. This would have advantages such as decreasing the risk of diseases being passed on.

EXAM TIP

Don't lose heart...

You could be asked to <u>evaluate</u> treatments for <u>cardiovascular disease</u>. Don't panic — just use any information you're given and your own knowledge to weigh up the <u>advantages</u> and <u>disadvantages</u>. Make sure your answer doesn't just focus on <u>one side</u> — e.g. don't just talk about the advantages and ignore the disadvantages — and don't forget to include a justified <u>conclusion</u>.

Warm-Up & Exam Questions

Hopefully I've persuaded you by now that it's a good idea to try these questions. Believe me, when you're sitting with your real exam paper in front of you, you'll feel so much better knowing that you've already been through loads of practice questions. So off you go...

Warm-Up Questions

1) Which vessels are affected in coronary heart disease?

2) a) What device can be used to keep an artery open?

   b) Give three risks associated with getting one of these devices fitted.

3) What is an artificial heart?

Exam Questions

1 Coronary heart disease is the main cause of death worldwide. **Figure 1** shows a cross-section of a blood vessel in someone with coronary heart disease.

Figure 1

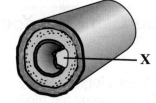

1.1 Name the substance labelled **X** on **Figure 1**.

[1 mark]

1.2 Explain how the presence of this substance can affect oxygen delivery to the heart muscle.

[2 marks]

2 A patient is taken into hospital. They are diagnosed as having a leaky heart valve.

2.1 Explain why a leaky valve could cause a health problem.

[2 marks]

The doctor decides that a surgeon should replace the valve.

2.2 Name and describe the **two** types of valve that the surgeon might use.

[4 marks]

2.3 Suggest **one** disadvantage of replacing the faulty valve.

[1 mark]

3 Some people with cardiovascular disease take statins. These are drugs that need to be taken every day.

3.1 Outline why statins are sometimes used in the treatment of coronary heart disease.

[2 marks]

3.2 Suggest **one** disadvantage to a patient of taking statins.

[1 mark]

Health and Disease

*Try as we might, it's unlikely that we'll be in tip-top condition for all of our lives — **disease** tends to get us all at some point. There are lots of **different types** of diseases we could get...*

Diseases are a Major Cause of Ill Health

Health is the state of physical and mental wellbeing.
Diseases are often responsible for causing ill health.

Diseases Can be Communicable or Non-Communicable

1) Communicable diseases are those that can spread from person to person or between animals and people. They can be caused by things like bacteria, viruses, parasites and fungi. They're sometimes described as contagious or infectious diseases. Measles and malaria are examples of communicable diseases. There's more about them on pages 81-84.

2) Non-communicable diseases are those that cannot spread between people or between animals and people. They generally last for a long time and get worse slowly. Asthma, cancer and coronary heart disease (see page 63) are examples of non-communicable diseases.

Different Types of Disease Sometimes Interact

Sometimes diseases can interact and cause other physical and mental health issues that don't immediately seem related. Here are a few examples:

1) People who have problems with their immune system (the system that your body uses to help fight off infection — see p.87) have an increased chance of suffering from communicable diseases such as influenza (flu), because their body is less likely to be able to defend itself against the pathogen that causes the disease.

Pathogen is just the fancy term for a microorganism that can cause a disease when it infects its host.

2) Some types of cancer can be triggered by infection by certain viruses. For example, infection with some types of hepatitis virus can cause long-term infections in the liver, where the virus lives in the cells. This can lead to an increased chance of developing liver cancer. Another example is infection with HPV (human papilloma virus), which can cause cervical cancer in women.

3) Immune system reactions in the body caused by infection by a pathogen can sometimes trigger allergic reactions such as skin rashes or worsen the symptoms of asthma for asthma sufferers.

4) Mental health issues such as depression can be triggered when someone is suffering from severe physical health problems, particularly if they have an impact on the person's ability to carry out everyday activities or if they affect the person's life expectancy.

Communicable diseases can spread...

...but non-communicable diseases can't. Remember that — it's really important.

Health and Disease

*Ill health isn't just about having a disease — there are plenty of **other causes**.*
*And then there's the **cost** of ill health to consider too — there might be more to it than you'd first thought...*

Other Factors Can Also Affect Your Health

There are plenty of factors other than diseases that can also affect your health. For example:

1) Whether or not you have a good, balanced diet that provides your body with everything it needs, and in the right amounts. A poor diet can affect your physical and mental health.

2) The stress you are under — being constantly under lots of stress can lead to health issues.

3) Your life situation — for example, whether you have easy access to medicines to treat illness, or whether you have access to things that can prevent you from getting ill in the first place, e.g. being able to buy healthy food or access condoms to prevent the transmission of some sexually transmitted diseases.

Non-Communicable Diseases Can Be Costly

The Human Cost

1) The human cost of non-communicable diseases is obvious. Tens of millions of people around the world die from non-communicable diseases per year.

2) People with these diseases may have a lower quality of life or a shorter lifespan. This not only affects the sufferers themselves, but their loved ones too.

The Financial Cost

1) It's also important to think about the financial cost.

2) The cost to the NHS of researching and treating these diseases is huge — and it's the same for other health services and organisations around the world.

3) Families may have to move or adapt their home to help a family member with a disease, which can be costly.

4) Also, if the family member with the disease has to give up work or dies, the family's income will be reduced.

5) A reduction in the number of people able to work can also affect a country's economy.

Lots of things affect health, and ill health can be costly

A human cost is the effect something has on humans. A financial cost is to do with how much spending something results in. When you're studying biology, you'll come across lots of things that have a human cost or a financial cost (or both). Some things can have quite far-reaching knock-on effects.

Risk Factors for Non-Communicable Diseases

You've probably heard the term 'risk factor' before. These next couple of pages have lots of info on them.
There's nothing too tricky, but there's quite a bit to read — take it slowly and make sure it goes in.

Risk Factors Increase Your Chance of Getting a Disease

1) <u>Risk factors</u> are things that are linked to an <u>increase</u> in the <u>likelihood</u> that a person will develop a certain disease during their lifetime. They <u>don't guarantee</u> that someone <u>will</u> get the disease.

2) Risk factors are often aspects of a person's <u>lifestyle</u> (e.g. how much exercise they do).

3) They can also be the presence of certain substances in the <u>environment</u> (e.g. air pollution) or <u>substances</u> in your <u>body</u> (e.g. asbestos fibres — asbestos was a material used in buildings until it was realised that the fibres could build up in your airways and cause diseases such as cancer later in life).

4) Many <u>non-communicable</u> diseases are caused by several different risk factors <u>interacting</u> with each other rather than one factor alone.

5) Lifestyle factors can have different impacts <u>locally</u>, <u>nationally</u> and <u>globally</u>. E.g. in <u>developed countries</u>, non-communicable diseases are <u>more common</u> as people generally have a <u>higher income</u> and can buy <u>high-fat</u> food. <u>Nationally</u>, people from <u>deprived areas</u> are <u>more likely</u> to smoke, have a poor diet and not exercise. This means the incidence of <u>cardiovascular disease</u>, <u>obesity</u> and <u>Type 2 diabetes</u> is <u>higher</u> in those areas. Your <u>individual choices</u> affect the <u>local</u> incidence of disease.

Some Risk Factors Can Cause a Disease Directly

Some risk factors <u>are</u> able to <u>directly cause</u> a disease. For example:

> <u>Smoking</u> has been proven to directly cause <u>cardiovascular disease</u>, <u>lung disease</u> and <u>lung cancer</u>. It damages the <u>walls</u> of <u>arteries</u> and the <u>cells</u> in the <u>lining</u> of the <u>lungs</u>.

> It's thought that <u>obesity</u> can directly cause <u>Type 2 diabetes</u> by making the body <u>less sensitive</u> or <u>resistant</u> to insulin, meaning that it struggles to <u>control</u> the <u>concentration</u> of <u>glucose</u> in the blood.

There's more about Type 2 diabetes on page 133.

Risk Factors for Non-Communicable Diseases

Here are a few more risk factors that can directly cause disease:

1) Drinking too much alcohol has been shown to cause liver disease. The liver breaks down alcohol, but the reaction can damage its cells.

2) Liver cells may also be damaged when toxic chemicals leak from the gut due to damage to the intestines caused by alcohol.

3) Too much alcohol can affect brain function too. It can damage the nerve cells in the brain, causing the brain to lose volume.

Smoking when pregnant reduces the amount of oxygen the baby receives in the womb and can cause lots of health problems for the unborn baby. Drinking alcohol has similar effects. Alcohol can damage the baby's cells, affecting its development and causing a wide range of health issues.

There's more about cancer coming up on the next page.

Cancer can be directly caused by exposure to certain substances or radiation. Things that cause cancer are known as carcinogens. Carcinogens work in different ways. For example, some damage a cell's DNA in a way that makes the cell more likely to divide uncontrollably. Ionising radiation (e.g. from X-rays) is an example of a carcinogen.

Risk Factors Can be Identified Using Correlation

1) Risk factors are identified by scientists looking for correlations in data. However, correlation doesn't always equal cause.

2) Some risk factors aren't capable of directly causing a disease, but are related to another risk factor that is.

3) For example:

See pages 10 and 13 for more about correlations.

A lack of exercise and a high fat diet are heavily linked to an increased chance of cardiovascular disease, but they can't cause the disease directly. It's the resulting high blood pressure and high 'bad' cholesterol levels (see p.64) that can actually cause it.

It's hard to avoid all risk factors of disease...

...but remember that risk factors that cause disease don't mean you'll definitely get the disease — they just increase the chance of it happening. Also, remember that not all risk factors cause disease. Many are just correlated with the disease, meaning there is a relationship between them.

Cancer

*The more we understand about **cancer**, the better our chances of **avoiding** and **beating** it. Hoorah.*

Cancer is Caused by Uncontrolled Cell Growth and Division

This <u>uncontrolled</u> growth and division is a result of <u>changes</u> that occur to the <u>cells</u> and results in the formation of a <u>tumour</u> (a mass of cells). Not all tumours are cancerous. They can be <u>benign</u> or <u>malignant</u>:

Benign

1) This is where the tumour <u>grows</u> until there's no more room.
2) The tumour <u>stays</u> in one place (usually within a membrane) rather than invading other tissues in the body.
3) This type <u>isn't</u> normally dangerous, and the tumour <u>isn't</u> cancerous.

Malignant

1) This is where the tumour grows and <u>spreads</u> to neighbouring healthy tissues.
2) Cells can <u>break off</u> and spread to other parts of the body by travelling in the <u>bloodstream</u>.
3) The malignant cells then <u>invade</u> healthy tissues elsewhere in the body and form <u>secondary tumours</u>.
4) Malignant tumours are <u>dangerous</u> and can be fatal — <u>they are cancers</u>.

Risk Factors Can Increase the Chance of Some Cancers

<u>Anyone</u> can develop cancer. Having risk factors <u>doesn't</u> mean that you'll definitely get cancer. It just means that you're at an <u>increased risk</u> of developing the disease. Cancer <u>survival rates</u> have <u>increased</u> due to medical advances such as <u>improved treatment</u>, being able to <u>diagnose</u> cancer <u>earlier</u> and <u>increased screening</u> for the disease.

Risk Factors Can Be Associated With Lifestyle

Scientists have identified <u>lots</u> of lifestyle risk factors for various types of cancer. For example:

1) <u>Smoking</u> — It's a well known fact that smoking is linked to <u>lung cancer</u>, but research has also linked it to <u>other types</u> of cancer too, including mouth, bowel, stomach and cervical cancer.
2) <u>Obesity</u> — Obesity has been linked to <u>many different cancers</u>, including bowel, liver and kidney cancer. It's the <u>second biggest</u> preventable cause of cancer after smoking.
3) <u>UV exposure</u> — People who are often exposed to <u>UV radiation</u> from the Sun have an increased chance of developing <u>skin cancer</u>. People who live in <u>sunny climates</u> and people who spend a lot of time <u>outside</u> are at <u>higher risk</u> of the disease. People who frequently use <u>sun beds</u> are also putting themselves at higher risk of developing skin cancer.
4) <u>Viral infection</u> — Infection with some viruses has been shown to <u>increase</u> the chances of developing <u>certain types</u> of cancer. For example, infection with <u>hepatitis B</u> and <u>hepatitis C</u> viruses can increase the risk of developing <u>liver cancer</u>. The likelihood of becoming infected with these viruses sometimes depends on lifestyle — e.g. they can be spread between people through <u>unprotected sex</u> or <u>sharing needles</u>.

Risk Factors Can Also Be Associated With Genetics

Sometimes you can <u>inherit faulty genes</u> that make you <u>more susceptible</u> to cancer.   For example:

Mutations in the <u>BRCA</u> genes have been linked to an <u>increased likelihood</u> of developing <u>breast</u> and <u>ovarian cancer</u>.

Topic 2 — Organisation

Warm-Up & Exam Questions

It's time for some more questions — don't just assume that you've remembered everything you just read on the past few pages. Give these a go, and then go back over anything that you struggled with.

Warm-Up Questions

1) What is meant by 'health'?
2) What does it mean if a disease is 'communicable'?
3) Give an example of a national financial cost associated with non-communicable diseases.
4) Give an example of a type of risk factor other than an aspect of a person's lifestyle.

Exam Questions

1 Many diseases have risk factors. (Grade 4-6)

1.1 What is meant by the term risk factor?

[1 mark]

1.2 Give **one** risk factor for lung disease.

[1 mark]

1.3 Name **one** carcinogen that is a risk factor for cancer.

[1 mark]

2 Cancer results from a tumour. (Grade 4-6)

2.1 What causes tumours to form? Tick **one** box.

☐ Uncontrolled cell division.

☐ Slow cell division.

☐ Cell division stopping.

☐ Cells dying.

[1 mark]

2.2 Name the type of tumour that causes cancer.

[1 mark]

2.3 Explain how secondary tumours form in the body.

[2 marks]

3 Diseases can be communicable or non-communicable. (Grade 6-7)

3.1 What is meant by a non-communicable disease?

[1 mark]

3.2 Influenza is a communicable disease.
Why might someone who has a problem with their immune system have an increased chance of suffering from influenza?

[1 mark]

Plant Cell Organisation

*You saw on pages 45-46 how animals keep their **specialised cells** neat and tidy — plants are in on the act too.*

Plant Cells Are Organised Into Tissues And Organs

<u>Plants</u> are made of <u>organs</u> like <u>stems</u>, <u>roots</u> and <u>leaves</u>. Plant organs work together to make <u>organ systems</u>.
These can perform the various tasks that a plant needs to carry out to survive and grow — for example,
<u>transporting substances</u> around the plant. Plant organs are made of <u>tissues</u>. Examples of plant tissues are:

1) <u>Epidermal tissue</u> — this <u>covers</u> the whole plant.
2) <u>Palisade mesophyll tissue</u> — this is the part of the leaf where most <u>photosynthesis</u> happens.
3) <u>Spongy mesophyll tissue</u> — this is also in the leaf, and contains big <u>air spaces</u> to allow
   gases to <u>diffuse</u> in and out of cells.
4) <u>Xylem</u> and <u>phloem</u> — they <u>transport</u> things like <u>water</u>, <u>mineral ions</u> and <u>food</u>
   around the plant (through the roots, stems and leaves — see next page for more).
5) <u>Meristem tissue</u> — this is found at the <u>growing tips</u> of <u>shoots</u> and <u>roots</u> and is able to
   <u>differentiate</u> (change) into lots of <u>different types</u> of plant cell, allowing the plant to <u>grow</u>.

For more on photosynthesis, see page 101.

The Leaf is an Organ Made Up of Several Types of Tissue

Leaves contain <u>epidermal</u>, <u>mesophyll</u>, <u>xylem</u> and <u>phloem</u> tissues.

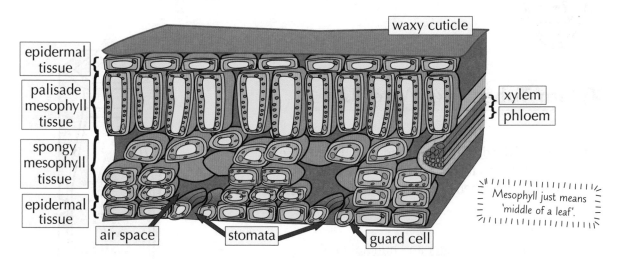

Mesophyll just means 'middle of a leaf'.

Here's how the <u>structures</u> of the tissues that make up the leaf are <u>related</u> to their <u>function</u>:

1) The epidermal tissues are covered with a <u>waxy cuticle</u>, which helps to <u>reduce water loss</u>
   by evaporation.
2) The <u>upper epidermis</u> is <u>transparent</u> so that light can pass through it to the <u>palisade layer</u>.
3) The <u>palisade layer</u> has lots of <u>chloroplasts</u> (the little structures where photosynthesis takes place).
   This means that they're near the top of the leaf where they can get the most <u>light</u>.
4) The <u>xylem</u> and <u>phloem</u> form a network of vascular bundles, which <u>deliver water</u> and
   other <u>nutrients</u> to the entire leaf and take away the <u>glucose</u> produced by photosynthesis.
   They also help <u>support</u> the structure.
5) The <u>tissues</u> of leaves are also adapted for efficient <u>gas exchange</u> (see page 40). E.g. the <u>lower
   epidermis</u> is full of little holes called <u>stomata</u>, which let CO_2 diffuse directly into the leaf.
   The opening and closing of stomata is controlled by <u>guard cells</u> in response to environmental
   conditions. The <u>air spaces</u> in the <u>spongy mesophyll</u> tissue <u>increase</u> the rate of diffusion of gases.

Transpiration and Translocation

*Flowering plants have **two** separate types of vessel — **xylem** and **phloem** — for transporting stuff around.*
***Both** types of vessel go to **every part** of the plant, but they are totally **separate**.*

Phloem Tubes Transport Food:

1) Made of columns of <u>elongated</u> living cells with small <u>pores in the end walls</u> to allow <u>cell sap</u> to flow through.

Cell sap is a liquid that's made up of the substances being transported and water.

2) They transport <u>food substances</u> (mainly dissolved <u>sugars</u>) made in the leaves to the rest of the plant for <u>immediate use</u> (e.g. in growing regions) or for <u>storage</u>.

3) The transport goes in <u>both directions</u>.

4) This process is called <u>translocation</u>.

Xylem Tubes Take Water Up:

1) Made of <u>dead cells</u> joined end to end with <u>no</u> end walls between them and a hole down the middle. They're strengthened with a material called <u>lignin</u>.

2) They carry <u>water</u> and <u>mineral</u> ions from the <u>roots</u> to the <u>stem</u> and <u>leaves</u>.

3) The movement of water <u>from</u> the <u>roots</u>, <u>through</u> the <u>xylem</u> and <u>out</u> of the <u>leaves</u> is called the <u>transpiration stream</u> (see next page).

Water and minerals

REVISION TIP

Xylem vessels carry water, phloem vessels carry sugars

Make sure you don't get your phloem <u>mixed up</u> with your xylem. To help you to learn which is which, you could remember that ph<u>l</u>oem transports substances in b<u>o</u>th directions, but xylem only transports things upwards — x<u>y</u> to the sky. It might just bag you a mark or two on exam day...

Transparation

*If you don't water a house plant for a few days it starts to go all droopy. Plants need **water**.*

Transparation is the Loss of Water from the Plant

1) Transpiration is caused by the <u>evaporation</u> and <u>diffusion</u> (see page 34) of water from a plant's surface. Most transpiration happens at the <u>leaves</u>.

2) This evaporation creates a slight <u>shortage</u> of water in the leaf, and so more water is drawn up from the rest of the plant through the <u>xylem vessels</u> to replace it.

3) This in turn means more water is drawn up from the <u>roots</u>, and so there's a constant <u>transpiration stream</u> of water through the plant.

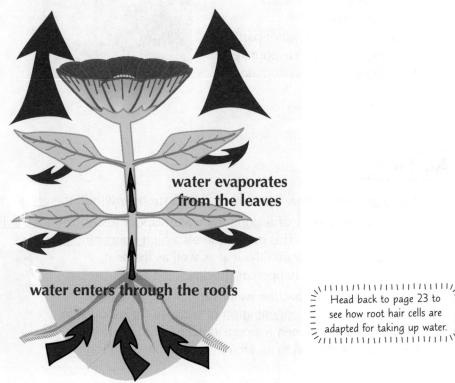

water evaporates from the leaves

water enters through the roots

Head back to page 23 to see how root hair cells are adapted for taking up water.

Transparation is just a <u>side-effect</u> of the way leaves are adapted for <u>photosynthesis</u>. They have to have <u>stomata</u> in them so that gases can be exchanged easily (see page 40). Because there's more water <u>inside</u> the plant than in the <u>air outside</u>, the water escapes from the leaves through the stomata by diffusion.

Transparation involves evaporation and diffusion

A big tree loses about a <u>thousand litres</u> of water from its leaves <u>every single day</u> — it's a fact. That's as much water as the average person drinks in a whole year, so the <u>roots</u> have to be very effective at drawing in water from the soil. Which is why they have all those root <u>hairs</u>, you see.

The Rate of Transpiration

*The **rate of transpiration** varies according to the **environmental conditions**...*

Transpiration Rate is Affected by Four Main Things

Light Intensity

1) The <u>brighter</u> the light, the <u>greater</u> the transpiration rate.
2) <u>Stomata</u> begin to <u>close</u> as it gets darker. Photosynthesis can't happen in the dark, so they don't need to be open to let <u>CO_2</u> in. When the stomata are closed, very little water can escape.

Temperature

1) The <u>warmer</u> it is, the <u>faster</u> transpiration happens.
2) When it's warm the water particles have <u>more energy</u> to evaporate and diffuse out of the stomata.

Air Flow

1) The <u>better</u> the air flow around a leaf (e.g. stronger wind), the <u>greater</u> the transpiration rate.
2) If air flow around a leaf is <u>poor</u>, the water vapour just <u>surrounds the leaf</u> and doesn't move away. This means there's a <u>high concentration</u> of water particles outside the leaf as well as inside it, so <u>diffusion</u> doesn't happen as quickly.
3) If there's <u>good</u> air flow, the water vapour is <u>swept away</u>, maintaining a <u>low concentration</u> of water in the air outside the leaf. Diffusion then happens quickly, from an area of higher concentration to an area of lower concentration.

Humidity

1) The <u>drier</u> the air around a leaf, the <u>faster</u> transpiration happens.
2) This is like what happens with air flow. If the air is <u>humid</u> there's a lot of water in it already, so there's not much of a <u>difference</u> between the inside and the outside of the leaf.
3) Diffusion happens <u>fastest</u> if there's a <u>really high concentration</u> in one place, and a <u>really low concentration</u> in the other.

Measuring Transpiration and Stomata

*Sorry, more on **transpiration**. But then it's a quick dash through **stomata** and out of the other end of the topic.*

A **Potometer** can be Used to **Estimate Transpiration Rate**

1) You can estimate the <u>rate of transpiration</u> by measuring the <u>uptake of water</u> by a plant.

2) This is because you can assume that <u>water uptake</u> by the plant is directly related to <u>water loss</u> by the leaves (transpiration).

3) Set up the apparatus as in the diagram, and then record the <u>starting position</u> of the air bubble.

4) Start a stopwatch and record the <u>distance moved</u> by the bubble per unit time, e.g. per hour.

5) Keep the <u>conditions constant</u> throughout the experiment, e.g. the <u>temperature</u> and <u>air humidity</u>.

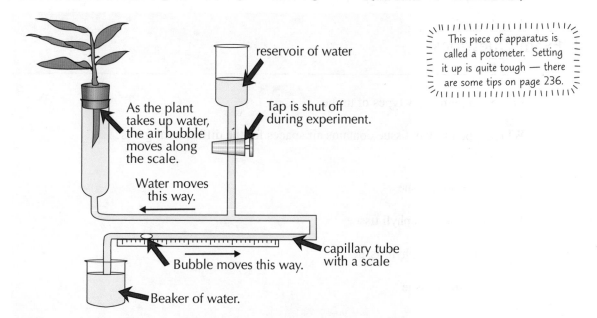

As the plant takes up water, the air bubble moves along the scale.

reservoir of water

Tap is shut off during experiment.

Water moves this way.

Bubble moves this way.

capillary tube with a scale

Beaker of water.

This piece of apparatus is called a potometer. Setting it up is quite tough — there are some tips on page 236.

Guard Cells Are Adapted to **Open and Close Stomata**

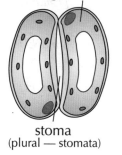

guard cell

stoma
(plural — stomata)

1) They have a kidney shape which <u>opens</u> and <u>closes</u> the <u>stomata</u> (page 40) in a leaf.

2) When the plant has <u>lots</u> of water the guard cells fill with it and go plump and <u>turgid</u>. This makes the stomata <u>open</u> so <u>gases</u> can be exchanged for <u>photosynthesis</u>.

3) When the plant is <u>short</u> of water, the guard cells lose water and become <u>flaccid</u>, making the stomata <u>close</u>. This helps stop too much water vapour <u>escaping</u>.

4) <u>Thin</u> outer walls and <u>thickened</u> inner walls make the opening and closing work.

5) They're also <u>sensitive to light</u> and <u>close at night</u> to save water without losing out on photosynthesis.

6) You usually find <u>more</u> stomata on the <u>undersides</u> of leaves than on the top. The <u>lower surface</u> is <u>shaded</u> and <u>cooler</u> — so <u>less water</u> is <u>lost</u> through the stomata than if they were on the upper surface.

7) Guard cells are therefore adapted for <u>gas exchange</u> and <u>controlling water loss</u> within a <u>leaf</u>.

The opening and closing of stomata allows plants to survive

Different leaves will have different <u>distributions</u> of <u>stomata</u>. You can peel the epidermal tissue off some leaves and then mount them on <u>microscope slides</u> (see page 19) to <u>compare</u> them.

Q1   Aloe vera plants grow in hot, dry areas. Primroses grow in cool, wet areas.
Predict which plant will have fewer stomata per cm² on the underside of its leaves.
Explain your answer.

[2 marks]

Q1 Video Solution

Warm-Up & Exam Questions

Just a few simple Warm-Up Questions and a few slightly harder Exam Questions stand between you and mastering cell organisation and transport in plants...

Warm-Up Questions

1) Describe the characteristics of meristem tissue.
2) Which layer of plant tissue contains lots of chloroplasts?
3) True or false? Substances pass in both directions through xylem vessels.
4) State the four main factors that affect the rate of transpiration in plants.

Exam Questions

1   Leaves contain many types of tissue. **(Grade 4-6)**

Which type of plant tissue contains air spaces for the diffusion of gases?
Tick **one** box.

☐   epidermal tissue

☐   palisade mesophyll tissue

☐   spongy mesophyll tissue

☐   meristem tissue

[1 mark]

2   Plants absorb water and mineral ions through their root hair cells. **(Grade 4-6)**

2.1   Name the vessels that transport water and mineral ions from the roots of a plant to the leaves.

[1 mark]

2.2   Describe the structure of the vessels you named in **2.1**.

[3 marks]

2.3   Name the process of water transport through a plant.

[1 mark]

3   Aphids are insects which feed on plant cell sap. Cell sap is the name given to the liquids carried around the plant in transport vessels. **(Grade 6-7)**

3.1   The cell sap the aphids feed on contains sugars.
What type of transport vessel does the cell sap come from?

[1 mark]

3.2   Explain how the structure of these transport vessels is adapted to their function.

[2 marks]

3.3   Name the movement of cell sap through the plant's transport vessels.

[1 mark]

Exam Questions

4   A student used a rose plant in his garden to carry out some investigations. **(Grade 7-9)**

4.1   The student cut several stems from the plant and put them in a glass vase on his kitchen windowsill.
He added a layer of oil to the surface of the water to prevent evaporation.
Over the next few days, he noticed that the level of water in the vase gradually decreased.
How would the reduction of water in the vase differ if the kitchen was not as warm?
Explain your answer.

[3 marks]

4.2*   The student investigated the appearance of guard cells on the underside of a rose leaf at different
times on a humid day. He took a leaf from his rose plant at 10 am, 4 pm and 11 pm and immediately
examined it under a microscope. He drew diagrams to show the appearance of the guard cells at each
time, as shown in **Figure 1**.

Figure 1

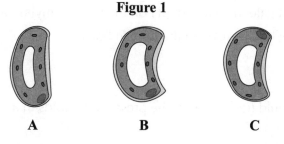

       A   **B**   **C**

Suggest which diagram (A-C), shows the appearance of the guard cells observed at 11 pm.
Explain your answer.

[4 marks]

5   A student was investigating transpiration in basil plants under different conditions. **(Grade 7-9)**
She used twelve plants, three plants in each of the four different conditions.
The plants were weighed before and after the experiment. She calculated the
% loss in the mass per day and recorded her results in **Table 1**.

Table 1

plant	in a room (% loss in mass)	next to a fan (% loss in mass)	by a lamp (% loss in mass)	next to a fan and by a lamp (% loss in mass)
1	5	8	10	13
2	5	9	11	15
3	4	11	9	13
mean	4.7	9.3		13.6

5.1   Calculate the mean % loss in plant mass for the three plants by a lamp.

[2 marks]

5.2   Explain why the plants located next to a fan lost more mass than those in a still room.

[3 marks]

5.3   The student then covered the undersides of the leaves with petroleum jelly.
Suggest how this would affect the rate of transpiration from the leaves.

[2 marks]

5.4   Suggest how you could alter the student's experiment to investigate the effects of humidity
on the rate of transpiration in basil plants.

[2 marks]

Revision Summary for Topic 2

Well, that's <u>Topic 2</u> finished. Now it's time to test how much you've taken in...

For even more practice, try the Retrieval Quiz for Topic 2 — just scan this QR code!

Topic 2 Quiz

- Try these questions and <u>tick off each one</u> when you <u>get it right</u>.
- When you're <u>completely happy</u> with a sub-topic, tick it off.

Cell Organisation (p.45-46) ☑

1) What is a tissue?
2) Give an example of a human organ system.

The Role of Enzymes and Food Tests (p.47-53) ☑

3) Why can enzymes be described as biological catalysts?
4) What does it mean when an enzyme has been 'denatured'?
5) Describe how you could investigate the effect of pH on the rate of amylase activity.
6) List the three places where amylase is made in the human body.
7) What is the role of lipases?
8) Where is bile stored?
9) Name the solution that you would use to test for the presence of lipids in a food sample.

The Lungs and Circulatory System (p.56-60) ☑

10) Explain the role that alveoli play in gas exchange.
11) Explain why the circulatory system in humans is described as a 'double circulatory system'.
12) Name the four chambers of the heart.
13) How are arteries adapted to carry blood away from the heart?
14) Why do red blood cells not have a nucleus?
15) Name the pigment in red blood cells.
16) What is the function of plasma?

Diseases and Risk Factors (p.63-71) ☑

17) Give two advantages of statins.
18) What name is given to a replacement heart valve that has been man-made?
19) Give a factor other than disease that can affect health.
20) Give an example of where different types of disease might interact in the body.
21) Give one risk factor for Type 2 diabetes.
22) Which type of tumour is not cancerous?

Plant Cell Organisation and Transport (p.73-77) ☑

23) List the tissues that make up a leaf.
24) Explain how the structure of the upper epidermal tissue in a leaf is related to its function.
25) What is the function of phloem?
26) What is transpiration?
27) How could you measure the rate of transpiration?
28) Name the type of cell that helps open and close stomata.

Communicable Disease

*If you're hoping I'll ease you gently into this new topic... no such luck. Straight on to the **baddies** of biology.*

There Are **Several Types** of **Pathogen**

1) Pathogens are <u>microorganisms</u> that enter the body and cause <u>disease</u>.
2) They cause <u>communicable</u> (infectious) diseases — diseases that can <u>easily spread</u> (see p.67).
3) Both <u>plants</u> and <u>animals</u> can be infected by pathogens.
4) Pathogens can be <u>bacteria</u> or <u>viruses</u> (see below), or <u>protists</u> or <u>fungi</u> (see next page).

1. **Bacteria** Are Very Small **Living Cells**

1) Bacteria are <u>very small cells</u> (about 1/100th the size of your body cells), which can reproduce rapidly inside your body.

2) They can make you <u>feel ill</u> by <u>producing toxins</u> (poisons) that <u>damage your cells and tissues</u>.

2. **Viruses** Are **Not** Cells — They're Much Smaller

1) Viruses are <u>not cells</u>. They're <u>tiny</u>, about 1/100th the size of a bacterium.

2) Like bacteria, they can <u>reproduce rapidly</u> inside your body.

3) They live inside your cells and <u>replicate themselves</u> using the cells' <u>machinery</u> to produce many <u>copies</u> of themselves.

4) The cell will usually then <u>burst</u>, releasing all the new viruses.

5) This <u>cell damage</u> is what makes you feel ill.

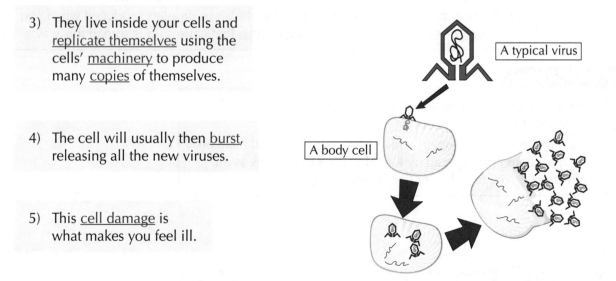

A typical virus

A body cell

Communicable Disease

3. Protists are Single-Celled Eukaryotes

1) There are lots of different types of protists. But they're all eukaryotes (see page 16) and most of them are single-celled.

2) Some protists are parasites. Parasites live on or inside other organisms and can cause them damage. They are often transferred to the organism by a vector, which doesn't get the disease itself — e.g. an insect that carries the protist.

4. Fungi Come in Different Shapes

1) Some fungi are single-celled.

2) Others have a body which is made up of hyphae (thread-like structures).

3) These hyphae can grow and penetrate human skin and the surface of plants, causing diseases.

4) The hyphae can produce spores, which can be spread to other plants and animals.

Pathogens Can Be Spread in Different Ways

Pathogens can be spread in many ways. Here are just a few...

Water

1) Some pathogens can be picked up by drinking or bathing in dirty water.

2) E.g. cholera is a bacterial infection that's spread by drinking water contaminated with the diarrhoea of other sufferers.

Air

1) Pathogens can be carried in the air and can then be breathed in.

2) Some airborne pathogens are carried in the air in droplets produced when you cough or sneeze — e.g. the influenza virus that causes flu is spread this way.

Direct Contact

1) Some pathogens can be picked up by touching contaminated surfaces, including the skin.

2) E.g. athlete's foot is a fungus which makes skin itch and flake off. It's most commonly spread by touching the same things as an infected person, e.g. shower floors and towels.

Watch yourself, there are a lot of nasties out there...

Plants need to be worried too, as you'll find out. It's strange to think such small things can have such massive effects on your body, but bacteria and viruses in particular can multiply extremely quickly.

Viral and Fungal Diseases

*There are heaps of diseases caused by **viruses** or **fungi** — here are four of them...*

Measles, HIV and TMV are Viral Diseases

1. Measles

1) Measles is spread by droplets from an infected person's sneeze or cough.
2) People with measles develop a red skin rash, and they show signs of a fever (a high temperature).
3) Measles can be very serious, or even fatal, if there are complications. For example, measles can sometimes lead to pneumonia (a lung infection) or inflammation of the brain (encephalitis).
4) Most people are vaccinated against measles when they're young.

2. HIV

1) HIV is a virus spread by sexual contact, or by exchanging bodily fluids such as blood. This can happen when people share needles when taking drugs.
2) HIV initially causes flu-like symptoms for a few weeks. Usually, the person doesn't then experience any symptoms for several years. During this time, HIV can be controlled with antiretroviral drugs. These stop the virus replicating in the body.
3) The virus attacks the immune cells (see page 87).
4) If the body's immune system is badly damaged, it can't cope with other infections or cancers. At this stage, the virus is known as late stage HIV infection, or AIDS.

3. Tobacco Mosaic Virus

1) Tobacco mosaic virus (TMV) is a virus that affects many species of plants, e.g. tomatoes.
2) It causes a mosaic pattern on the leaves of the plants — parts of the leaves become discoloured.
3) The discolouration means the plant can't carry out photosynthesis as well, so the virus affects growth.

Photosynthesis is important for plant growth because it produces glucose — see page 101.

Rose Black Spot is a Fungal Disease

1) Rose black spot is a fungus that causes purple or black spots to develop on the leaves of rose plants. The leaves can then turn yellow and drop off.
2) This means that less photosynthesis can happen, so the plant doesn't grow very well.
3) It spreads through the environment in water or by the wind.
4) Gardeners can treat the disease using fungicides and by stripping the plant of its affected leaves. These leaves then need to be destroyed so that the fungus can't spread to other rose plants.

Protist and Bacterial Diseases

*Sorry — I'm afraid there are some more diseases to learn about here. This time, there's one disease caused by a protist and a couple caused by **bacteria**. I don't know about you, but I'm starting to feel a bit itchy...*

Malaria is a Disease Caused by a Protist

1) Part of the malarial protist's <u>life cycle</u> takes place inside a mosquito.

2) The mosquitoes are <u>vectors</u> (see page 82) — they <u>pick up</u> the malarial protist when they <u>feed</u> on an <u>infected animal</u>.

3) Every time the mosquito feeds on another animal, it <u>infects it</u> by inserting the protist into the animal's blood vessels.

4) Malaria causes <u>repeating</u> episodes of <u>fever</u>. It can be <u>fatal</u>.

5) People can be protected from mosquitoes using <u>insecticides</u> and <u>mosquito nets</u>.

There's more on protists on page 82.

Salmonella and Gonorrhea Are Two Bacterial Diseases

1. *Salmonella*

1) *Salmonella* is a type of <u>bacteria</u> that causes <u>food poisoning</u>.

2) Infected people can suffer from <u>fever</u>, <u>stomach cramps</u>, <u>vomiting</u> and <u>diarrhoea</u>.

3) These symptoms are caused by the <u>toxins</u> that the bacteria produce (see page 81).

4) You can get *Salmonella* food poisoning by eating <u>food</u> that's been <u>contaminated</u> with *Salmonella* bacteria, e.g. eating chicken that caught the disease whilst it was alive, or eating food that has been contaminated by being prepared in unhygienic conditions.

2. Gonorrhoea

1) <u>Gonorrhoea</u> is a <u>sexually transmitted disease</u> (STD).

2) STDs are passed on by <u>sexual contact</u>, e.g. having unprotected sex.

3) Gonorrhoea is caused by <u>bacteria</u>.

4) A person with gonorrhoea will get <u>pain</u> when they <u>urinate</u>. Another symptom is a thick yellow or green <u>discharge</u> from the <u>vagina</u> or the <u>penis</u>.

5) Gonorrhoea was originally treated with an <u>antibiotic</u> called <u>penicillin</u>, but this has become trickier now because strains of the bacteria have become <u>resistant</u> to it (see page 90).

6) To prevent the <u>spread</u> of gonorrhoea, people can be treated with <u>antibiotics</u> and should use <u>barrier methods</u> of contraception (see page 142), such as <u>condoms</u>.

Hang in there, this stuff is pretty gross, but it's nearly over...

Try drawing out a <u>table</u> with columns for 'disease', 'type of organism it's caused by', 'symptoms' and 'how it's spread', then fill it in for all the diseases on this page and the previous one. See how much you can write down <u>without</u> looking back at the page.

Preventing Disease

*Pathogens can make life very **difficult**, but there are lots of things we can do to **protect** ourselves...*

The **Spread** of Disease Can Be **Reduced** or **Prevented**

There are things that we can do to <u>reduce</u>, and even <u>prevent</u>, the spread of disease. For example:

1. Being **Hygienic**

Using <u>simple hygiene measures</u> can prevent the spread of disease.

> Doing things like <u>washing your hands</u> thoroughly before preparing food or after you've sneezed can stop you infecting another person.

2. **Destroying Vectors**

1) By <u>getting rid</u> of the <u>organisms</u> that spread disease, you can prevent the disease from being <u>passed on</u>.
2) Vectors that are <u>insects</u> can be killed using <u>insecticides</u> or by <u>destroying</u> their <u>habitat</u> so that they can no longer breed.

> The <u>spread</u> of malaria (see previous page) can be reduced by stopping <u>mosquitoes</u> from <u>breeding</u>.

3. **Isolating** Infected Individuals

If you <u>isolate</u> someone who has a communicable disease, it <u>prevents</u> them from <u>passing it on</u> to anyone else.

4. **Vaccination**

<u>Vaccinating</u> people and animals against communicable diseases means that they <u>can't</u> develop the infection and then <u>pass it on</u> to someone else.

There's more about how vaccination works on page 88.

> For example, in the UK, most <u>poultry</u> (e.g. chickens and turkeys) is given a <u>vaccination</u> against *Salmonella*. This is to control the <u>spread</u> of the disease.

There you go, basic hygiene can be a real life saver...

There are <u>lots of ways</u> to prevent the spread of diseases and often the method used <u>depends</u> on the disease. As well as the methods on this page, don't forget about the different ways of preventing the spread of the diseases you learnt about on the <u>previous two pages</u> — e.g. using condoms.

Warm-Up & Exam Questions

Have a go at these questions to test whether you know about each of the diseases covered on the previous pages — their symptoms, how they are transmitted and how their spread can be limited.

Warm-Up Questions

1) What is meant by a communicable disease?
2) List three viral diseases.
3) What symptom of measles is shown on the skin?
4) What effect does rose black spot disease have on plants?
5) How is gonorrhoea transmitted between individuals?
6) How can vaccinations help to limit the spread of a disease?

Exam Questions

1 Diseases are often recognised by their symptoms. **(Grade 4-6)**

1.1 Describe the initial symptoms of HIV infection.

[1 mark]

1.2 Give **two** symptoms of gonorrhoea.

[2 marks]

1.3 A person has food poisoning caused by *Salmonella*. Give **two** symptoms that they may have.

[2 marks]

2 Viruses are a type of pathogen. They can infect every type of living organism. **(Grade 6-7)**

2.1 What is meant by the term 'pathogen'?

[1 mark]

2.2 The leaves of a tobacco plant can become discoloured if it is infected by a particular virus. Name the virus that affects tobacco plants in this way and describe what effect the discolouration of the leaves can have on a plant.

[2 marks]

2.3 HIV is a virus that can infect humans. Outline how HIV can be spread.

[2 marks]

3 The methods used to prevent the spread of a disease depend on how the disease is transmitted. **(Grade 6-7)**

3.1 It is important for chefs to wash their hands thoroughly before cooking. Suggest why.

[1 mark]

3.2 Explain why hand washing may not be helpful in limiting the spread of malaria.

[2 marks]

3.3 Suggest and explain **one** reason why efforts to limit the spread of malaria often focus on the mosquito.

[1 mark]

Fighting Disease

*The human body has some pretty neat features when it comes to **fighting disease**.*

Your Body Has a Pretty Sophisticated **Defence System**

1) The human body has got features that stop a lot of nasties getting inside in the first place.
2) The <u>skin</u> acts as a <u>barrier</u> to pathogens. It also secretes <u>antimicrobial substances</u> which kill pathogens.
3) <u>Hairs</u> and <u>mucus</u> in your nose <u>trap</u> particles that could contain pathogens.
4) The <u>trachea</u> and <u>bronchi</u> (breathing pipework — see page 56) secrete <u>mucus</u> to trap pathogens.
5) The trachea and bronchi are lined with <u>cilia</u>. These are hair-like structures, which <u>waft the mucus</u> up to the back of the throat where it can be <u>swallowed</u>.
6) The <u>stomach</u> produces <u>hydrochloric acid</u>. This kills pathogens that make it that far from the mouth.

Your **Immune System** Can **Attack Pathogens**

1) If pathogens do make it into your body, your <u>immune system</u> kicks in to destroy them.
2) The most important part of your immune system is the <u>white blood cells</u>. They travel around in your blood and crawl into every part of you, constantly patrolling for microbes. When they come across an invading microbe they have three lines of attack.

1. **Consuming** Them

White blood cells can <u>engulf</u> foreign cells and <u>digest</u> them. This is called <u>phagocytosis</u>.

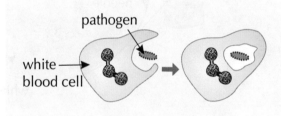

2. Producing **Antibodies**

1) Every invading pathogen has unique molecules (called <u>antigens</u>) on its surface.
2) When some types of white blood cell come across a <u>foreign antigen</u> (i.e. one they don't recognise), they will start to produce <u>proteins</u> called <u>antibodies</u> to lock onto the invading cells so that they can be <u>found</u> and <u>destroyed</u> by other white blood cells. The antibodies produced are specific to that type of antigen — they won't lock on to any others.
3) Antibodies are then produced <u>rapidly</u> and carried around the body to find all similar bacteria or viruses.
4) If the person is infected with the same pathogen again the white blood cells will rapidly produce the antibodies to kill it — the person is <u>naturally immune</u> to that pathogen and won't get ill.

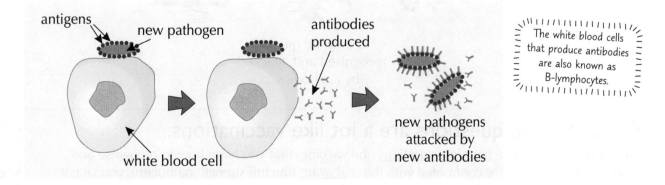

The white blood cells that produce antibodies are also known as B-lymphocytes.

3. Producing **Antitoxins**   These counteract toxins produced by the <u>invading bacteria</u>.

Fighting Disease — Vaccination

*Vaccinations have changed the way we fight disease. We don't always have to deal with the problem once it's happened — we can **prevent** it happening in the first place.*

Vaccination — **Protects** from **Future Infections**

1) When you're infected with a new <u>pathogen</u>, it takes your white blood cells a few days to <u>learn</u> how to deal with it. But by that time, you can be pretty <u>ill</u>.

2) <u>Vaccinations</u> involve injecting small amounts of <u>dead</u> or <u>inactive</u> pathogens. These carry <u>antigens</u>, which cause your body to produce <u>antibodies</u> to attack them — even though the pathogen is <u>harmless</u> (since it's dead or inactive).

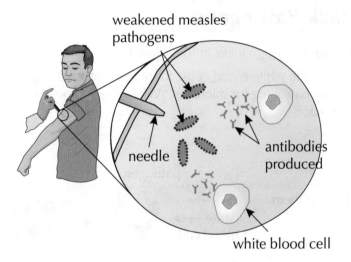

weakened measles pathogens

needle

antibodies produced

white blood cell

> The MMR vaccine contains <u>weakened</u> versions of the viruses that cause <u>measles</u>, <u>mumps</u> and <u>rubella</u> (German measles) all in one vaccine.

3) But if live pathogens of the same type appear after that, the white blood cells can <u>rapidly</u> mass-produce antibodies to kill off the pathogen.

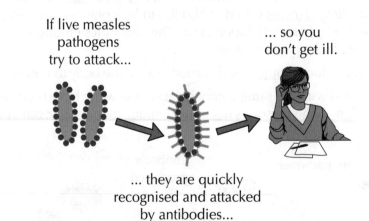

If live measles pathogens try to attack...

... they are quickly recognised and attacked by antibodies...

... so you don't get ill.

Practice exam questions are a lot like vaccinations...

We expose you to some <u>harmless questions</u> (the vaccine) that you learn how to recognise and answer, then when you're confronted with the <u>real exam</u> (the full strength pathogen), you've got the necessary <u>knowledge</u> (antibodies) to answer (kill) them. Gosh, you'd best get revising...

Q1 Basia is vaccinated against flu and Cassian isn't. They are both exposed to a flu virus. Cassian falls ill whereas Basia doesn't. Explain why. [2 marks]

Q1 Video Solution

Fighting Disease — Vaccination

*Having a whole range of **vaccinations** is pretty much standard now, so children today are **much less likely** to catch the kinds of diseases that they might have in the past. That doesn't mean that vaccination is without its problems though...*

There are **Pros** and **Cons** of **Vaccination**

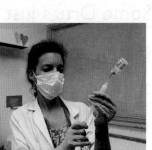

Pros:

1) Vaccines have helped <u>control</u> lots of communicable diseases that were once <u>common</u> in the UK (e.g. polio, measles, whooping cough, rubella, mumps, tetanus...).

> Because of vaccinations, <u>smallpox</u> no longer occurs at all, and <u>polio</u> infections have fallen by 99%.

2) Big outbreaks of disease — called <u>epidemics</u> — can be prevented if a <u>large percentage</u> of the population is vaccinated. That way, even the people who aren't vaccinated are <u>unlikely</u> to catch the disease because there are <u>fewer</u> people able to pass it on. But if a significant number of people <u>aren't</u> vaccinated, the disease can <u>spread</u> quickly through them and lots of people will be <u>ill</u> at the same time.

Cons:

1) Vaccines don't always work — sometimes they <u>don't</u> give you <u>immunity</u>.

2) You can sometimes have a <u>bad reaction</u> to a vaccine (e.g. swelling, or maybe something more serious like a fever or seizures). But bad reactions are very <u>rare</u>.

Prevention is better than cure...

Deciding whether to have a vaccination means <u>balancing risks</u> — the risk of catching the disease if you don't have a vaccine, against the risk of having a bad reaction if you do. As always, you need to look at the <u>evidence</u>. For example, if you get measles (the disease), there's about a 1 in 15 chance that you'll get complications (e.g. pneumonia) — and about 1 in 500 people who get measles actually die. However, the number of people who have a problem with the vaccine is more like 1 in 1 000 000.

Fighting Disease — Drugs

*You've probably had to take some sort of **medicine** if you've been ill, e.g. cough remedies, painkillers. And you're about to find out why it's important to only take **antibiotics** when you **really need them**.*

Some Drugs Just **Relieve Symptoms** — Others **Cure** the Problem

1) <u>Painkillers</u> (e.g. aspirin) are drugs that relieve pain. However, they don't actually tackle the <u>cause</u> of the disease or kill pathogens, they just help to reduce the <u>symptoms</u>.

2) Other drugs do a similar kind of thing — reduce the <u>symptoms</u> without tackling the underlying <u>cause</u>. For example, lots of "cold remedies" don't actually <u>cure</u> colds.

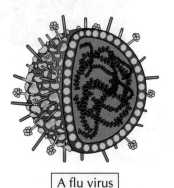

A flu virus

3) <u>Antibiotics</u> (e.g. penicillin) work differently — they actually <u>kill</u> (or prevent the growth of) the bacteria causing the problem without killing your own body cells. <u>Different antibiotics</u> kill <u>different types</u> of bacteria, so it's important to be treated with the <u>right one</u>.

4) But antibiotics <u>don't destroy viruses</u> (e.g. <u>flu</u> or <u>cold</u> viruses). Viruses reproduce <u>using your own body cells</u>, which makes it very difficult to develop drugs that destroy just the virus without killing the body's cells.

5) The use of antibiotics has greatly reduced the number of deaths from communicable diseases caused by <u>bacteria</u>.

Bacteria Can Become **Resistant** to **Antibiotics**

1) Bacteria can <u>mutate</u> — sometimes the mutations cause them to be <u>resistant</u> to (not killed by) an <u>antibiotic</u>.

2) If you have an <u>infection</u>, some of the bacteria might be <u>resistant</u> to antibiotics.

3) This means that when you <u>treat</u> the infection, only the <u>non-resistant</u> strains of bacteria will be <u>killed</u>.

4) The individual <u>resistant</u> bacteria will <u>survive</u> and <u>reproduce</u>, and the population of the resistant strain will <u>increase</u>. This is an example of natural selection (see page 176).

5) This resistant strain could cause a <u>serious infection</u> that <u>can't</u> be treated by antibiotics. E.g. <u>MRSA</u> (meticillin-resistant *Staphylococcus aureus*) causes serious wound infections and is resistant to the powerful antibiotic <u>meticillin</u>.

6) To <u>slow down</u> the <u>rate</u> of development of <u>resistant strains</u>, it's important for doctors to <u>avoid</u> <u>over-prescribing</u> antibiotics. So you <u>won't</u> get them for a <u>sore throat</u>, only for something more serious.

7) It's also important that you <u>finish</u> the <u>whole course</u> of antibiotics and don't just stop once you feel better.

Antibiotic resistance is inevitable...

Antibiotic resistance is <u>scary</u>. Bacteria reproduce quickly, and so are pretty <u>fast at evolving</u> to deal with threats (e.g. antibiotics). If we were back in the situation where we had no way to treat bacterial infections, it'd be a bit of a nightmare. So do your bit, and <u>finish your courses</u> of antibiotics.

Fighting Disease — Drugs

*New drugs against diseases don't just appear out of nowhere. There's a **very lengthy process** which a new drug has to go through before it can be used in **humans** (more on that on the next page). **First of all**, though, a new drug has to be **discovered** — this is where plants and microorganisms come in...*

Many **Drugs** Originally Came From **Plants**

1) Plants produce a variety of chemicals to defend themselves against pests and pathogens (see page 98).

2) Some of these chemicals can be used as drugs to treat human diseases or relieve symptoms.

3) A lot of our current medicines were discovered by studying plants used in traditional cures. For example:

> 1) Aspirin is used as a painkiller and to lower fever. It was developed from a chemical found in willow.
> 2) Digitalis is used to treat heart conditions. It was developed from a chemical found in foxgloves.

4) Some drugs were extracted from microorganisms. For example:

> 1) Alexander Fleming was clearing out some Petri dishes containing bacteria.
> 2) He noticed that one of the dishes of bacteria also had mould on it and the area around the mould was free of the bacteria.
> 3) He found that the mould (called *Penicillium notatum*) on the Petri dish was producing a substance that killed the bacteria — this substance was penicillin.

5) These days, drugs are made on a large scale in the pharmaceutical industry — they're synthesised by chemists in labs.

6) However, the process still might start with a chemical extracted from a plant.

Good old mould — saving lives since 1928...

Drug development is a big industry. A lot of money and time goes into developing new and better drugs, but it can all start with something as humble as a plant or a microorganism.

Developing Drugs

New drugs are constantly being developed. But before they can be given to the general public,
*they have to go through a thorough **testing** procedure. This is what usually happens...*

There are **Three Main Stages** in Drug Testing

1) In preclinical testing, drugs are tested on <u>human cells and tissues</u> in the lab.

> However, you can't use human cells and tissues to test drugs that affect <u>whole</u>
> or <u>multiple</u> body systems, e.g. testing a drug for blood pressure must be done
> on a whole animal because it has an intact circulatory system.

2) The next step in preclinical testing is to test the drug on <u>live animals</u>.

   1) This is to test <u>efficacy</u> (whether the drug <u>works</u> and produces
      the effect you're looking for), to find out about its <u>toxicity</u>
      (how harmful it is) and to find the best <u>dosage</u> (the concentration
      that should be given, and how often it should be given).

   2) The law in Britain states that any new drug must be tested on
      <u>two</u> different <u>live mammals</u>. Some people think it's <u>cruel</u> to test
      on animals, but others believe this is the <u>safest</u> way to make sure
      a drug isn't dangerous before it's given to humans.

   > But some people think that
   > animals are so different from
   > humans that testing on
   > animals is pointless.

3) If the drug <u>passes</u> the tests on animals then it's tested on <u>human volunteers</u> in a <u>clinical trial</u>.

   1) First, the drug is tested on <u>healthy</u> volunteers. This is to make sure that it doesn't have
      any <u>harmful side effects</u> when the body is working normally. At the start of the trial,
      a <u>very low dose</u> of the drug is given and this is gradually increased.

   2) If the results of the tests on healthy volunteers are good, the drugs can be tested on people
      suffering from the <u>illness</u>. The <u>optimum dose</u> is found — this is the dose of drug that is the
      <u>most effective</u> and has <u>few side effects</u>.

   3) To test how well the drug works, patients are <u>randomly</u> put into <u>two groups</u>. One is given
      the <u>new drug</u>, the other is given a <u>placebo</u> (a substance that's like the drug being tested but
      doesn't do anything). This is so the <u>doctor</u> can see the actual difference the drug makes
      — it allows for the <u>placebo effect</u> (when the patient expects the treatment to work and so
      <u>feels better</u>, even though the treatment isn't doing anything).

   4) Clinical trials are <u>blind</u> — the patient in the study <u>doesn't know</u> whether they're getting
      the drug or the placebo. In fact, they're often <u>double-blind</u> — neither the patient nor the
      <u>doctor</u> knows until all the <u>results</u> have been gathered. This is so the doctors <u>monitoring</u>
      the patients and <u>analysing</u> the results aren't <u>subconsciously influenced</u> by their knowledge.

   5) The results of drug testing and drug trials aren't published until they've
      been through <u>peer review</u>. This helps to prevent <u>false claims</u>.

> Peer review is when other scientists check that the work is valid and has been carried out rigorously — see page 1.

The placebo effect doesn't work with revision...

... you can't just expect to get a good mark and then magically get it. I know, I know, there's a lot of
information to take in on this page, but just <u>read it through slowly</u>. There's nothing too tricky here —
it's just a case of going over it <u>again</u> and <u>again</u> until you've got it all firmly lodged in your memory.

Warm-Up & Exam Questions

It's easy to think you've learnt everything in the section until you try the Warm-Up Questions.
Don't panic if there's a bit you've forgotten, just go back over that bit until it's firmly fixed in your brain.

Warm-Up Questions

1) How is the skin adapted to defend against the entry of pathogens?
2) What is the role of the immune system?
3) From what organism was the drug digitalis sourced originally?
4) What is meant by the efficacy of a drug?
5) What is a placebo?
6) Why are placebos used in drug trials?

Exam Questions

1 There are many different lines of defence in the human body (Grade 4-6) that help to prevent pathogens from entering the blood.

1.1 What is the role of the hairs and mucus in the nose?

[1 mark]

1.2 How do the cilia in the trachea and bronchi help to defend the body?

[1 mark]

1.3 What does the stomach produce to kill pathogens?

[1 mark]

2 A scientist is carrying out a clinical trial. (Grade 6-7)

2.1 What is a drug tested on in a clinical trial? Tick **one** box.

☐ human cells

☐ human volunteers

☐ live animals

☐ human tissue

[1 mark]

2.2 The clinical trial is double blind. Explain what this means.

[2 marks]

2.3 Apart from the toxicity of the drug, give **two** other factors that scientists research during drug testing.

[2 marks]

2.4 The results from drug testing are assessed by peer review. Explain what this means and why it is done.

[2 marks]

Topic 3 — Infection and Response

Exam Questions

3 White blood cells play an important role in defence against pathogens, including the production of antibodies and antitoxins.

3.1 Apart from producing antibodies and antitoxins, give **one** other method that white blood cells use to defend the body against pathogens.

[1 mark]

3.2 Explain why the production of antibodies is specific to a certain disease.

[1 mark]

4 The development of antibiotics has helped to save many lives. However, the overuse of antibiotics may be a threat to global health in the future. Penicillin is an example of an antibiotic.

4.1 Name the organism that penicillin originates from.

[1 mark]

4.2 Explain why the overuse of antibiotics may be a threat to global health in the future.

[2 marks]

4.3 Infection with rhinovirus causes the common cold. Explain why antibiotics such as penicillin are not used to treat a cold.

[1 mark]

5 Rubella is a communicable viral disease.

The rubella virus is spread in droplets through the air when an infected person coughs, sneezes or talks. The virus causes several symptoms including fever and painful joints. Fortunately, the spread of the disease can be reduced by vaccination.

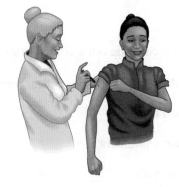

5.1 Suggest a drug that patients with rubella may be given to relieve their symptoms.

[1 mark]

5.2 Explain why it might be difficult to develop a drug which destroys rubella in the body.

[2 marks]

5.3* Explain how being vaccinated against rubella can prevent a person from catching the disease and suggest why vaccinating a large proportion of the population reduces the risk of someone who hasn't been vaccinated from catching rubella.

[6 marks]

5.4 Suggest **one** reason why some individuals may choose not to receive a vaccination against a disease.

[1 mark]

Monoclonal Antibodies

Antibodies aren't only used by the immune system — scientists have engineered them for lots of new uses.

Monoclonal Antibodies are Identical Antibodies

1) Antibodies are produced by <u>B-lymphocytes</u> — a type of white blood cell (see page 87).

2) <u>Monoclonal antibodies</u> are produced from <u>lots of clones</u> of a single white blood cell. This means all the antibodies are <u>identical</u> and will only target <u>one</u> specific <u>protein antigen</u>.

3) However, you can't just grab the lymphocyte that made the antibody and grow more — lymphocytes <u>don't divide very easily</u>.

4) <u>Tumour cells</u>, on the other hand, don't produce antibodies but <u>divide lots</u> — so they can be <u>grown really easily</u>.

5) It's possible to <u>fuse</u> a mouse <u>B-lymphocyte</u> with a <u>tumour cell</u> to create a cell called a <u>hybridoma</u>.

6) Hybridoma cells can be <u>cloned</u> to get <u>lots</u> of identical cells. These cells all produce the same <u>antibodies</u> (<u>monoclonal antibodies</u>). The antibodies can be <u>collected</u> and <u>purified</u>.

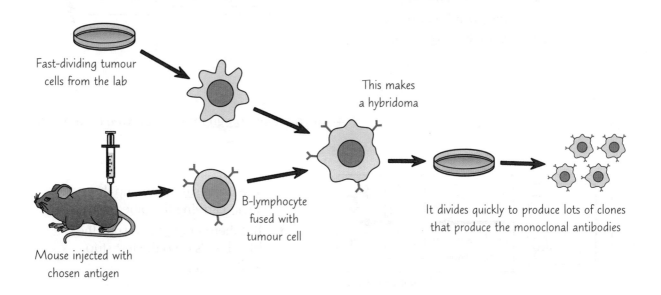

Fast-dividing tumour cells from the lab

This makes a hybridoma

B-lymphocyte fused with tumour cell

It divides quickly to produce lots of clones that produce the monoclonal antibodies

Mouse injected with chosen antigen

7) You can make monoclonal antibodies that <u>bind to anything</u> you want, e.g. an antigen that's only found on the surface of <u>one type of cell</u>. Monoclonal antibodies are really useful because they will <u>only</u> bind to (target) <u>this molecule</u> — this means you can use them to target a specific cell or chemical in the body.

Monoclonal Antibodies

Monoclonal Antibodies Are Used In Pregnancy Tests

A <u>hormone</u> called HCG is found in the <u>urine</u> of women <u>only</u> when they are <u>pregnant</u>.
<u>Pregnancy testing sticks</u> detect this hormone. Here's how they work:

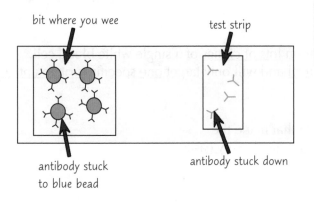

bit where you wee

test strip

antibody stuck
to blue bead

antibody stuck down

1) The bit of the stick you <u>wee on</u> has some <u>antibodies</u> to the hormone, with <u>blue beads attached</u>.

2) The <u>test strip</u> (the bit of the stick that turns blue if you're pregnant) has some more antibodies to the hormone <u>stuck onto it</u> (so that they can't move).

3) If you're <u>pregnant</u> and you wee on the stick:

- The <u>hormone binds</u> to the <u>antibodies</u> on the <u>blue beads</u>.
- The urine <u>moves up</u> the stick, <u>carrying</u> the hormone and the beads.
- The beads and hormone <u>bind</u> to the antibodies on the strip.
- So the <u>blue beads</u> get <u>stuck</u> on the strip, turning it <u>blue</u>.

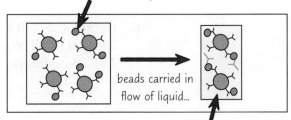

hormone stuck to antibody stuck to bead

beads carried in
flow of liquid...

...and stick to strip

4) If you're <u>not pregnant</u> and you wee on the stick:

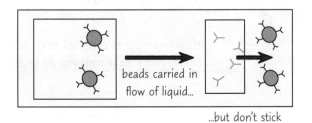

beads carried in
flow of liquid...

...but don't stick

- The urine <u>still</u> moves up the stick, carrying the <u>blue beads</u>.
- But there's <u>nothing</u> to stick the blue beads onto the <u>test strip</u>, so it <u>doesn't go blue</u>.

Handy little things, these monoclonal antibodies...

Monoclonal antibodies have lots <u>more uses</u> in <u>medicine</u>, e.g. a test similar to a pregnancy test can be used to detect the <u>antigens</u> of <u>pathogens</u> in a <u>blood sample</u>. There's more about their uses on the next page.

Monoclonal Antibodies

*Because monoclonal antibodies can be produced to **target** a **specific** chemical or cell, they have lots of uses.*

Monoclonal Antibodies Can be Used to **Treat Diseases**...

1) <u>Different cells</u> in the body have <u>different antigens</u> on their cell <u>surface</u>. So you can make monoclonal antibodies that will bind to <u>specific cells</u> in the body (e.g. just liver cells).

2) Cancer cells have <u>antigens</u> on their <u>cell membranes</u> that <u>aren't</u> found on normal body cells. They're called <u>tumour markers</u>.

3) In the lab, you can make <u>monoclonal antibodies</u> that will <u>bind</u> to these tumour markers.

4) An <u>anti-cancer drug</u> can be attached to these monoclonal antibodies. This might be a <u>radioactive</u> substance, a <u>toxic drug</u> or a chemical which stops cancer cells <u>growing</u> and <u>dividing</u>.

5) The antibodies are <u>given</u> to the patient through a drip.

6) The antibodies <u>target specific cells</u> (the cancer cells) because they only bind to the <u>tumour markers</u>.

7) The drug <u>kills</u> the <u>cancer cells</u> but <u>doesn't</u> kill any <u>normal body cells</u> near the tumour.

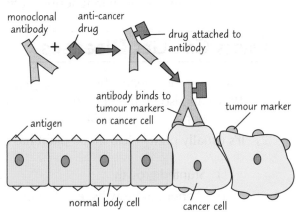

...and in **Laboratories** and **Research** to **Find Specific Substances**

Monoclonal antibodies can be used to:

1) Bind to <u>hormones</u> and other <u>chemicals</u> in <u>blood</u> to measure their levels.

2) Test blood samples in laboratories for certain <u>pathogens</u>.

3) <u>Locate</u> specific molecules on a <u>cell</u> or in a <u>tissue</u>:

> 1) First, monoclonal antibodies are made that will bind to the specific molecules you're looking for.
> 2) The antibodies are then bound to a <u>fluorescent dye</u>.
> 3) If the molecules are present in the sample you're analysing, the monoclonal antibodies will <u>attach</u> to them, and they can be <u>detected</u> using the dye.

Monoclonal Antibodies Do Have Some **Problems** Though

1) There are some obvious <u>advantages</u> of monoclonal antibodies. One big one is in cancer treatment. Other cancer treatments (like standard chemotherapy and radiotherapy) can <u>affect normal body cells</u> as well as killing cancer cells, whereas monoclonal antibodies target specific cells. This means the <u>side effects</u> of an antibody-based drug are <u>lower</u> than for standard chemotherapy or radiotherapy.

2) However, monoclonal antibodies do cause <u>more side effects</u> than were <u>originally expected</u>, e.g. they can cause fever, vomiting and low blood pressure. When they were first developed, scientists thought that because they targeted a very specific cell or molecule, they wouldn't create a lot of side effects.

3) This means that they are <u>not as widely used</u> as treatments as scientists had originally thought they might be.

Monoclonal antibodies have many uses in research and medicine

Q1 A scientist has a sample of tissue from a patient with a suspected bacterial infection. He sticks it to a microscope slide. Then he adds a solution of monoclonal antibodies against the bacteria that have been joined to a fluorescent dye. Finally, he washes off any unbound antibodies and looks at the slide under a microscope. Explain how the test works to confirm that the bacteria are present. [2 marks]

Plant Diseases and Defences

*It's not just us humans that can get diseases — **plants** get their fair share too.*

Plants Need **Mineral Ions**

1) Plants need <u>mineral ions</u> from the <u>soil</u>. If there aren't enough, plants suffer <u>deficiency symptoms</u>.

2) <u>Nitrates</u> are needed to make <u>proteins</u> and therefore for <u>growth</u>. A lack of nitrates causes <u>stunted growth</u>.

3) <u>Magnesium ions</u> are needed for making <u>chlorophyll</u>, which is needed for <u>photosynthesis</u>.
   Plants without enough magnesium suffer from <u>chlorosis</u> and have <u>yellow leaves</u>.

Plants Can Get **Diseases**

1) Plants can be infected by <u>viral</u>, <u>bacterial</u> and <u>fungal pathogens</u> — see page 83 for some examples.
   They can also be <u>infested</u> and damaged by <u>insects</u>. For example, <u>aphids</u> are an <u>insect</u> that can
   cause huge <u>damage</u> to plants.

2) It's usually pretty clear that a plant has a disease. The common signs are:

1) Stunted <u>growth</u>	2) <u>Spots</u> on the leaves	3) Patches of <u>decay</u> (rot)
4) Abnormal <u>growths</u>, e.g. lumps	5) <u>Malformed</u> stems or leaves	6) <u>Discolouration</u>

3) Infestations of <u>pests</u> are easy to spot too — you should be able to <u>see them</u> on the plants.

4) Different plant diseases have different <u>signs</u>. They can be <u>identified</u> by:

   1) Looking up the signs in a <u>gardening manual</u> or on a <u>gardening website</u>.
   2) Taking the infected plant to a <u>laboratory</u>, where scientists can identify the pathogen.
   3) Using <u>testing kits</u> that identify the pathogen using <u>monoclonal antibodies</u> (see page 95).

Plants Have **Physical, Chemical** and **Mechanical Defences...**

Physical defences

1) Most plant leaves and stems have a <u>waxy cuticle</u>, which provides a <u>barrier</u> to stop pathogens entering.

2) Plant cells themselves are surrounded by <u>cell walls</u> made from <u>cellulose</u>.
   These form a <u>physical barrier</u> against pathogens that make it past the waxy cuticle.

3) Plants have <u>layers</u> of <u>dead cells</u> around their <u>stems</u>, for example, the outer part of the <u>bark</u> on trees.
   These act as a <u>barrier</u> to stop pathogens entering.

Chemical defences

1) Some can produce <u>antibacterial chemicals</u> which kill bacteria — e.g. the <u>mint plant</u> and <u>witch hazel</u>.

2) Other plants produce <u>poisons</u> which can deter herbivores (organisms that eat plants)
   — e.g. <u>tobacco plants</u>, <u>foxgloves</u> and <u>deadly nightshade</u>.

Mechanical defences

1) Some plants have adapted to have <u>thorns</u> and <u>hairs</u> which <u>stop</u> animals from <u>touching</u> and <u>eating</u> them.

2) Other plants have leaves that <u>droop</u> or <u>curl</u> when something touches them. This means that they can
   prevent themselves from being eaten by knocking <u>insects</u> off themselves and <u>moving away</u> from things.

3) Some plants can cleverly <u>mimic</u> other organisms. E.g. the <u>passion flower</u> has <u>bright yellow spots</u> on
   its leaves which look like <u>butterfly eggs</u>. This stops other butterflies laying their eggs there. Several
   species of plant in the 'ice plant family' in southern Africa look like <u>stones</u> and <u>pebbles</u>. This <u>tricks</u>
   other organisms into not eating them.

Warm-Up & Exam Questions

It's that time again — time to test just how much of the previous pages you really remember...

Warm-Up Questions

1) What type of white blood cell produces antibodies?
2) What is a hybridoma cell made from?
3) Give a symptom of nitrate deficiency in plants.
4) How does bark prevent a tree from being infected with pathogens?

Exam Questions

1 Which of the following is a term used to describe yellow leaves on a plant? Tick **one** box. *Grade 4-6*

☐ chlorophyll ☐ chlorosis ☐ cellulose ☐ cuticle

[1 mark]

2 Plant diseases can be caused by deficiencies in nutrients or by pathogens. *Grade 6-7*
Plants have many methods to protect themselves against diseases.

2.1 Give **three** methods of physical defence used by plants to stop pathogens entering.

[3 marks]

2.2 Explain why plants with a magnesium deficiency are less able to photosynthesise.

[1 mark]

2.3 Apart from discoloured leaves, state **two** signs which may indicate that a plant is diseased.

[2 marks]

3 Monoclonal antibodies have many uses in medicine. *Grade 6-7*

3.1 List **three** things that can be bound to a monoclonal antibody to treat cancer.

[3 marks]

3.2 Explain **one** advantage of using monoclonal antibodies to treat cancer
instead of using normal treatment methods.

[2 marks]

4 **Figure 1** shows a pregnancy testing stick, which uses monoclonal antibodies to test a urine
sample for the pregnancy hormone HCG. When urine is applied to the end containing *Grade 7-9*
the beads, it travels up the stick towards strips **A** and **B**. If the woman is pregnant,
both **A** and **B** will turn blue.

Figure 1

antibodies that bind HCG
attached to blue beads

A: contains antibodies that bind HCG
B: contains antibodies that bind to
the antibodies on the blue beads

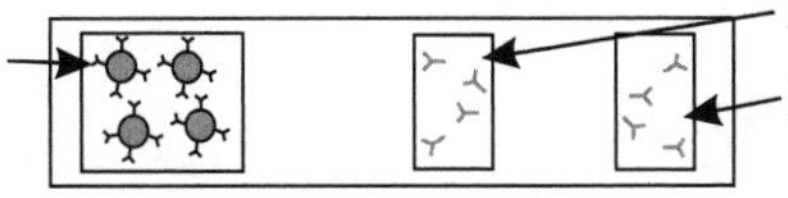

Strip **B** in **Figure 1** is designed to always turn blue, even if the woman is not pregnant.
Suggest why strip **B** is included on the testing stick. Explain your answer.

[3 marks]

Revision Summary for Topic 3

Well, that wraps up <u>Topic 3</u> — time to put yourself to the test and find out <u>how much you really know</u>.

- Try these questions and <u>tick off each one</u> when you <u>get it right</u>.
- When you're <u>completely happy</u> with a sub-topic, tick it off.

For even more practice, try the Retrieval Quiz for Topic 3 — just scan this QR code!

Topic 3 Quiz

Types of Disease (p.81-85) ☑

1) How can bacteria make us feel ill? ☑
2) Give one way that fungi can cause disease. ☑
3) Give three ways that pathogens can be spread between people. ☑
4) How are mosquitoes involved in the spread of malaria? ☑
5) What type of pathogen causes *Salmonella* food poisoning? ☑
6) How can the spread of gonorrhoea be prevented? ☑
7) How can destroying vectors help to prevent the spread of disease? ☑

Fighting Disease (p.87-92) ☑

8) What is the name for the molecules which antibodies lock onto on the surface of a pathogen? ☑
9) What are antitoxins? ☑
10) How does antibiotic resistance arise in a population of bacteria? ☑
11) Which plant does the painkiller aspirin originate from? ☑
12) Name the scientist who discovered penicillin. ☑
13) What two things are drugs tested on in preclinical testing? ☑
14) What is meant by a drug's toxicity? ☑

Antibodies (p.95-97) ☑

15) What is a monoclonal antibody? ☑
16) Where are the B-lymphocytes taken from when making monoclonal antibodies? ☑
17) Why might a fluorescent dye be added to a monoclonal antibody? ☑
18) Why aren't monoclonal antibodies used to deliver drugs as much as scientists hoped they would be? ☑

Plant Diseases and Defences (p.98) ☑

19) What do plants use magnesium ions for? ☑
20) Give one way of identifying which disease a plant has. ☑
21) Give one chemical defence that a plant may have to defend itself. ☑
22) Give one mechanical defence that a plant may have to defend itself. ☑

Photosynthesis

*First, **photosynthesis equations**. Then onto how plants use **glucose**...*

Photosynthesis Produces Glucose Using Light

1) Photosynthesis uses energy to change carbon dioxide and water into glucose and oxygen.
2) It takes place in chloroplasts in green plant cells — they contain pigments like chlorophyll that absorb light.
3) Energy is transferred to the chloroplasts from the environment by light.
4) Photosynthesis is endothermic — this means energy is transferred from the environment in the process.
5) The word equation for photosynthesis is:

$$\text{carbon dioxide} + \text{water} \xrightarrow{\text{light}} \text{glucose} + \text{oxygen}$$

6) Here's the symbol equation too:

$$6CO_2 + 6H_2O \xrightarrow{\text{light}} C_6H_{12}O_6 + 6O_2$$

Plants Use Glucose in Five Main Ways...

1) For respiration — This transfers energy from glucose (see p.110) which enables the plants to convert the rest of the glucose into various other useful substances.

2) Making cellulose — Glucose is converted into cellulose for making strong plant cell walls (see p.17).

3) Making amino acids — Glucose is combined with nitrate ions (absorbed from the soil) to make amino acids, which are then made into proteins.

4) Stored as oils or fats — Glucose is turned into lipids (fats and oils) for storing in seeds.

5) Stored as starch — Glucose is turned into starch and stored in roots, stems and leaves, ready for use when photosynthesis isn't happening, like in the winter. Starch is insoluble, which makes it much better for storing than glucose — a cell with lots of glucose in would draw in loads of water and swell up.

'Photo' means light and 'synthesis' means putting together...

...so photosynthesis means 'putting together using light'. And of course the thing being put together is glucose. Well, I guess that's one way of remembering it... (Maybe just learn the word equation instead.)

The Rate of Photosynthesis

*The rate of photosynthesis is affected by the intensity of **light**, the concentration of **CO₂**, and the **temperature**. Plants also need **water** for photosynthesis, but when a plant is so short of water that it becomes the **limiting factor** in photosynthesis, it's already in such **trouble** that this is the least of its worries.*

Limiting Factors Affect the Rate of Photosynthesis

1) Any of these three factors can become the <u>limiting factor</u> — this just means that it's stopping photosynthesis from happening any <u>faster</u>.

2) These factors have a <u>combined effect</u> on the rate of photosynthesis, but which factor is limiting at a particular time depends on the <u>environmental conditions</u>:

- at <u>night</u> it's pretty obvious that <u>light</u> is the limiting factor,
- in <u>winter</u> it's often the <u>temperature</u>,
- if it's warm enough and bright enough, the amount of <u>CO₂</u> is usually limiting.

3) <u>Chlorophyll</u> can also be a <u>limiting factor</u> of photosynthesis.

The <u>amount of chlorophyll</u> in a plant can be affected by <u>disease</u> (e.g. infection with the tobacco mosaic virus) or <u>environmental stress</u>, such as a <u>lack of nutrients</u>. These factors can cause <u>chloroplasts</u> to become <u>damaged</u> or to <u>not</u> make <u>enough chlorophyll</u>. This means the rate of photosynthesis is <u>reduced</u> because they <u>can't absorb</u> as much <u>light</u>.

Not Enough Light Slows Down the Rate of Photosynthesis

1) Light provides the <u>energy</u> needed for photosynthesis.

2) As the <u>light level</u> is raised, the rate of photosynthesis <u>increases steadily</u> — but only up to a <u>certain point</u>.

3) Beyond that, it <u>won't</u> make any difference — as light intensity increases, the rate will <u>no longer increase</u>. This is because it'll be either the <u>temperature</u> or the <u>CO₂ level</u> which is now the limiting factor, not light.

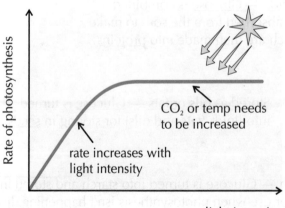

Rate of photosynthesis

CO₂ or temp needs to be increased

rate increases with light intensity

light intensity

4) In the lab, you can change the light intensity by <u>moving a lamp</u> closer to or further away from your plant (see page 105 for this experiment).

5) But if you just plot the rate of photosynthesis against "distance of lamp from the plant", you get a <u>weird-shaped graph</u>. To get a graph like the one above you either need to <u>measure</u> the light intensity at the plant using a <u>light meter</u> or do a bit of nifty maths with your results.

The Rate of Photosynthesis

Too Little **Carbon Dioxide** Also Slows it Down

CO_2 is one of the <u>raw materials</u> needed for photosynthesis.

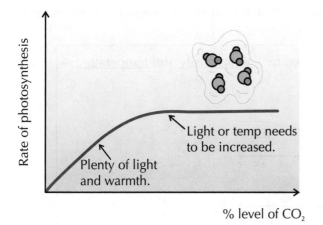

Plenty of light and warmth.

Light or temp needs to be increased.

% level of CO_2

1) As with light intensity, the amount of <u>CO_2</u> will only increase the rate of photosynthesis up to a point.

2) After this, the graph <u>flattens out</u> — as the amount of CO_2 increases, the rate <u>no longer increases</u>. This shows that CO_2 is no longer the <u>limiting factor</u>.

3) As long as <u>light</u> and <u>CO_2</u> are in plentiful supply then the factor limiting photosynthesis must be <u>temperature</u>.

The **Temperature** has to be Just Right

Temperature affects the rate of photosynthesis because it affects the <u>enzymes</u> involved.

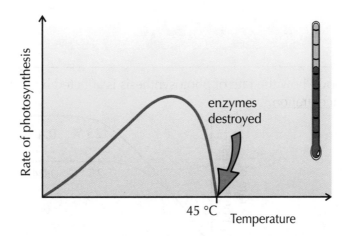

enzymes destroyed

45 °C   Temperature

1) Usually, if the temperature is the <u>limiting factor</u> it's because it's <u>too low</u> — the <u>enzymes</u> needed for photosynthesis work more <u>slowly</u> at low temperatures.

2) But if the plant gets <u>too hot</u>, the enzymes it needs for photosynthesis and its other reactions will be <u>damaged</u>.

3) This happens at about <u>45 °C</u> (which is pretty hot for outdoors, although <u>greenhouses</u> can get that hot if you're not careful).

Graphs, graphs and more graphs...

It's really vital that you've got your head around <u>limiting factors</u>, particularly the <u>graphs</u>. I say this because on the next page you're going to have to tackle graphs that have <u>more than one</u> limiting factor — so there's <u>no point</u> moving on until you're completely happy with dealing with just one on its own first.

The Rate of Photosynthesis

*Now that you know all about **limiting factors**, it's time to take it to the next level...*

One Graph May Show the Effect of Many Limiting Factors

You could get a graph that shows <u>more than one</u> limiting factor on the rate of photosynthesis, for example:

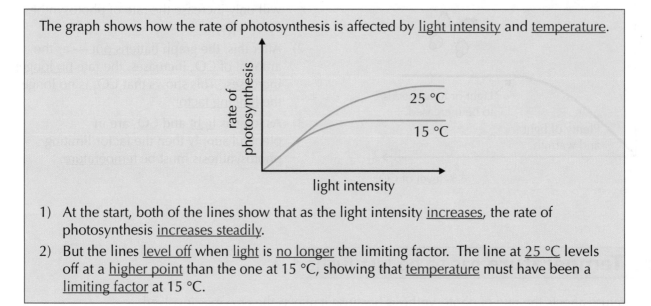

The graph shows how the rate of photosynthesis is affected by <u>light intensity</u> and <u>temperature</u>.

1) At the start, both of the lines show that as the light intensity <u>increases</u>, the rate of photosynthesis <u>increases steadily</u>.

2) But the lines <u>level off</u> when <u>light</u> is <u>no longer</u> the limiting factor. The line at <u>25 °C</u> levels off at a <u>higher point</u> than the one at 15 °C, showing that <u>temperature</u> must have been a <u>limiting factor</u> at 15 °C.

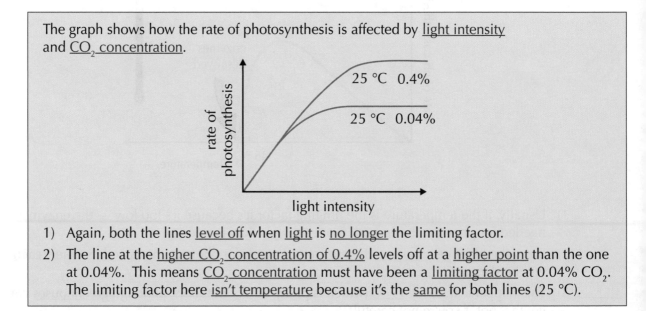

The graph shows how the rate of photosynthesis is affected by <u>light intensity</u> and <u>CO_2 concentration</u>.

1) Again, both the lines <u>level off</u> when <u>light</u> is <u>no longer</u> the limiting factor.

2) The line at the <u>higher CO_2 concentration of 0.4%</u> levels off at a <u>higher point</u> than the one at 0.04%. This means <u>CO_2 concentration</u> must have been a <u>limiting factor</u> at 0.04% CO_2. The limiting factor here <u>isn't temperature</u> because it's the <u>same</u> for both lines (25 °C).

Make sure you know how to read from graphs

In the exam, you might have to describe what's going on in a graph of limiting factors. <u>Don't panic</u> — just look at the graph <u>carefully</u>, making sure you pay attention to the <u>axes</u>, as well as any additional <u>labels</u>, to see how the factors shown are affecting the <u>rate of photosynthesis</u>.

Measuring the Rate of Photosynthesis

*It's practical time again. This one lets you see how changing **light intensity** affects the **rate of photosynthesis**.*

Oxygen Production Shows the Rate of Photosynthesis

PRACTICAL

<u>Canadian pondweed</u> can be used to measure the effect of <u>light intensity</u> on the <u>rate of photosynthesis</u>. The rate at which the pondweed produces <u>oxygen</u> corresponds to the rate at which it's photosynthesising — the <u>faster</u> the rate of oxygen production, the <u>faster</u> the rate of photosynthesis.

Here's how the experiment works:

1) A source of <u>white light</u> is placed at a <u>specific distance</u> from the pondweed.

2) The pondweed is left to photosynthesise for a <u>set amount of time</u>.
   As it photosynthesises, the oxygen released will collect in the <u>capillary tube</u>.

3) At the end of the experiment, the <u>syringe</u> is used to draw the gas bubble in the tube up alongside a ruler and the <u>length</u> of the <u>gas bubble</u> is <u>measured</u>. This is <u>proportional</u> to the <u>volume of O$_2$</u> produced.

4) For this experiment, any <u>variables</u> that could affect the results should be <u>controlled</u>, e.g. the <u>temperature</u> and <u>time</u> the pondweed is left to photosynthesise.

5) The experiment is <u>repeated</u> twice with the <u>light source</u> at the <u>same</u> distance and the <u>mean</u> volume of O$_2$ produced is calculated.

6) Then the whole experiment is repeated with the <u>light source</u> at <u>different distances</u> from the pondweed.

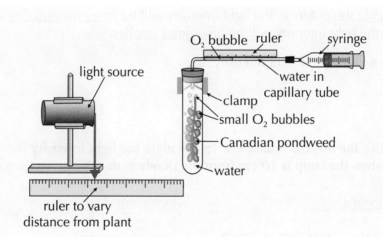

You can compare the results at different light intensities by giving the rate as the length of the bubble per unit time, e.g. cm/min.

The apparatus above can be altered to measure the effect of <u>temperature</u> or <u>CO$_2$</u> on photosynthesis. For example:

> 1) The test tube of pondweed can be put into a <u>water bath</u> at a <u>set temperature</u>, or a measured amount of <u>sodium hydrogencarbonate</u> can be dissolved in the water (which <u>gives off</u> CO$_2$).
> 2) The experiment can then be repeated with different temperatures of water / concentrations of sodium hydrogencarbonate.

Measuring the Rate of Photosynthesis

*This page is all about the **inverse square law**. It can be a bit tricky to get your head around, so focus...*

The **Inverse Square Law** Links **Light Intensity** and **Distance**

1) In the experiment on the previous page, when the <u>lamp</u> is <u>moved away</u> from the pondweed, the amount of <u>light</u> that reaches the pondweed <u>decreases</u>.

2) You can say that as the <u>distance increases</u>, the <u>light intensity decreases</u>. In other words, distance and light intensity are <u>inversely proportional</u> to each other.

3) However, it's not quite as simple as that. It turns out that light intensity decreases in <u>proportion</u> to the <u>square</u> of the distance. This is called the <u>inverse square law</u> and is written out like this:

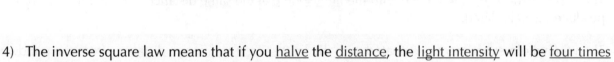

This is the 'proportional to' symbol.

Putting one over the distance shows the <u>inverse</u>.

$$\text{light intensity} \propto \frac{1}{\text{distance (d)}^2}$$

The distance is <u>squared</u>.

4) The inverse square law means that if you <u>halve</u> the <u>distance</u>, the <u>light intensity</u> will be <u>four times greater</u> and if you <u>divide</u> the distance by <u>three</u>, the light intensity will be <u>nine times greater</u>.

5) Likewise, if you <u>double</u> the distance, the light intensity will be <u>four times smaller</u> and if you <u>treble</u> the distance, the light intensity will be <u>nine times smaller</u>.

6) You can use $1/d^2$ as a measure of light intensity.

> **EXAMPLE**   **Use the inverse square law to calculate the light intensity when the lamp is 10 cm from the pondweed.**
>
> 1) <u>Use the formula</u> $\frac{1}{d^2}$. $\text{light intensity} = \frac{1}{d^2}$
>
> 2) Fill in the <u>values</u> you know — you're given the distance, so put that in. $\text{light intensity} = \frac{1}{10^2}$
>
> 3) Calculate the <u>answer</u>. $= 0.01$ a.u.   'a.u.' stands for 'arbitrary units'.

As one thing goes up, the other goes down...

That's what <u>inverse proportion</u> is all about. So here, as distance <u>decreases</u>, light intensity <u>increases</u>.

Q2 Video Solution

Q1 According to the inverse square law, describe what happens to the light intensity when the distance between a plant and its light source is doubled. [1 mark]

Q2 A plant is moved from 15 cm away from its light source to 5 cm away from its light source. Using the inverse square law, show that the light intensity becomes nine times greater. [3 marks]

Ideal Conditions for Photosynthesis

*Growing plants outdoors can be **very difficult**, especially on a **large scale** — it's almost impossible to control the weather and other conditions. But there's a way around that...*

You can **Artificially Create** the **Ideal Conditions** for **Farming**

1) The most common way to artificially create the <u>ideal environment</u> for plants is to grow them in a <u>greenhouse</u>.

2) Greenhouses help to <u>trap</u> the Sun's <u>heat</u>, and make sure that the <u>temperature</u> doesn't become <u>limiting</u>. In winter a farmer or gardener might use a <u>heater</u> as well to keep the temperature at the ideal level. In summer it could get <u>too hot</u>, so they might use <u>shades</u> and <u>ventilation</u> to cool things down.

3) <u>Light</u> is always needed for photosynthesis, so commercial farmers often supply <u>artificial light</u> after the Sun goes down to give their plants more quality photosynthesis time.

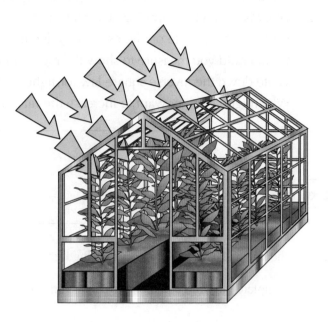

Greenhouses are used to grow plants, including food crops, flowers and tobacco plants.

4) Farmers and gardeners can also increase the level of <u>carbon dioxide</u> in the greenhouse. A fairly common way is to use a <u>paraffin heater</u> to heat the greenhouse. As the paraffin burns, it makes carbon dioxide as a <u>by-product</u>.

5) Keeping plants <u>enclosed</u> in a greenhouse also makes it easier to keep them free from <u>pests</u> and <u>diseases</u>. The farmer can add <u>fertilisers</u> to the soil as well, to provide all the <u>minerals</u> needed for healthy growth.

6) Sorting all this out <u>costs money</u> — but if the farmer can keep the conditions <u>just right</u> for photosynthesis, the plants will grow much <u>faster</u> and a <u>decent crop</u> can be harvested much more <u>often</u>, which can then be <u>sold</u>. It's important that a farmer supplies just the <u>right amount</u> of heat, light, etc. — enough to make the plants grow well, but <u>not</u> more than the plants <u>need</u>, as this would just be <u>wasting money</u>.

Greenhouses control the growing environment

Farmers use <u>greenhouses</u> to make sure crops get the <u>right amount</u> of <u>carbon dioxide</u>, <u>light</u> and <u>heat</u>. They can alter the conditions using paraffin heaters, artificial light and ventilation. This ensures nothing becomes a <u>limiting factor</u> for photosynthesis, which means a <u>good crop</u> is produced.

Warm-Up & Exam Questions

Time for a break in the topic and some questions. Do them now, whilst all that learning is fresh in your mind. Using that knowledge will help you to remember it all, and that's what this game is all about.

Warm-Up Questions

1) What does the chemical symbol $C_6H_{12}O_6$ represent?
2) What is meant by a limiting factor for the rate of photosynthesis?
3) Explain why the rate of photosynthesis decreases if the temperature is too high.
4) What could you measure to show the rate of photosynthesis?
5) Write down the inverse square law for light intensity.
6) Why might a farmer want to increase the rate of photosynthesis in her greenhouse of tomatoes?

Exam Questions

1   Photosynthesis produces glucose using light.   (Grade 4-6)

1.1   Complete the word equation for photosynthesis.

carbon dioxide + ... $\xrightarrow{\text{light}}$ glucose + ...

[2 marks]

1.2   Plants use some of the glucose they produce to make a substance which strengthens their cell walls. Which of the following strengthens cells walls?
Tick **one** box.

☐ cellulose   ☐ oils   ☐ starch   ☐ fats

[1 mark]

1.3   Give **two** others way that plants use the glucose they produce in photosynthesis.

[2 marks]

PRACTICAL

2   A student did an experiment to see how the rate of photosynthesis depends on light intensity. **Figure 1** shows some of her apparatus.   (Grade 4-6)

2.1   How can the student measure the rate of photosynthesis?

[1 mark]

2.2   State the dependent variable and the independent variable in this experiment.

[2 marks]

2.3   State **one** factor that should be kept constant during this experiment.

[1 mark]

Figure 1

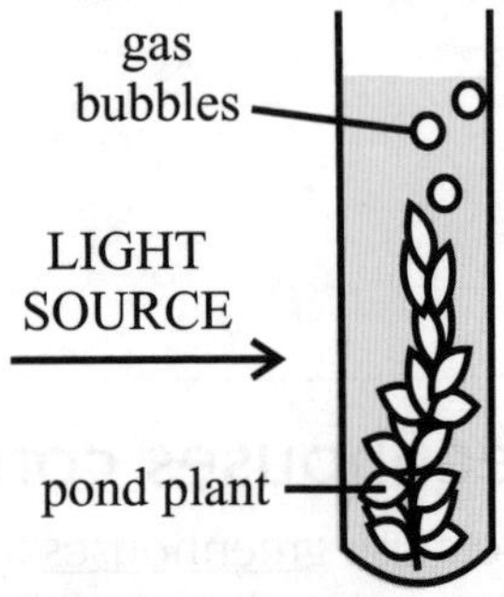

gas bubbles

LIGHT SOURCE

pond plant

Exam Questions

3 A student investigated the effect of different concentrations of carbon dioxide on the rate of photosynthesis of his Swiss cheese plant. The results are shown in **Figure 2**. *Grade 6-7*

Figure 2

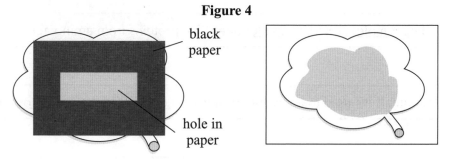

- - - - - 0.1% CO_2
——— 0.07% CO_2
——— 0.04% CO_2

rate of photosynthesis

light intensity

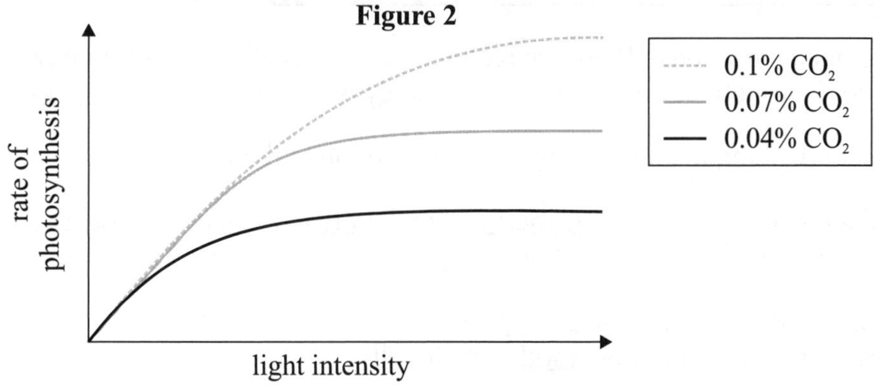

3.1 Describe the effect that increasing the concentration of CO_2 has on the rate of photosynthesis as light intensity increases.

[2 marks]

3.2 Explain why all the lines on the graph level off eventually.

[1 mark]

4 **Figure 3** shows a variegated leaf. *Grade 6-7* It is partly green and partly white. Chlorophyll is present in the green parts of the leaf but not the white parts.

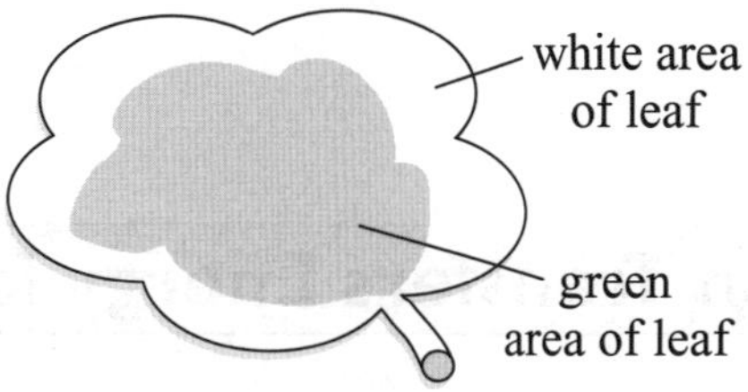

A student did an experiment in which part of the leaf was covered with black paper, as shown in **Figure 4**. The leaf was then exposed to light for four hours and was then tested for starch.

Figure 3

white area of leaf

green area of leaf

Figure 4

black paper

hole in paper

4.1 Complete **Figure 4** by shading in the part(s) of the leaf that you would expect to contain **starch**.

[1 mark]

4.2 Explain your answer to **4.1**.

[2 marks]

5 A student is investigating the effect of light intensity on the rate of photosynthesis by placing *Grade 7-9* a lamp at various distances from a plant and measuring the rate of photosynthesis. Use the inverse square law to calculate the light intensity when the lamp is 7.5 cm from the plant. Give your answer in arbitrary units (a.u.) to 2 significant figures.

[2 marks]

Respiration

*You need **energy** to keep your body going. Energy comes from **food**, and it's **transferred** by **respiration**.*

Respiration is NOT "Breathing In and Out"

Respiration involves many reactions. These are really important reactions, as respiration transfers the energy that the cell needs to do just about everything — this energy is used for all living processes.

1) Respiration is not breathing in and breathing out, as you might think.

2) Respiration is the process of transferring energy from the breakdown of glucose (sugar) — and it goes on in every cell in your body continuously.

3) It happens in plants too. All living things respire.
It's how they transfer energy from their food to their cells.

> RESPIRATION is the process of TRANSFERRING ENERGY
> FROM GLUCOSE, which goes on IN EVERY CELL.

4) Respiration is exothermic — it transfers energy to the environment.

Respiration Transfers Energy for All Kinds of Things

Here are three examples of how organisms use the energy transferred by respiration:

1) To build up larger molecules from smaller ones (like proteins from amino acids).

2) In animals it's used to allow the muscles to contract (so they can move about).

3) In mammals and birds the energy is used to keep their body temperature steady in colder surroundings. (Unlike other animals, mammals and birds keep their bodies constantly warm.)

Respiration releases energy from glucose

So... respiration is a pretty important thing. Cyanide is a really nasty toxin that stops respiration by stopping enzymes involved in the process from working — so it's pretty poisonous (it can kill you).
Your brain, heart and liver are affected first because they have the highest energy demands... nice.

Metabolism

*Metabolism is going on **all of the time**. Right now. And now. Even now.
Okay, you get the picture. Time to read all about it.*

Metabolism is ALL the Chemical Reactions in an Organism

1) In a cell there are lots of chemical reactions happening all the time, which are controlled by enzymes.

Enzymes are biological catalysts — see p.47.

2) Many of these reactions are linked together to form bigger reactions:

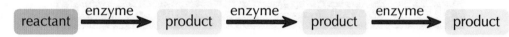

reactant → enzyme → product → enzyme → product → enzyme → product

3) In some of these reactions, larger molecules are made from smaller ones. For example:

> 1) Lots of small glucose molecules are joined together in reactions to form starch (a storage molecule in plant cells), glycogen (a storage molecule in animal cells) and cellulose (a component of plant cell walls).

> 2) Lipid molecules are each made from one molecule of glycerol and three fatty acids.

> 3) Glucose is combined with nitrate ions to make amino acids, which are then made into proteins.

4) In other reactions, larger molecules are broken down into smaller ones. For example:

> 1) Glucose is broken down in respiration. Respiration transfers energy to power all the reactions in the body that make molecules.

> 2) Excess protein is broken down in a reaction to produce urea. Urea is then excreted in urine.

5) The sum (total) of all of the reactions that happen in a cell or the body is called its metabolism.

It's still going on now

Enzymes are key to metabolism, so if you need a reminder about them, now is a good time to head back to page 47. Even if you are happy with enzymes, don't move on just yet — check you've taken in everything on this page before you flip over to continue on through the world of respiration. It's all important stuff.

Aerobic and Anaerobic Respiration

*There are **two types** of **respiration** — aerobic and anaerobic.*

Aerobic Respiration Needs Plenty of Oxygen

1) <u>Aerobic respiration</u> is respiration using <u>oxygen</u>.
It's the most <u>efficient</u> way to transfer energy from glucose.

2) Aerobic respiration goes on <u>all the time</u> in <u>plants</u> and <u>animals</u>.

3) Most of the reactions in <u>aerobic respiration</u> happen inside <u>mitochondria</u> (see page 16).

4) Here are the <u>word</u> and <u>symbol equations</u> for aerobic respiration:

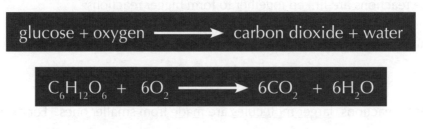

glucose + oxygen $\longrightarrow$ carbon dioxide + water

$$C_6H_{12}O_6 + 6O_2 \longrightarrow 6CO_2 + 6H_2O$$

Anaerobic Respiration is Used if There's Not Enough Oxygen

When you do vigorous exercise and your body can't supply enough <u>oxygen</u> to your muscles, they start doing <u>anaerobic respiration</u> as well as aerobic respiration.

1) "<u>Anaerobic</u>" just means "<u>without</u> oxygen". It's the <u>incomplete breakdown</u> of glucose, making <u>lactic acid</u>.

2) Here's the <u>word equation</u> for anaerobic respiration in muscle cells:

glucose $\longrightarrow$ lactic acid

3) <u>Anaerobic respiration</u> does <u>not transfer nearly as much energy</u> as aerobic respiration. This is because glucose <u>isn't fully oxidised</u> (because it doesn't combine with oxygen).

4) So, anaerobic respiration is only useful in <u>emergencies</u>, e.g. during exercise when it allows you to keep on using your muscles for a while longer.

Anaerobic Respiration in Plants and Yeast is Slightly Different

1) <u>Plants</u> and <u>yeast cells</u> can respire <u>without oxygen</u> too, but they produce <u>ethanol</u> (alcohol) and <u>carbon dioxide</u> instead of lactic acid.

2) Here's <u>the word equation</u> for anaerobic respiration in <u>plants</u> and <u>yeast cells</u>:

glucose $\longrightarrow$ ethanol + carbon dioxide

Yeast are single-celled organisms.

3) Anaerobic respiration in <u>yeast cells</u> is called <u>fermentation</u>.

4) In the <u>food and drinks industry</u>, <u>fermentation</u> by yeast is of <u>great value</u> because it's used to make <u>bread</u> and <u>alcoholic drinks</u>, e.g. beer and wine.

5) In <u>bread-making</u>, it's the <u>carbon dioxide</u> from fermentation that makes bread <u>rise</u>.

6) In <u>beer</u> and <u>wine-making</u>, it's the fermentation process that produces <u>alcohol</u>.

Exercise

*When you **exercise**, your body responds in a number of helpful ways...*

When You **Exercise** You **Respire More**

1) Muscles need <u>energy</u> from respiration to <u>contract</u>. When you exercise, some of your muscles contract more frequently than normal so you need <u>more energy</u>. This energy comes from <u>increased respiration</u>.

2) The increase in respiration in your cells means you need to get <u>more oxygen</u> into them.

3) Your <u>breathing rate</u> and <u>breath volume increase</u> to get more oxygen into the blood, and your <u>heart rate increases</u> to get this oxygenated blood around the body faster. This <u>removes CO_2</u> more quickly at the same time.

4) When you do <u>really vigorous exercise</u> (like sprinting) your body can't supply <u>oxygen</u> to your muscles quickly enough, so they start <u>respiring anaerobically</u> (see the previous page).

5) This is <u>NOT the best way to transfer energy from glucose</u> because <u>lactic acid</u> builds up in the muscles, which gets <u>painful</u>.

6) Long periods of exercise also cause <u>muscle fatigue</u> — the muscles get <u>tired</u> and then <u>stop contracting efficiently</u>.

Remember, lactic acid is formed from the incomplete oxidation of glucose.

Anaerobic Respiration Leads to an **Oxygen Debt**

1) After resorting to anaerobic respiration, when you stop exercising you'll have an "<u>oxygen debt</u>".

2) An oxygen debt is the <u>amount of extra oxygen</u> your body needs to <u>react</u> with the <u>build up</u> of <u>lactic acid</u> and <u>remove</u> it from the cells. Oxygen reacts with the lactic acid to form harmless CO_2 and <u>water</u>.

3) In other words you have to "<u>repay</u>" the oxygen that you didn't get to your muscles in time, because your <u>lungs</u>, <u>heart</u> and <u>blood</u> couldn't keep up with the <u>demand</u> earlier on.

4) This means you have to keep breathing hard for a while <u>after you stop</u>, to get <u>more oxygen</u> into your blood, which is transported to the muscle cells.

5) The <u>pulse</u> and <u>breathing rate</u> stay high whilst there are <u>high levels</u> of <u>lactic acid</u> and CO_2.

6) Your body also has another way of coping with the high level of lactic acid — the <u>blood</u> that enters your muscles <u>transports</u> the <u>lactic acid</u> to the <u>liver</u>. In the liver, the lactic acid is <u>converted</u> back to <u>glucose</u>.

You Can Investigate The **Effect of Exercise** on **The Body**

1) You can measure <u>breathing rate</u> by <u>counting breaths</u>, and <u>heart rate</u> by <u>taking the pulse</u>.

2) To take the pulse, you put two fingers on the inside of your <u>wrist</u> or your <u>neck</u> and count the number of pulses in <u>1 minute</u>.

3) E.g. you could take your <u>pulse</u> after:

- <u>sitting down</u> for 5 minutes,
- then after 5 minutes of <u>gentle walking</u>,
- then again after 5 minutes of <u>slow jogging</u>,
- then again after <u>running</u> for 5 minutes.

You could then <u>plot</u> your results in a bar chart.

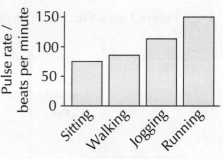

4) Your pulse rate will <u>increase</u> the more <u>intense</u> the exercise is, as your body needs to get <u>more oxygen</u> to the <u>muscles</u> and take more <u>carbon dioxide away</u> from the muscles.

5) To <u>reduce</u> the effect of any <u>random errors</u> on your results, do it as a <u>group</u> and plot the <u>average pulse rate</u> for each exercise.

There's more about random error on page 7.

Very vigorous exercise = anaerobic respiration = oxygen debt

Q1 Look at the graph above. Predict which type of exercise would lead to the highest concentration of lactic acid in the blood after 10 minutes. Explain your answer. [4 marks]

Q1 Video Solution

Warm-Up & Exam Questions

You know the drill by now — work your way through the Warm-Up questions, then the Exam Questions.

Warm-Up Questions

1) Give two examples of how animals use the energy transferred by respiration.
2) What is metabolism?
3) What are the reactants of aerobic respiration?
4) What is the process of anaerobic respiration in yeast called?
5) State three changes that take place in the body during vigorous exercise.

Exam Questions

1 Respiration is a process carried out by all living cells. It can take place aerobically or anaerobically.   *(Grade 4-6)*

1.1 State the purpose of respiration.

[1 mark]

1.2 Give **two** differences between aerobic and anaerobic respiration.

[2 marks]

1.3 Write the word equation for aerobic respiration.

[2 marks]

2 In the human body, respiration may be aerobic or anaerobic at different times.   *(Grade 6-7)*

2.1 Write down the word equation for anaerobic respiration in humans.

[1 mark]

2.2 Explain why the body uses anaerobic respiration during vigorous exercise.

[2 marks]

3 **Figure 1** shows the rate of oxygen use by a person before, during and after a period of exercise.   *(Grade 6-7)*

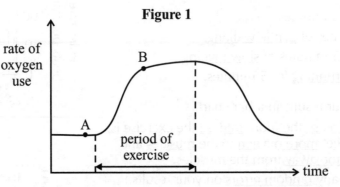

Figure 1

3.1 Explain why the rate of oxygen consumption is higher at **B** than at **A**.

[2 marks]

3.2 Suggest why oxygen use remains high, even after the period of exercise ends.

[1 mark]

Revision Summary for Topic 4

Well, it's all over for <u>Topic 4</u> folks — but I know how much you'll miss it, so here are some questions on it...

- Try these questions and <u>tick off each one</u> when you <u>get it right</u>.
- When you're <u>completely happy</u> with a sub-topic, tick it off.

For even more practice, try the Retrieval Quiz for Topic 4 — just scan this QR code!

Topic 4 Quiz

Photosynthesis (p.101-107) ☑

1) Where in a plant cell does photosynthesis take place? ☑
2) How is energy transferred to a plant from its environment for photosynthesis? ☑
3) What is an endothermic reaction? ☑
4) Name the products of photosynthesis. ☑
5) What type of molecule is formed from combining glucose molecules with nitrate ions? ☑
6) Why do plants store glucose as starch? ☑
7) What effect would a low carbon dioxide concentration have on the rate of photosynthesis? ☑
8) What effect would a very low temperature have on the rate of photosynthesis? ☑
9) Describe a method that could be used to measure the effect of light intensity on the rate of photosynthesis. ☑
10) In the inverse square law, how are light intensity and distance linked? ☑
11) Give one way that the temperature can be decreased in a greenhouse. ☑
12) Give one way that the level of carbon dioxide can be increased in a greenhouse. ☑

Respiration and Metabolism (p.110-113) ☐

13) What is respiration? ☑
14) What is an exothermic reaction? ☑
15) What process transfers energy to make new molecules in cells? ☑
16) Give three examples of metabolic reactions. ☑
17) Name the products of aerobic respiration. ☑
18) What is produced by anaerobic respiration in muscle cells? ☑
19) What is the word equation for anaerobic respiration in yeast cells? ☑
20) Name two products of the food and drink industry that fermentation is needed for. ☑
21) What happens to muscles when they become fatigued? ☑
22) In what organ is lactic acid converted back to glucose? ☑

Topic 5 — Homeostasis and Response

Homeostasis

*Homeostasis — a word that strikes fear into the heart of many a GCSE student. But it's really not that bad at all. This page is a brief **introduction** to the topic, so you need to **nail all of this** before you can move on.*

Homeostasis — Maintaining a **Stable Internal Environment**

1) The conditions inside your body need to be kept <u>steady</u>, even when the <u>external environment changes</u>.

2) This is really important because your <u>cells</u> need the <u>right conditions</u> in order to <u>function properly</u>, including the right conditions for <u>enzyme action</u> (see p.48).

3) <u>Homeostasis</u> is all about the <u>regulation</u> of the conditions inside your body (and cells) to <u>maintain a stable internal environment</u>, in response to <u>changes</u> in both internal and external conditions.

4) You have loads of <u>automatic control systems</u> in your body that regulate your internal environment — these include both <u>nervous</u> and <u>hormonal</u> communication systems. For example, there are control systems that maintain your <u>body temperature</u> (see pages 126-127), your <u>blood glucose</u> level (see page 132) and your <u>water content</u> (see page 136).

5) All your automatic control systems are made up of <u>three main components</u> which work together to maintain a steady condition — cells called <u>receptors</u>, <u>coordination centres</u> (including the brain, spinal cord and pancreas) and <u>effectors</u>.

Negative Feedback **Counteracts Changes**

Your automatic control systems keep your internal environment stable using a mechanism called <u>negative feedback</u>. When the level of something (e.g. water or temperature) gets <u>too high</u> or <u>too low</u>, your body uses negative feedback to bring it back to <u>normal</u>.

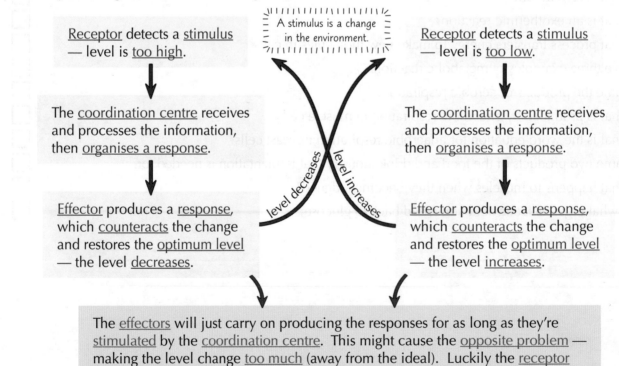

This process happens without you thinking about it — it's all <u>automatic</u>.

The Nervous System

*The **nervous system** means that humans can **react to their surroundings** and **coordinate their behaviour**.*

The **Nervous System Detects** and **Reacts** to **Stimuli**

1) Organisms need to respond to stimuli (changes in the environment) in order to survive.

2) A single-celled organism can just respond to its environment, but the cells of multicellular organisms need to communicate with each other first.

3) So as multicellular organisms evolved, they developed nervous and hormonal communication systems.

The **Nervous System** is made up of **Different Parts**

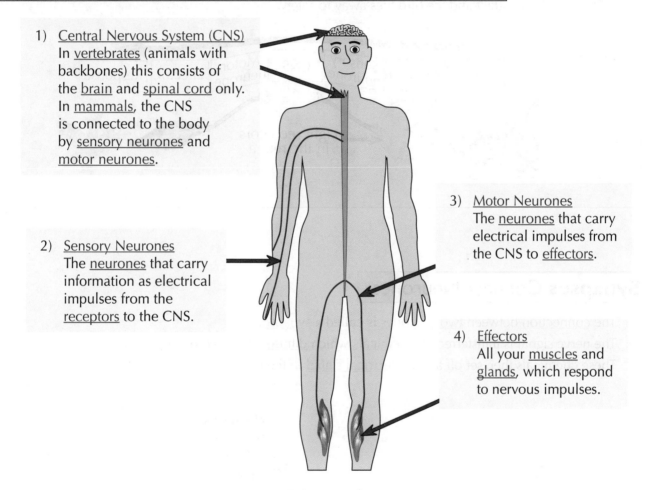

1) Central Nervous System (CNS)
In vertebrates (animals with backbones) this consists of the brain and spinal cord only. In mammals, the CNS is connected to the body by sensory neurones and motor neurones.

2) Sensory Neurones
The neurones that carry information as electrical impulses from the receptors to the CNS.

3) Motor Neurones
The neurones that carry electrical impulses from the CNS to effectors.

4) Effectors
All your muscles and glands, which respond to nervous impulses.

Receptors and **Effectors** can form part of **Complex Organs**

1) Receptors are the cells that detect stimuli.

2) There are many different types of receptors, such as taste receptors on the tongue and sound receptors in the ears.

3) Receptors can form part of larger, complex organs, e.g. the retina of the eye is covered in light receptor cells.

4) Effectors respond to nervous impulses and bring about a change.

5) Muscles and glands are known as effectors — they respond in different ways. Muscles contract in response to a nervous impulse, whereas glands secrete hormones.

The Nervous System

The **Central Nervous System (CNS) Coordinates** the **Response**

The CNS is a <u>coordination centre</u> — it receives information from the <u>receptors</u> and then <u>coordinates a response</u> (decides what to do about it). The response is carried out by <u>effectors</u>.

For example, a small bird is eating some seed...

1) ...when, out of the corner of its eye, it spots a cat skulking towards it (this is the <u>stimulus</u>).

2) The <u>receptors</u> in the bird's eye are <u>stimulated</u>.

3) <u>Sensory neurones</u> carry the information <u>from</u> the <u>receptors</u> to the <u>CNS</u>.

4) The CNS <u>decides</u> what to do about it.

5) The CNS sends information to the muscles in the bird's wings (the <u>effectors</u>) along <u>motor neurones</u>.

6) The muscles contract and the bird flies away to safety.

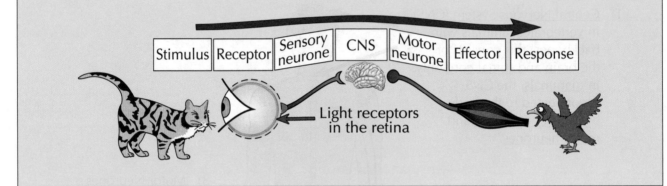

| Stimulus | Receptor | Sensory neurone | CNS | Motor neurone | Effector | Response |

Light receptors in the retina

Synapses Connect Neurones

1) The <u>connection</u> between <u>two neurones</u> is called a <u>synapse</u>.

2) The nerve signal is transferred by <u>chemicals</u> which <u>diffuse</u> (move) across the gap.

3) These chemicals then set off a <u>new electrical signal</u> in the <u>next</u> neurone.

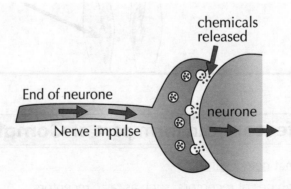

chemicals released

End of neurone

Nerve impulse

neurone

Don't let the thought of exams play on your nerves...

Don't forget that it's only <u>large animals</u> like mammals and birds that have <u>complex nervous systems</u>. <u>Simple animals</u> like jellyfish <u>don't</u> — everything they do is a <u>reflex response</u> (see next page).

Reflexes

*Neurones transmit information **very quickly** to and from the brain, and your brain **quickly decides** how to respond to a stimulus. But **reflexes** are even quicker...*

Reflexes Help Prevent Injury

1) <u>Reflexes</u> are <u>rapid</u>, <u>automatic</u> responses to certain stimuli that <u>don't involve</u> the <u>conscious</u> part of the brain — they can reduce the chances of being injured.

> • For example, if someone shines a <u>bright light</u> in your eyes, your <u>pupils</u> automatically get smaller so that less light gets into the eye — this stops it getting <u>damaged</u>.

> • Or if you get a shock, your body releases the <u>hormone</u> adrenaline automatically — it doesn't wait for you to <u>decide</u> that you're shocked.

2) The passage of information in a reflex (from receptor to effector) is called a <u>reflex arc</u>.

The Reflex Arc Goes Through the Central Nervous System

1) The neurones in reflex arcs go through the <u>spinal cord</u> or through an <u>unconscious part of the brain</u>.

2) When a <u>stimulus</u> (e.g. a painful bee sting) is detected by receptors, <u>impulses</u> are sent along a <u>sensory neurone</u> to the CNS.

3) When the impulses reach a <u>synapse</u> between the sensory neurone and a relay neurone, they trigger chemicals to be released (see previous page). These chemicals cause impulses to be sent along the <u>relay neurone</u>.

4) When the impulses reach a <u>synapse</u> between the relay neurone and a motor neurone, the same thing happens. Chemicals are released and cause impulses to be sent along the <u>motor neurone</u>.

5) The impulses then travel along the motor neurone to the <u>effector</u> (in this example it's a muscle).

6) The <u>muscle</u> then <u>contracts</u> and moves your hand away from the bee.

7) Because you don't have to think about the response (which takes time) it's <u>quicker</u> than normal responses.

Relay neurones connect sensory neurones to motor neurones.

3. Impulses travel along a sensory neurone.

4. Impulses are passed along a relay neurone, via a synapse.

5. Impulses travel along a motor neurone, via a synapse.

6. When impulses reach muscle, it contracts.

1. Bee stings finger.

2. Stimulation of pain receptors.

Don't get all twitchy — just learn it...

Reflexes <u>bypass</u> your <u>conscious brain</u> completely when a <u>quick response</u> is <u>essential</u>.

Q1   What is a reflex action?   [1 mark]

Q2   A chef touches a hot pan. A reflex reaction causes him to immediately move his hand away.
    a) State the effector in this reflex reaction.   [1 mark]
    b) Describe the pathway of the reflex from stimulus to effector.   [4 marks]

Q2 Video Solution

PRACTICAL # Investigating Reaction Time

*Reaction time is the time it takes to **respond to a stimulus** — it's often **less** than a **second**.*
*It can be **affected** by factors such as **age**, **gender** or **drugs**.*

You Can Measure **Reaction Time**

Caffeine is a drug that can speed up a person's reaction time.
The effect of caffeine on reaction time can be measured like this...

1) The person being tested should sit with their arm resting on the edge of a table
(this should stop them moving their arm up or down during the test).

2) Hold a ruler vertically between their thumb and forefinger. Make sure that the zero end of
the ruler is level with their thumb and finger. Then let go without giving any warning.

3) The person being tested should try to catch the ruler
as quickly as they can — as soon as they see it fall.

4) Reaction time is measured by the number on the ruler where it's caught — the
further down it's caught (i.e. the higher the number), the slower their reaction time.

5) Repeat the test several times then calculate the mean distance that the ruler fell.

6) The person being tested should then have a caffeinated drink
(e.g. 300 ml of cola). After ten minutes, repeat steps 1 to 5.

> With a little bit of maths, it's possible to work out the reaction time in seconds using the mean distance.

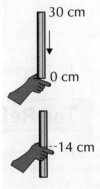

30 cm

0 cm

14 cm

7) You need to control any variables to make sure that this is a fair test.

> For example, you should use the same person to catch the ruler each time, and that person
> should always use the same hand to catch the ruler. Also, the ruler should always be dropped
> from the same height, and you should make sure that the person being tested has not had any
> caffeine (or anything else that may affect their reaction time) before the start of the experiment.

8) Too much caffeine can cause unpleasant side-effects, so the person being tested should
avoid drinking any more caffeine for the rest of the day after the experiment is completed.

Reaction Time Can Be Measured Using a **Computer**

1) Simple computer tests
can also be used to
measure reaction time.

> For example, the person being tested has to click the mouse (or press a key)
> as soon as they see a stimulus on the screen, e.g. a box change colour.

2) Computers can give a more precise reaction time because they remove
the possibility of human error from the measurement.

3) As the computer can record reaction time in milliseconds, it can also give a more accurate measurement.

4) Using a computer can also remove the possibility that the person can predict when to respond — using
the ruler test, the catcher may learn to anticipate the drop by reading the tester's body language.

As with any practical, you need to control the variables

Q1 Video
Solution

Q1 Some students investigated the effect of an energy drink on reaction time.
They measured their reaction times using a computer test. They had to click
the mouse when the screen changed from red to green. Each student repeated
the test five times before having an energy drink, and five times afterwards.

   a) The results for one of the students before having the energy drink were as follows:
     242 ms, 256 ms, 253 ms, 249 ms, 235 ms. Calculate the mean reaction time. [2 marks]

   b) Suggest two variables that the students needed to control
     during their investigation. [2 marks]

Warm-Up & Exam Questions

Welcome to some questions. There are quite a few of them, but that's because they're pretty important...

Warm-Up Questions

1) What is homeostasis?
2) State three things that are controlled by homeostasis in the human body.
3) What name is given to the connection between two neurones?
4) Name the three types of neurone in a reflex arc.
5) State one factor that affects human reaction time.

Exam Questions

PRACTICAL

1   A student is taking part in an experiment to test reaction times. Every time a red triangle   *Grade 4-6*
appears on the computer screen in front of her, she has to click the mouse.

1.1   Suggest what the stimulus, receptors and effectors are in this experiment.

[3 marks]

1.2   The student took the test three times. Her reaction time in test 1 was 328 ms.
Her reaction time in test 2 was 346 ms. Her mean reaction time was 343 ms.
Calculate her reaction time for test 3.

[2 marks]

2   Young babies have several reflexes not usually present in adults. For example, if an object is   *Grade 6-7*
placed in the palm of a newborn baby's hand, the baby will move their fingers to grasp the
object. The reflex arc for this reflex is shown in **Figure 1**.

Figure 1

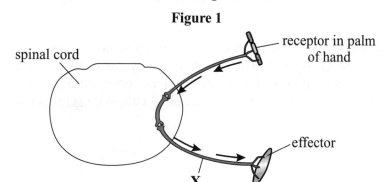

2.1   Name the structure labelled **X** on **Figure 1**.

[1 mark]

2.2   State the type of effector in this response and describe its action.

[2 marks]

2.3   Explain how an electrical impulse in one neurone is able to pass to the next neurone.

[2 marks]

2.4   If an object is placed in the palm of a baby over 6 months old, it can choose whether it wants to grasp
hold of the object. Describe **one** way in which the pathway of nervous impulses involved in
grasping an object differs between a newborn baby and a baby older than 6 months.

[1 mark]

The Brain

*Scientists know a bit about the **brain** but **not as much** as they'd like.*

The **Brain** is Responsible for **Complex Behaviours**

1) Along with the spinal cord, the brain is part of the <u>central nervous system</u>.

2) It's made up of <u>billions</u> of <u>interconnected neurones</u> (neurones that are connected together).

3) The brain is in charge of all of our <u>complex behaviours</u>. It controls and coordinates everything you do — running, breathing, sleeping, remembering your gym kit...

4) We know that <u>different regions</u> of the brain carry out <u>different functions</u>:

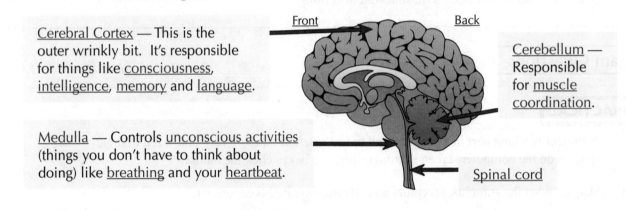

Front   Back

<u>Cerebral Cortex</u> — This is the outer wrinkly bit. It's responsible for things like <u>consciousness</u>, <u>intelligence</u>, <u>memory</u> and <u>language</u>.

<u>Cerebellum</u> — Responsible for <u>muscle coordination</u>.

<u>Medulla</u> — Controls <u>unconscious activities</u> (things you don't have to think about doing) like <u>breathing</u> and your <u>heartbeat</u>.

<u>Spinal cord</u>

Scientists Use a Range of **Methods** to **Study** the **Brain**

Scientists use a few different methods to study the brain and map out <u>which bits do what</u>:

<u>Studying patients with brain damage</u> — If a <u>small</u> part of the brain has been <u>damaged</u>, the <u>effect</u> this has on the patient can tell you a lot about what the damaged part of the brain does. E.g. if an area at the back of the brain was damaged by a stroke and the patient went <u>blind</u>, you know that that area has something to do with <u>vision</u>.

Scientists that study the brain are called neuroscientists.

<u>Electrically stimulating the brain</u> — The brain can be <u>stimulated electrically</u> by pushing a tiny <u>electrode</u> into the tissue and giving it a small zap of electricity. By observing what stimulating <u>different parts</u> of the brain does, it's possible to get an idea of what those parts do. E.g. when a certain part of the brain (known as the <u>motor area</u>) is stimulated, it causes <u>muscle contraction</u> and <u>movement</u>.

<u>MRI Scans</u> — A <u>magnetic resonance imaging (MRI) scanner</u> is a big fancy tube-like machine that can produce a very <u>detailed picture</u> of the brain's structures. Scientists use it to find out what areas of the brain are <u>active</u> when people are doing things like listening to music or trying to recall a memory.

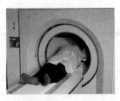

Messing With the **Brain** Can Have **Consequences**

1) Knowledge of how the brain works has led to the development of <u>treatments</u> for <u>disorders</u> of the nervous system. For example, <u>electrical stimulation</u> of the brain can help reduce <u>muscle tremors</u> caused by nervous system disorders such as Parkinson's disease.

2) However, the brain is incredibly <u>complex</u> and <u>delicate</u> — the investigation of brain function and any treatment of brain damage or disease is difficult. It also carries <u>risks</u>, such as <u>physical damage</u> to the brain or <u>increased problems</u> with brain function (e.g. difficulties with speech).

The Eye

*The **eye** is a **sense organ**. There's a lot to get your head around, so get **focused**.*

Learn the Eye with All Its Labels

1) The SCLERA is the <u>tough</u>, <u>supporting wall</u> of the eye.

2) The CORNEA is the <u>transparent</u> outer layer found at the <u>front</u> of the eye. It <u>refracts</u> (bends) light into the eye.

3) The IRIS contains <u>muscles</u> that allow it to control the <u>diameter</u> of the PUPIL (the <u>hole</u> in the <u>middle</u>) and therefore <u>how much light</u> enters the eye.

4) The LENS <u>focuses</u> the <u>light</u> onto the RETINA (which contains receptor cells sensitive to <u>light intensity</u> and <u>colour</u>).

5) The shape of the lens is controlled by the CILIARY MUSCLES and SUSPENSORY LIGAMENTS.

6) The OPTIC NERVE carries impulses from the receptors on the retina to the <u>brain</u>.

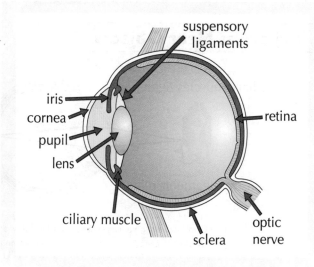

The Iris Reflex — Adjusting for Bright Light

<u>Very bright</u> light can <u>damage</u> the retina — so you have a reflex to protect it.

1) When <u>light receptors</u> in the eye detect very bright light, a <u>reflex</u> is triggered that makes the pupil <u>smaller</u>. The <u>circular muscles</u> in the iris <u>contract</u> and the <u>radial muscles relax</u>. This reduces the amount of light that can enter the eye.

2) The opposite process happens in dim light. This time, the <u>radial muscles</u> contract and the <u>circular muscles</u> relax, which makes the pupil <u>wider</u>.

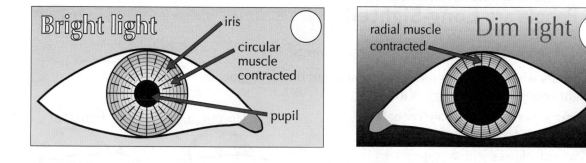

Learn that diagram of the eye...

It'll help if you <u>sketch</u> the diagram out roughly, <u>close this book</u> and then try to <u>label</u> your sketch. If your artistic skills aren't up to much, you could even <u>trace it</u>, then label the traced version.

The Eye and Correcting Vision Defects

*As you saw on the previous page, the way the eye works is quite **complex**. It's not surprising really that sometimes it **doesn't work so well**. Thankfully, we have ways of **correcting** it...*

Focusing on Near and Distant Objects — Another Reflex

The eye focuses light on the retina by <u>changing</u> the <u>shape</u> of the <u>lens</u> — this is known as <u>accommodation</u>.

To Look at **Near Objects**:

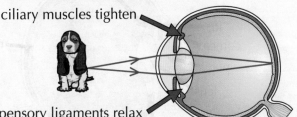

ciliary muscles tighten

suspensory ligaments relax

1) The <u>ciliary muscles contract</u>, which <u>slackens</u> the <u>suspensory ligaments</u>.
2) The lens becomes <u>fat</u> (more curved).
3) This <u>increases</u> the amount by which it <u>refracts</u> (bends) light.

As you get older, your eye's lens loses flexibility, so it can't easily spring back to a round shape. This means light can't be focused well for near viewing, so older people often have to use reading glasses.

To Look at **Distant Objects**:

1) The <u>ciliary muscles relax</u>, which allows the <u>suspensory ligaments</u> to <u>pull tight</u>.
2) This makes the lens go <u>thin</u> (less curved).
3) So it <u>refracts</u> light by a <u>smaller</u> amount.

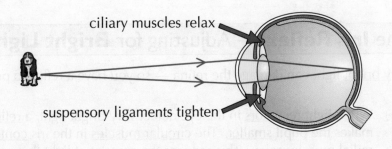

ciliary muscles relax

suspensory ligaments tighten

If the lens cannot refract the light by the <u>right amount</u> (so that it focuses on the <u>retina</u>), the person will be <u>short-</u> or <u>long-sighted</u> — see below and the next page for more.

Some People are Long-Sighted

<u>Long-sighted</u> people are <u>unable to focus</u> on <u>near</u> objects:

1) This occurs when the <u>lens</u> is the wrong shape and doesn't <u>refract</u> the light enough or the <u>eyeball</u> is too <u>short</u>.
2) The images of near objects are brought into focus <u>behind</u> the <u>retina</u>.
3) You can use glasses with a <u>convex lens</u> (a lens which <u>curves outwards</u>) to correct it.
4) The lens <u>refracts</u> the light rays so they focus on the <u>retina</u>.
5) The medical term for long-sightedness is <u>hyperopia</u>.

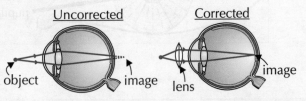

<u>Uncorrected</u>   <u>Corrected</u>

object   image   lens   image

More on Correcting Vision Defects

Some People are Short-Sighted

Short-sighted people are unable to focus on distant objects:

1) This occurs when the lens is the wrong shape and refracts the light too much or the eyeball is too long.

2) The images of distant objects are brought into focus in front of the retina.

3) You can use glasses with a concave lens (a lens which curves inwards) to correct it, so that the light rays focus on the retina.

4) The medical term for short-sightedness is myopia.

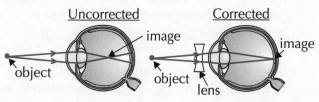

There are Several Treatments for Vision Defects

Wearing glasses isn't for everyone. Here are some alternatives:

Contact lenses

1) Contact lenses are thin lenses that sit on the surface of the eye and are shaped to compensate for the fault in focusing.

2) They're popular because they are lightweight and almost invisible. They're also more convenient than glasses for activities like sports.

3) The two main types of contact lenses are hard lenses and soft lenses. Soft lenses are generally more comfortable, but carry a higher risk of eye infections than hard lenses.

Laser eye surgery

1) Bad eyesight can sometimes be corrected with laser eye surgery.

2) A laser can be used to vaporise tissue, changing the shape of the cornea (and so changing how strongly it refracts light into the eye).

3) Slimming it down makes it less powerful and can improve short sight. Changing the shape so that it's more powerful will improve long sight.

4) The surgeon can precisely control how much tissue the laser takes off, completely correcting the vision.

5) However, like all surgical procedures, there is a risk of complications, such as infection or the eye reacting in a way that makes your vision worse than before.

Replacement lens surgery

1) Sometimes long-sightedness may be more effectively treated by replacing the lens of the eye (rather than altering the shape of the cornea with laser eye surgery).

2) In replacement lens surgery, the natural lens of the eye is removed and an artificial lens, made of clear plastic, is inserted in its place.

3) As it involves work inside the eye, replacing a lens carries higher risks than laser eye surgery, including possible damage to the retina (which could lead to loss of sight).

A convex lens increases refraction...

...and a concave lens reduces it. So if the lenses in your eye aren't refracting the light enough, you need a convex lens to correct it. Simple. Well, it will be once you've read through these two pages a few times.

Controlling Body Temperature

*The body has to keep its insides at around **37 °C** — the **optimum temperature** for **enzymes** in the body.*

Body Temperature Must be Kept Constant

1) The body has to <u>balance</u> the amount of <u>energy gained</u> (e.g. through respiration) and <u>lost</u> to keep the <u>core body temperature constant</u>.

Core body temperature is the temperature inside your body, where your internal organs are.

2) There is a <u>thermoregulatory centre</u> in the <u>brain</u>, which contains <u>receptors</u> that are sensitive to the temperature of the <u>blood</u> flowing through the brain.

3) The thermoregulatory centre also receives impulses from <u>temperature receptors</u> in the <u>skin</u>, giving information about <u>skin temperature</u>.

Body Temperature is Controlled via Negative Feedback

Here's how it works:

<u>Temperature receptors</u> detect that core body temperature is <u>too high</u>.

⬇

The <u>thermoregulatory centre</u> acts as a <u>coordination centre</u> — it receives information from the temperature receptors and <u>triggers</u> the <u>effectors</u> automatically.

⬇

<u>Effectors</u>, e.g. sweat glands, produce a <u>response</u> (see next page) and <u>counteract</u> the change.

body cools down   *body warms up*

<u>Temperature receptors</u> detect that core body temperature is <u>too low</u>.

⬇

The <u>thermoregulatory centre</u> acts as a <u>coordination centre</u> — it receives information from the temperature receptors and <u>triggers</u> the <u>effectors</u> automatically.

⬇

<u>Effectors</u>, e.g. muscles, produce a <u>response</u> (see next page) and <u>counteract</u> the change.

Antagonistic Effectors Oppose Each Other's Actions

1) Some effectors work <u>antagonistically</u>, e.g. one effector heats and another cools — they'll work at the same time to achieve a very precise temperature.

2) This mechanism allows a <u>more sensitive response</u>.

If you do enough revision, you can avoid negative feedback...

<u>Negative feedback</u> is a fancy-sounding name for a not-very-complicated idea. Basically, when something <u>increases</u> or <u>decreases</u> from the <u>normal level</u>, negative feedback kicks in to <u>bring it back</u> to normal.

Controlling Body Temperature

The **Body** has Some Nifty Tricks for **Altering** its Temperature

Different responses are produced by effectors to counteract an increase or decrease in body temperature.

When You're **Too Hot**:

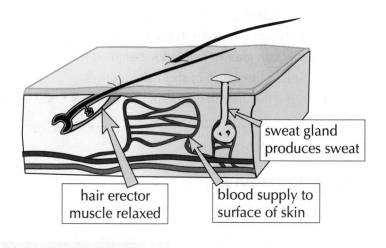

sweat gland produces sweat

hair erector muscle relaxed

blood supply to surface of skin

1) Hairs lie flat.

2) Sweat is produced by sweat glands and evaporates from the skin. This transfers energy to the environment.

3) The blood vessels supplying the skin dilate so more blood flows close to the surface of the skin. This is called vasodilation. This helps transfer energy from the skin to the environment.

When You're **Too Cold**:

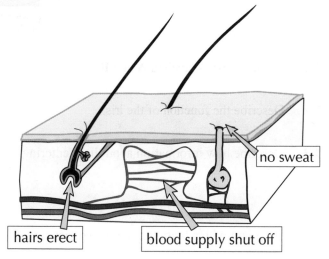

no sweat

hairs erect

blood supply shut off

1) Hairs stand up to trap an insulating layer of air.

2) No sweat is produced.

3) Blood vessels supplying skin capillaries constrict to close off the skin's blood supply. This is called vasoconstriction.

4) When you're cold you shiver too (your muscles contract automatically). This needs respiration, which transfers some energy to warm the body.

Goose bumps are the result of hairs standing up when you're cold

People exposed to extreme cold for a long time without protection can get frostbite — the blood supply to the fingers and toes is cut off to reduce the amount of energy lost (this kills the cells, and they go black).

Warm-Up & Exam Questions

Without a good warm-up you're likely to strain a brain cell or two. So take the time to run through these simple questions and get the basic facts straight before plunging into the Exam Questions.

1) Name the region of the brain that controls coordinated movement.
2) What name is given to the transparent layer at the front on the eye?
3) How can glasses help a long-sighted person focus on something nearby?
4) Explain the cause of short-sightedness.
5) Name the area of the brain that controls body temperature.

Exam Questions

1 **Figure 1** shows a cross section through the eye. *Grade 4-6*

Figure 1

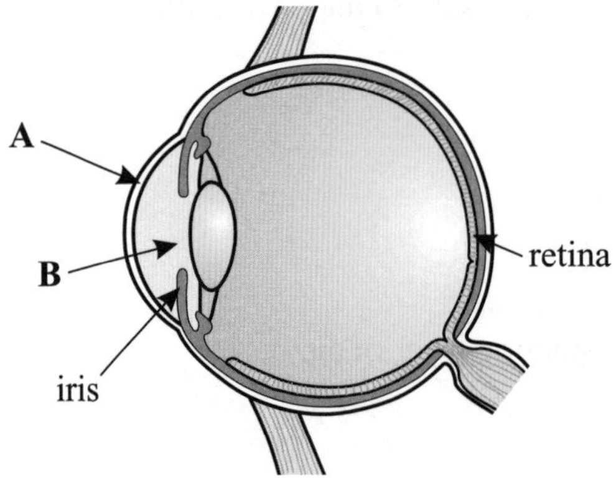

1.1 Name the parts labelled **A** and **B**.

[2 marks]

1.2 Describe the function of the iris.

[1 mark]

1.3 Describe how information about light entering the eye is passed to the brain.

[2 marks]

2 A patient with a brain tumour is experiencing difficulties with memory and language. *Grade 6-7*

2.1 Which of the following areas of the brain is most likely to be affected by the tumour?
Tick **one** box.

☐ medulla   ☐ cerebral cortex   ☐ cerebellum   ☐ hypothalamus

[1 mark]

2.2 The patient's doctor has concerns about operating to remove the tumour.
Suggest **two** possible concerns the doctor may have about possible effects on the brain.

[2 marks]

Topic 5 — Homeostasis and Response

Exam Questions

3   Changes in the skin are an important part of temperature regulation.

    Figure 2 shows a cross section through the skin of a person who is cold.

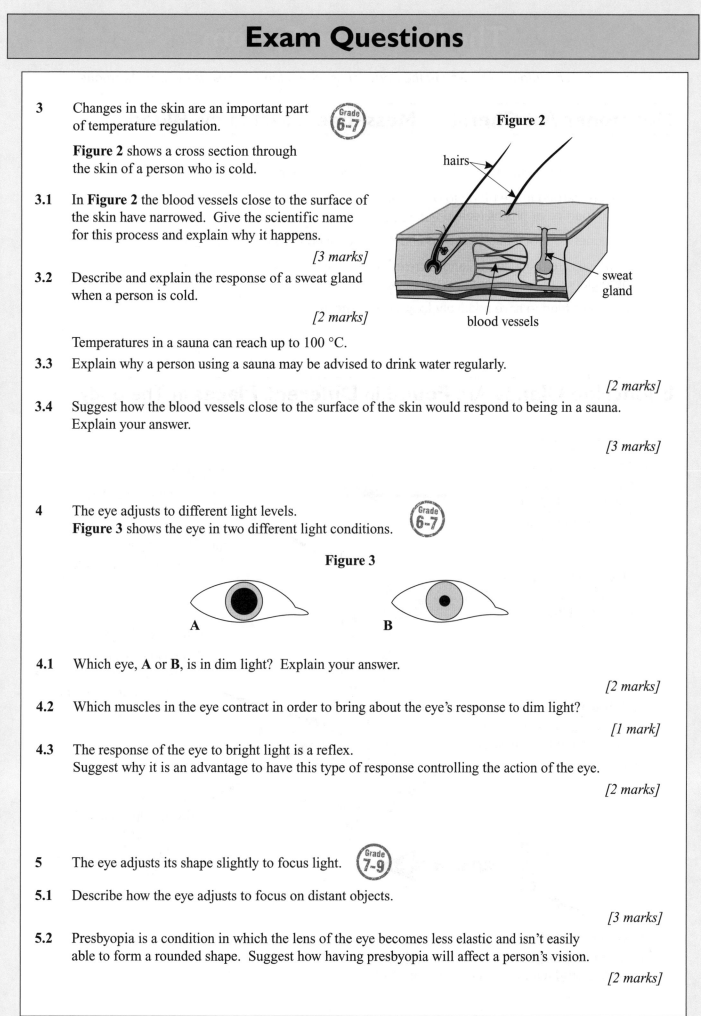

Figure 2

hairs

sweat gland

blood vessels

3.1   In **Figure 2** the blood vessels close to the surface of the skin have narrowed. Give the scientific name for this process and explain why it happens.

[3 marks]

3.2   Describe and explain the response of a sweat gland when a person is cold.

[2 marks]

Temperatures in a sauna can reach up to 100 °C.

3.3   Explain why a person using a sauna may be advised to drink water regularly.

[2 marks]

3.4   Suggest how the blood vessels close to the surface of the skin would respond to being in a sauna. Explain your answer.

[3 marks]

4   The eye adjusts to different light levels.
    Figure 3 shows the eye in two different light conditions.

Figure 3

A   B

4.1   Which eye, **A** or **B**, is in dim light? Explain your answer.

[2 marks]

4.2   Which muscles in the eye contract in order to bring about the eye's response to dim light?

[1 mark]

4.3   The response of the eye to bright light is a reflex.
      Suggest why it is an advantage to have this type of response controlling the action of the eye.

[2 marks]

5   The eye adjusts its shape slightly to focus light.

5.1   Describe how the eye adjusts to focus on distant objects.

[3 marks]

5.2   Presbyopia is a condition in which the lens of the eye becomes less elastic and isn't easily able to form a rounded shape. Suggest how having presbyopia will affect a person's vision.

[2 marks]

The Endocrine System

*The other way to send information around the body (apart from along nerves) is by using **hormones**.*

Hormones Are **Chemical Messengers** Sent in the **Blood**

1) Hormones are chemical molecules released directly into the blood.

2) They are carried in the blood to other parts of the body, but only affect particular cells in particular organs (called target organs).

3) Hormones control things in organs and cells that need constant adjustment.

4) Hormones are produced in (and secreted by) various glands, called endocrine glands. These glands make up your endocrine system.

5) Hormones tend to have relatively long-lasting effects.

Endocrine Glands Are **Found** in **Different Places** in The Body

PITUITARY GLAND

1) The pituitary gland produces many hormones that regulate body conditions.

2) It is sometimes called the 'master gland' because these hormones act on other glands, directing them to release hormones that bring about change.

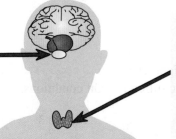

THYROID
This produces thyroxine, which is involved in regulating things like the rate of metabolism, heart rate and temperature.

ADRENAL GLAND
This produces adrenaline, which is used to prepare the body for a 'fight or flight' response (see page 144).

OVARIES (females only)
Produce oestrogen, which is involved in the menstrual cycle (see page 140).

PANCREAS
This produces insulin, which is used to regulate the blood glucose level (see page 132).

TESTES (males only)
Produce testosterone, which controls puberty and sperm production in males (see page 139).

Comparing Nerves and Hormones

*Now you know that there are **two** ways information can be sent round the body*
*— via the **nervous** or **hormonal** systems — here's a recap of the differences between them...*

Hormones and Nerves Carry Messages in Different Ways

Hormones and nerves do similar jobs — they both carry information and instructions around the body.
But there are some important differences between them:

Nerves

1) Very FAST action.

2) Act for a very SHORT TIME.

3) Act on a very PRECISE AREA.

Hormones

1) SLOWER action.

2) Act for a LONG TIME.

3) Act in a more GENERAL way.

If you're not sure whether a response is nervous or hormonal, have a think about the speed
of the reaction and how long it lasts.

If the Response is Really Quick, It's Probably Nervous

Some information needs to be passed to effectors really quickly (e.g. pain
signals, or information from your eyes telling you about the lion heading your
way), so it's no good using hormones to carry the message — they're too slow.

If a Response Lasts For a Long Time, It's Probably Hormonal

For example, when you get a shock, a hormone called adrenaline is released
into the body (causing the fight-or-flight response, where your body is hyped
up ready for action). You can tell it's a hormonal response (even though it
kicks in pretty quickly) because you feel a bit wobbly for a while afterwards.

Nerves, hormones — no wonder revision makes me tense...

Hormones control various organs and cells in the body, though they tend to control things that aren't
immediately life-threatening (so things like sexual development, blood sugar level, water content, etc.).

Controlling Blood Glucose

*On page 126, you saw that **body temperature** is controlled as part of **homeostasis** — well so is blood glucose level. **Insulin** and **glucagon** are **hormones** that control how much **glucose** there is in your **blood**.*

Insulin and Glucagon Control Blood Glucose Level

1) Eating foods containing <u>carbohydrate</u> puts <u>glucose</u> (a type of sugar) into the <u>blood</u> from the gut.

2) The normal <u>metabolism</u> of cells <u>removes glucose</u> from the blood.

3) Vigorous <u>exercise</u> removes <u>much more</u> glucose from the blood.

4) <u>Excess</u> glucose can be stored as <u>glycogen</u> in the <u>liver</u> and in the <u>muscles</u>.

5) The <u>level of glucose</u> in the <u>blood</u> must be kept <u>steady</u>. <u>Changes</u> are monitored and controlled by the <u>pancreas</u>, using the hormones <u>insulin</u> and <u>glucagon</u>, in a <u>negative feedback cycle</u>:

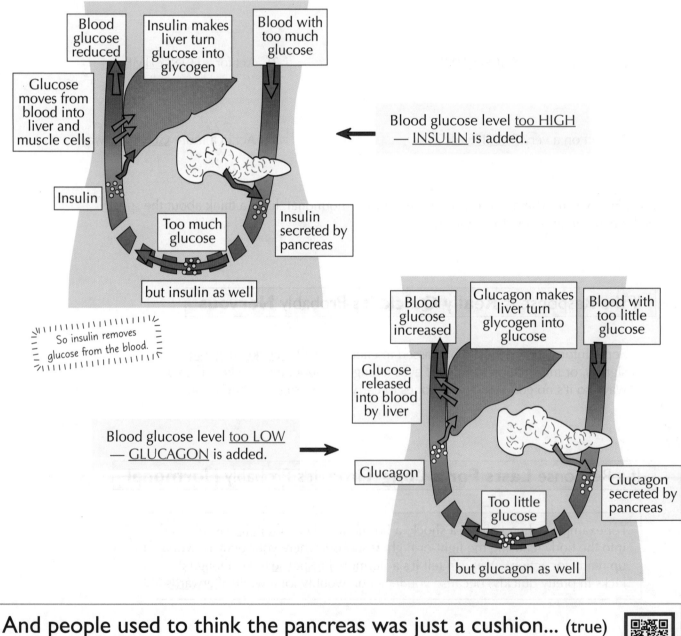

And people used to think the pancreas was just a cushion... (true)

This stuff can seem a bit confusing at first, but if you learn those <u>two diagrams</u>, it should get a bit easier.

Q1 The graph shows the relative secretion rates of insulin and glucagon as the blood glucose level increases. Which curve represents glucagon? Explain your answer. [2 marks]

Diabetes

Sometimes, homeostasis goes wrong. ***Diabetes*** *is an example of this.*

With **Diabetes**, You **Can't Control** Your **Blood Sugar Level**

Diabetes is a condition that affects your ability to control your blood sugar level. There are two types:

Type 1 Diabetes — **Little** or **No Insulin** is Made

1) Type 1 diabetes is where the pancreas produces little or no insulin.

2) This means a person's blood glucose level can rise to a level that can kill them.

3) People with Type 1 diabetes need insulin therapy — this usually involves several injections of insulin throughout the day, most likely at mealtimes. This makes sure that glucose is removed from the blood quickly once the food has been digested, stopping the level getting too high. It's a very effective treatment.

4) The amount of insulin that needs to be injected depends on the person's diet and how active they are.

5) As well as insulin therapy, people with Type 1 diabetes need to think about limiting the intake of food rich in simple carbohydrates, e.g. sugars (which cause the blood glucose to rise rapidly) and taking regular exercise (which helps to remove excess glucose from the blood).

Type 2 Diabetes — **Insulin Resistance**

1) Type 2 diabetes is where a person becomes resistant to their own insulin (they still produce insulin, but their body's cells don't respond properly to the hormone).

2) This can also cause a person's blood sugar level to rise to a dangerous level.

3) Being overweight can increase your chance of developing Type 2 diabetes, as obesity is a major risk factor in the development of the disease.

4) Type 2 diabetes can be controlled by eating a carbohydrate-controlled diet and getting regular exercise.

Be prepared to interpret graphs in the exam

You could be asked to interpret a graph showing the effects of insulin on the blood sugar levels of people with and without diabetes. Don't panic — just study the graph carefully (including the axes labels) so you know exactly what it's showing you. Then apply your blood sugar knowledge.

Warm-Up & Exam Questions

Right then, another lot of pages down. Now there's just the small matter of answering some questions...

Warm-Up Questions

1) How do hormones travel to their target organs?
2) Name five endocrine glands found in the male human body.
3) Which has longer lasting effects — a nervous response or a hormonal response?
4) What does insulin do?
5) What is Type 2 diabetes?

Exam Questions

1   **Figure 1** shows how the blood glucose level is regulated in humans.
Grade 6-7

Figure 1

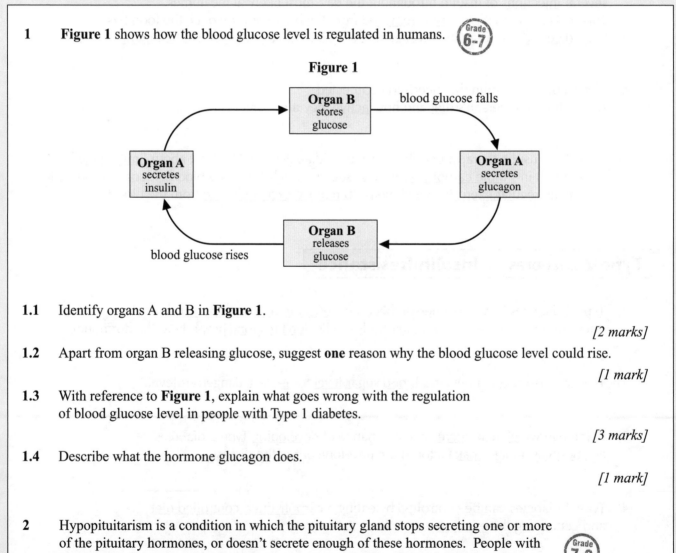

1.1   Identify organs A and B in **Figure 1**.

[2 marks]

1.2   Apart from organ B releasing glucose, suggest **one** reason why the blood glucose level could rise.

[1 mark]

1.3   With reference to **Figure 1**, explain what goes wrong with the regulation
of blood glucose level in people with Type 1 diabetes.

[3 marks]

1.4   Describe what the hormone glucagon does.

[1 mark]

2   Hypopituitarism is a condition in which the pituitary gland stops secreting one or more
of the pituitary hormones, or doesn't secrete enough of these hormones. People with
hypopituitarism may experience tiredness and weight gain. They may also feel the
cold more. These symptoms are all linked to low thyroid hormone levels.
Grade 7-9

Suggest and explain why someone with hypopituitarism may experience these symptoms.

[3 marks]

The Kidneys

*The **kidneys** are really important in this whole **homeostasis** thing.*

Kidneys Basically Act as Filters to "Clean the Blood"

1) The kidneys make urine by taking <u>waste products</u> (and other unwanted substances) out of your blood.

2) Substances are <u>filtered out</u> of the blood as it passes through the kidneys. This process is called <u>filtration</u>.

3) Useful substances like <u>glucose</u>, some <u>ions</u> and the right amount of <u>water</u> are then absorbed back into the blood. This process is called <u>selective reabsorption</u>.

Substances Removed from the Body in Urine Include:

1. Urea

1) <u>Proteins</u> (and the <u>amino acids</u> that they are broken down into) can't be <u>stored</u> by the body — so any <u>excess</u> amino acids are converted into <u>fats</u> and <u>carbohydrates</u>, which can be stored. This occurs in the <u>liver</u> and involves a process called <u>deamination</u>.

2) <u>Ammonia</u> is produced as a <u>waste product</u> from this process.

3) Ammonia is <u>toxic</u> so it's converted to <u>urea</u> in the liver. Urea is then transported to the <u>kidneys</u>, where it's <u>filtered out</u> of the blood and excreted from the body in <u>urine</u>.

A small, unregulated amount of urea is also lost from the skin in sweat.

2. Ions

1) <u>Ions</u> such as <u>sodium</u> are taken into the body in <u>food</u>, and then absorbed into the blood.

2) If the ion (or water) content of the body is <u>wrong</u>, this could upset the <u>balance</u> between ions and water, meaning too much or too little <u>water</u> is drawn into cells by <u>osmosis</u> (see page 35). Having the wrong amount of water can <u>damage</u> cells or mean they <u>don't work</u> as well as normal.

3) Some ions are lost in <u>sweat</u> (which tastes salty, you may have noticed). However, this amount is <u>not regulated</u>, so the right <u>balance</u> of ions in the body must be maintained by the <u>kidneys</u>. The right amount of ions is <u>reabsorbed</u> into the blood after filtration and the rest is removed from the body in <u>urine</u>.

3. Water

1) The body has to <u>constantly balance</u> the water coming in against the water going out.

2) We lose water from the <u>skin</u> in <u>sweat</u> and from the <u>lungs</u> when <u>breathing out</u>.

3) We can't control how much we lose in these ways, so the amount of water is balanced by the amount we <u>consume</u> and the amount <u>removed by the kidneys</u> in <u>urine</u>.

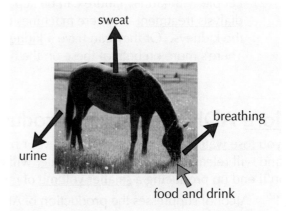

sweat

breathing

urine

food and drink

The Kidneys

*As you might have been expecting, the kidneys' work is controlled by a **hormone**.*

The **Concentration of Urine** is **Controlled** by a **Hormone**

1) The concentration of urine is controlled by a hormone called <u>anti-diuretic hormone</u> (ADH).
2) This is released into the <u>bloodstream</u> by the <u>pituitary gland</u>.
3) The brain <u>monitors the water content of the blood</u> and instructs the <u>pituitary gland</u> to release <u>ADH</u> into the blood according to how much is needed.

Negative Feedback Controls **Water Content**

1) The whole process of water content regulation is controlled by <u>negative feedback</u> (see page 116).
2) This means that if the water content gets <u>too high</u> or <u>too low</u> a mechanism will be triggered that brings it back to <u>normal</u>.
3) Here's how it works:

A <u>receptor</u> in the <u>brain</u> detects that the water content is <u>too high</u>.

⬇

The <u>coordination centre</u> in the brain receives the information and coordinates a <u>response</u>.

⬇

The <u>pituitary gland</u> releases <u>less</u> ADH, so <u>less water</u> is <u>reabsorbed</u> from the kidney tubules.

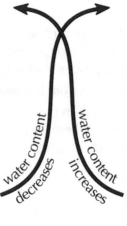

water content decreases / *water content increases*

A <u>receptor</u> in the <u>brain</u> detects that the water content is <u>too low</u>.

⬇

The <u>coordination centre</u> in the brain receives the information and coordinates a <u>response</u>.

⬇

The <u>pituitary gland</u> releases <u>more</u> ADH, so <u>more water</u> is <u>reabsorbed</u> from the kidney tubules.

The Kidneys Remove **Waste Substances** from the Blood

1) If the kidneys don't work properly, <u>waste substances build up</u> in the blood and you lose your ability to <u>control</u> the <u>levels of ions and water</u> in your body. Eventually, this results in <u>death</u>.

2) People with kidney failure can be kept alive by having <u>dialysis treatment</u> — where <u>machines</u> do the job of the kidneys. Or they can have a <u>kidney transplant</u>. There's more on both of these on the next page.

The kidneys are incredibly important — if they don't work as they should, you can get problems in the heart, bones, nervous system, stomach, mouth, etc.

<u>More</u> ADH = <u>less</u> urine produced...

If you <u>lose water</u> (e.g. by sweating a lot) your blood water content will drop and your pituitary gland will release more ADH. <u>More water</u> will be <u>reabsorbed</u> from the kidney tubules and you'll end up producing a <u>smaller volume</u> of <u>more concentrated</u> (darker) <u>urine</u>.

Q1 Video Solution

Q1 Alcohol suppresses the production of ADH.
    Suggest how this can lead to dehydration.

[2 marks]

Treatments for Kidney Failure

*If someone's kidneys stop working, there are basically two treatments — **regular dialysis** or a **transplant**.*

Dialysis Machines Filter the Blood

1) Dialysis has to be done <u>regularly</u> to keep the concentrations of <u>dissolved substances</u> in the blood at <u>normal levels</u>, and to remove waste substances.

2) In a <u>dialysis machine</u> the person's blood flows between <u>partially permeable membranes</u>, surrounded by dialysis fluid. The membranes are permeable to things like <u>ions</u> and <u>waste substances</u>, but not <u>big molecules</u> like proteins (just like the membranes in the kidney).

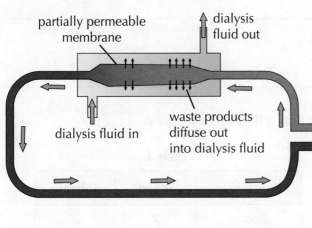

partially permeable membrane

dialysis fluid out

dialysis fluid in

waste products diffuse out into dialysis fluid

from person

back to person

3) The dialysis fluid has the <u>same concentration</u> of dissolved ions and glucose as <u>healthy blood</u>.

4) This means that useful <u>dissolved ions</u> and <u>glucose</u> won't be lost from the blood during dialysis.

5) Only <u>waste substances</u> (such as <u>urea</u>) and <u>excess ions and water</u> diffuse across the barrier.

6) Many patients with kidney failure have to have a dialysis session <u>three times a week</u>. Each session takes <u>3-4 hours</u> — not much fun.

7) Plus, dialysis may cause <u>blood clots</u> or <u>infections</u>.

8) Being on a dialysis machine is <u>not a pleasant experience</u> and it is <u>expensive</u> for the NHS to run.

9) However, dialysis can buy a patient with kidney failure <u>valuable time</u> until a <u>donor organ</u> is found.

Kidney Transplants are a Cure, but can be Rejected

1) At the moment, the only <u>cure</u> for kidney failure is to have a <u>kidney transplant</u>.

2) Healthy kidneys are usually transplanted from people who have <u>died suddenly</u>.

3) The person who died has to be on the <u>organ donor register</u> or carry a <u>donor card</u> (provided their relatives agree too).

4) Kidneys can also be transplanted from people who are still <u>alive</u> (as we all have two of them) but there is a small <u>risk</u> to the <u>person donating</u> the kidney.

5) There is also a risk that the donor kidney can be <u>rejected</u> by the patient's <u>immune system</u>. The patient is treated with <u>drugs</u> to <u>prevent</u> this but it can still happen.

6) Transplants are <u>cheaper</u> (in the long run) than dialysis and they can put an end to the hours patients have to spend on dialysis, but there are long <u>waiting lists</u> for kidneys.

Dialysis or transplant? Both have their downsides...

<u>Donor kidneys</u> are ideally matched by <u>blood type</u> (and a few other things) to the recipient, which makes them less likely to be <u>rejected</u>. However, it means a potentially <u>long waiting time</u> for a suitable kidney.

Warm-Up & Exam Questions

Just a few simple Warm-Up Questions and a few slightly harder Exam Questions stand between you and the menstrual cycle...

Warm-Up Questions

1) Describe how urea is produced from excess amino acids.
2) Aside from urea, give two substances removed in the urine.
3) Which hormone controls the reabsorption of water in the kidneys?
4) Name the part of the brain where this hormone is released.
5) What is the purpose of the partially permeable membrane in a dialysis machine?

Exam Questions

1   Substances filtered out of the blood in the kidneys form a fluid called a filtrate. **(Grade 4-6)**

1.1   **Table 1** shows some substances that are present either in the blood or in the filtrate just after filtration has taken place. Complete **Table 1** by filling in the blanks in each column.

[2 marks]

Table 1

Substances	Blood	Filtrate
glucose	✗	✓
urea		
	✗	✓

1.2   Glucose is present in the blood that leaves the kidneys. By which of the following processes does glucose move from the filtrate into the blood? Tick **one** box.

☐ filtration   ☐ osmosis   ☐ selective reabsorption   ☐ deamination

[1 mark]

2   A hospital patient has kidney failure. She has dialysis three times a week. **(Grade 6-7)**

2.1   Explain how the dialysis machine removes urea from the patient's blood.

[2 marks]

2.2   Explain why the patient does not lose glucose from her blood during dialysis.

[2 marks]

The patient is on the waiting list to receive a kidney transplant.

2.3   Suggest **one** reason why this form of treatment may be preferable to dialysis.

[1 mark]

2.4   Give **one** disadvantage of kidney transplants.

[1 mark]

3*   A runner went for a 10 mile run on a warm day. When she got home she noticed that her urine was darker in colour than normal. Explain why she produced darker coloured urine.

[6 marks]

Puberty and the Menstrual Cycle

*The monthly **release of an egg** from a woman's ovaries is part of the **menstrual cycle**.*

Hormones Promote Sexual Characteristics at Puberty

At puberty, your body starts releasing sex hormones that trigger off secondary sexual characteristics (such as the development of facial hair in men and breasts in women) and cause eggs to mature in women.

- In men, the main reproductive hormone is testosterone. It's produced by the testes and stimulates sperm production.

- In women, the main reproductive hormone is oestrogen. It's produced by the ovaries. As well as bringing about physical changes, oestrogen is also involved in the menstrual cycle.

The Menstrual Cycle Has Four Stages

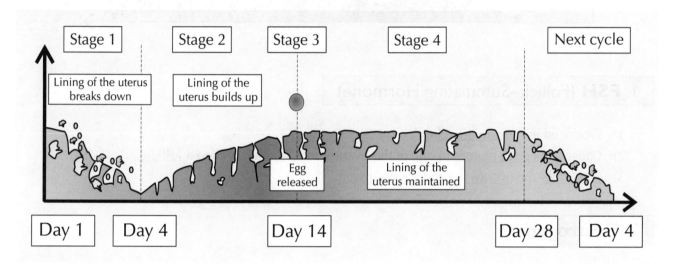

Stage 1

Day 1 — menstruation starts. The uterus lining breaks down for about four days.

Stage 2

The uterus lining builds up again, from day 4 to day 14, into a thick spongy layer full of blood vessels, ready to receive a fertilised egg.

Stage 3

An egg develops and is released from the ovary at day 14 — this is called ovulation.

Stage 4

The wall is then maintained for about 14 days until day 28. If no fertilised egg has landed on the uterus wall by day 28, the spongy lining starts to break down and the whole cycle starts again.

Puberty and the Menstrual Cycle

*There's **more than one** hormone involved in the menstrual cycle...*

The **Menstrual Cycle** is **Controlled** by **Four Hormones**

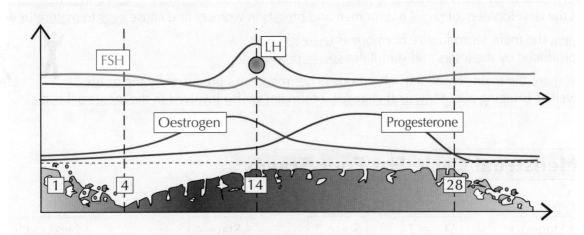

1. **FSH** (Follicle-Stimulating Hormone)

1) Produced in the <u>pituitary gland</u>.
2) Causes an <u>egg to mature</u> in one of the ovaries, in a structure called a <u>follicle</u>.
3) <u>Stimulates</u> the <u>ovaries</u> to produce <u>oestrogen</u>.

2. **Oestrogen**

1) Produced in the <u>ovaries</u>.
2) Causes the lining of the uterus to <u>grow</u>.
3) <u>Stimulates</u> the release of <u>LH</u> (which causes the release of an egg) and <u>inhibits</u> release of <u>FSH</u>.

3. **LH** (Luteinising Hormone)

1) Produced by the <u>pituitary gland</u>.
2) Stimulates the <u>release of an egg</u> at day 14 (<u>ovulation</u>).

4. **Progesterone**

1) Produced in the <u>ovaries</u> by the remains of the <u>follicle</u> after ovulation.
2) <u>Maintains</u> the lining of the uterus during the <u>second half</u> of the cycle.
   When the level of progesterone <u>falls</u>, the lining <u>breaks down</u>.
3) <u>Inhibits</u> the release of <u>LH</u> and <u>FSH</u>.

Examiners love a good menstrual cycle graph...

Learn this page until you know <u>which hormone does what</u>, and you understand the <u>graph</u> above.

Controlling Fertility

Pregnancy can happen if sperm reaches the ovulated egg. **Contraception** *tries to* **stop** *this happening.*

Hormones Can Be Used to **Reduce Fertility**

1) Oestrogen can be used to prevent the release of an egg —
   so it can be used as a method of contraception.

2) This may seem kind of strange (since naturally oestrogen helps stimulate the release of eggs).
   But if oestrogen is taken every day to keep the level of it permanently high, it inhibits the
   production of FSH, and after a while egg development and production stop and stay stopped.

3) Progesterone also reduces fertility, e.g. by stimulating the production of thick
   mucus which prevents any sperm getting through and reaching an egg.

Oestrogen and **Progesterone** Can Be Taken in a **Pill**

1) The pill is an oral contraceptive containing oestrogen and progesterone
   (known as the combined oral contraceptive pill).

2) It's over 99% effective at preventing pregnancy, but it can cause side effects like
   headaches and nausea and it doesn't protect against sexually transmitted diseases.

There's also a progesterone-only pill — it has fewer
side effects than the pill, and is just as effective.

Other Contraceptives Also **Contain Hormones**

Here are some examples:

1) The contraceptive patch contains oestrogen and progesterone (the same as the combined pill).
   It's a small (5 cm × 5 cm) patch that's stuck to the skin. Each patch lasts one week.

2) The contraceptive implant is inserted under the skin of the arm. It releases a continuous
   amount of progesterone, which stops the ovaries releasing eggs, makes it hard for sperm to
   swim to the egg, and stops any fertilised egg implanting in the uterus. An implant can last for
   three years.

3) The contraceptive injection also contains progesterone. Each dose lasts 2 to 3 months.

4) An intrauterine device (IUD) is a T-shaped device that is inserted into the uterus to kill sperm
   and prevent implantation of a fertilised egg. There are two main types — plastic IUDs that
   release progesterone and copper IUDs that prevent the sperm surviving in the uterus.

So oestrogen and progesterone can be used to prevent pregnancy...

As you probably already know, hormonal contraceptives are **not** the only contraceptives you can use.
You'll find out about non-hormonal methods on the next page — but get this lot learnt first.

Controlling Fertility

*Not everyone wants to avoid getting pregnant — **hormones** can also be used to **increase fertility**. First up though, a bit on **non-hormonal methods** of **contraception**...*

Barriers Stop Egg and Sperm Meeting

1) Non-hormonal forms of contraception are designed to stop the sperm from getting to the egg.
2) Condoms are worn over the penis during intercourse to prevent the sperm entering the vagina. There are also female condoms that are worn inside the vagina. Condoms are the only form of contraception that will protect against sexually transmitted diseases.
3) A diaphragm is a shallow plastic cup that fits over the cervix (the entrance to the uterus) to form a barrier. It has to be used with spermicide (a substance that disables or kills the sperm).
4) Spermicide can be used alone as a form of contraception, but it is not as effective (only about 70-80%).

There are Other Ways to Avoid Pregnancy

1) Sterilisation — this involves cutting or tying the fallopian tubes (which connect the ovaries to the uterus) in a female, or the sperm duct (the tube between the testes and penis) in a male. This is a permanent procedure. However, there is a very small chance that the tubes can rejoin.
2) 'Natural methods' — Pregnancy may be avoided by finding out when in the menstrual cycle the woman is most fertile and avoiding sexual intercourse on those days. It's popular with people who think that hormonal and barrier methods are unnatural, but it's not very effective.
3) Abstinence — The only way to be completely sure that sperm and egg don't meet is to not have intercourse.

Hormones Can Be Used to Increase Fertility

1) Some women have levels of FSH (follicle-stimulating hormone) that are too low to cause their eggs to mature. This means that no eggs are released and the women can't get pregnant.
2) The hormones FSH and LH can be given to women as a fertility drug to stimulate ovulation.
3) The use of hormones to increase fertility has one big pro:

   It helps a lot of women to get pregnant when previously they couldn't... pretty obvious.

4) There are some cons though:

   1) It doesn't always work — some women may have to do it many times, which can be expensive.
   2) Too many eggs could be stimulated, resulting in unexpected multiple pregnancies (twins, triplets, etc.).

The winner of best contraceptive ever — just not doing it...

You might be asked to evaluate the different hormonal and non-hormonal methods of contraception in your exam. If you do, make sure you weigh up and write about both the pros and the cons of each method.

Controlling Fertility

*If the use of FSH and LH alone can't help a woman to get pregnant, **IVF** may be considered...*

IVF Can Also Help Couples to **Have Children**

If a woman cannot get pregnant using medication, she may chose to try IVF ("*in vitro* fertilisation").

1) IVF involves collecting eggs from the woman's ovaries and fertilising them in a lab using the man's sperm.

2) IVF treatment can also involve a technique called Intra-Cytoplasmic Sperm Injection (ICSI), where the sperm is injected directly into an egg. It's useful if the man has a very low sperm count.

3) The fertilised eggs are then grown into embryos in a laboratory incubator.

4) Once the embryos are tiny balls of cells, one or two of them are transferred to the woman's uterus to improve the chance of pregnancy.

5) FSH and LH are given before egg collection to stimulate several eggs to mature (so more than one egg can be collected).

6) IVF has a pretty obvious benefit:

Fertility treatment can give an infertile couple a child.

7) But there are also downsides to IVF:

1) Multiple births can happen if more than one embryo grows into a baby — these are risky for the mother and babies (there's a higher risk of miscarriage, stillbirth...).

2) The success rate of IVF is low — the average success rate in the UK is about 26%. This makes the process incredibly stressful and often upsetting, especially if it ends in multiple failures.

3) As well as being emotionally stressful, the process is also physically stressful for the woman. Some women have a strong reaction to the hormones — e.g. abdominal pain, vomiting, dehydration.

Advances in Technology Have Improved IVF

1) Advances in microscope techniques have helped to improve the techniques (and therefore the success rate) of IVF.

2) Specialised micro-tools have been developed to use on the eggs and sperm under the microscope. They're also used to remove single cells from the embryo for genetic testing (to check that it is healthy — see page 169).

3) More recently, the development of time-lapse imaging (using a microscope and camera built into the incubator) means that the growth of the embryos can be continuously monitored to help identify those that are more likely to result in a successful pregnancy.

Some People Are **Against IVF**

1) The process of IVF often results in unused embryos that are eventually destroyed. Because of this, some people think it is unethical because each embryo is a potential human life.

2) The genetic testing of embryos before implantation also raises ethical issues as some people think it could lead to the selection of preferred characteristics, such as gender or eye colour.

Adrenaline and Thyroxine

*You've met a lot of human hormones so far, but **two more** won't hurt.*
Then that's it, I promise — before it's time to go onto plant hormones...

Adrenaline Prepares You for **"Fight or Flight"**

1) Adrenaline is a hormone released by the adrenal glands, which are just above the kidneys (see p.130).

2) Adrenaline is released in response to stressful or scary situations — your brain detects fear or stress and sends nervous impulses to the adrenal glands, which respond by secreting adrenaline.

3) It gets the body ready for 'fight or flight' by triggering mechanisms that increase the supply of oxygen and glucose to cells in the brain and muscles. E.g. adrenaline increases heart rate.

Hormone Release can be Affected by **Negative Feedback**

Your body can control the levels of hormones (and other substances) in the blood using negative feedback systems. When the body detects that the level of a substance has gone above or below the normal level, it triggers a response to bring the level back to normal again. Here's an example of just that:

Thyroxine Regulates **Metabolism**

1) Thyroxine is a hormone released by the thyroid gland, which is in the neck (see p.130).

2) It plays an important role in regulating the basal metabolic rate — the speed at which chemical reactions in the body occur while the body is at rest. Thyroxine is also important for loads of processes in the body, such as stimulating protein synthesis for growth and development.

3) Thyroxine is released in response to thyroid stimulating hormone (TSH), which is released from the pituitary gland.

4) A negative feedback system keeps the amount of thyroxine in the blood at the right level — when the level of thyroxine in the blood is higher than normal, the secretion of TSH from the pituitary gland is inhibited (stopped). This reduces the amount of thyroxine released from the thyroid gland, so the level in the blood falls back towards normal.

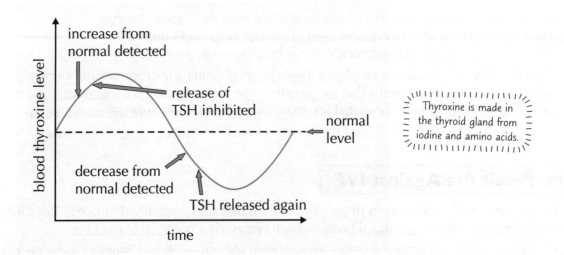

Thyroxine is made in the thyroid gland from iodine and amino acids.

Warm-Up & Exam Questions

If these questions don't get your adrenaline pumping, I don't know what will. Better get started...

Warm-Up Questions

1) Name the hormone that stimulates an egg to mature in the ovary.
2) Name three forms of contraception that reduce fertility using progesterone, not oestrogen.
3) Give one drawback to using hormones to increase fertility.
4) What is the role of FSH and LH during IVF?
5) Name the gland that releases thyroxine.

Exam Questions

1   The menstrual cycle is controlled by several different hormones.   *(Grade 4-6)*

1.1   What effect does oestrogen have on the release of FSH?

[1 mark]

1.2   Which hormone is responsible for maintaining the uterus lining?

[1 mark]

1.3   On what day of the menstrual cycle is the egg released?

[1 mark]

2   The combined oral contraceptive pill contains oestrogen and progesterone.   *(Grade 6-7)*

2.1   Explain how taking oestrogen can prevent pregnancy.

[2 marks]

2.2   Progesterone can prevent pregnancy by preventing ovulation.
Explain **one** other way in which taking progesterone can prevent pregnancy.

[2 marks]

The combined pill is taken once a day in a '21 day pill, 7 day no pill' cycle. One of the problems with the combined pill is that women may forget to take it on the days they are supposed to.

2.3   Suggest an alternative method of hormonal contraception that may be more suitable for a woman who is worried about remembering to take the combined pill. Explain your choice.

[2 marks]

2.4   A couple in their late 30s who have already had three children are looking for a more permanent method of contraception. Suggest **one** method of contraception that may be suitable for them.

[1 mark]

3   A dog suddenly runs towards a cat across the street, which frightens the cat.   *(Grade 7-9)*

Explain what would happen to the cat's heart rate when it sees the dog and explain why this response is beneficial.

[5 marks]

Plant Hormones

*Plants **don't** just grow randomly. Plant hormones make sure they grow in the **right direction**.*

Auxin is a Plant **Growth Hormone**

1) <u>Auxin</u> is a <u>plant hormone</u> that controls <u>growth</u> near the <u>tips</u> of <u>shoots</u> and <u>roots</u>.

2) It controls the growth of a plant in response to <u>light</u> (<u>phototropism</u>) and <u>gravity</u> (<u>gravitropism</u> or <u>geotropism</u>).

3) Auxin is produced in the <u>tips</u> and <u>moves backwards</u> to stimulate the <u>cell elongation (enlargement) process</u> which occurs in the cells <u>just behind</u> the tips.

4) If the tip of a shoot is <u>removed</u>, no auxin is available and the shoot may <u>stop growing</u>.

5) Extra auxin <u>promotes</u> growth in the <u>shoot</u> but <u>inhibits</u> growth in the <u>root</u> — producing the <u>desired result</u>...

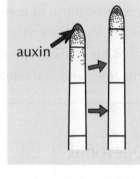

Shoots Grow **Towards Light**

1) When a <u>shoot tip</u> is exposed to <u>light</u>, <u>more auxin</u> accumulates on the side that's in the <u>shade</u> than the side that's in the light.

2) This makes the cells grow (elongate) <u>faster</u> on the <u>shaded side</u>, so the shoot bends <u>towards</u> the light.

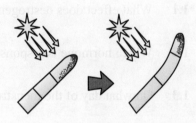

Shoots Grow **Away From Gravity**

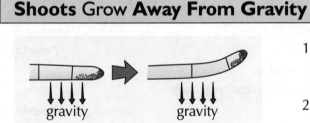

1) When a <u>shoot</u> is growing sideways, <u>gravity</u> produces an unequal distribution of auxin in the tip, with <u>more auxin</u> on the <u>lower side</u>.

2) This causes the lower side to grow <u>faster</u>, bending the shoot <u>upwards</u>.

Roots Grow **Towards Gravity**

1) A <u>root</u> growing sideways will also have more auxin on its <u>lower side</u>.

2) But in a root the <u>extra</u> auxin <u>inhibits</u> growth. This means the cells on <u>top</u> elongate faster, and the root bends <u>downwards</u>.

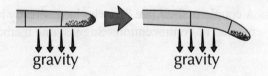

One hormone, three different responses

By responding to stimuli in their environment, plants <u>increase</u> their chances of <u>survival</u>. For example, by growing towards the light, plants increase the amount of light they receive for <u>photosynthesis</u>.

Investigating Plant Growth Responses

*Time to find out if what you've just learnt is **really true**...*

You can **Investigate Plant Growth Responses**

You can investigate the effect of <u>light</u> on the <u>growth</u> of cress seeds like this...

1) Put <u>10 cress seeds</u> into three different Petri dishes, each lined with <u>moist filter paper</u>. (Remember to label your dishes, e.g. A, B, C.)

2) Shine a <u>light</u> onto one of the dishes from <u>above</u> and two of the dishes from <u>different directions</u>.

3) Leave your cress seeds alone for <u>one week</u> until you can <u>observe</u> their <u>responses</u> — and hey presto, you'll find the seedlings <u>grow towards the light</u>.

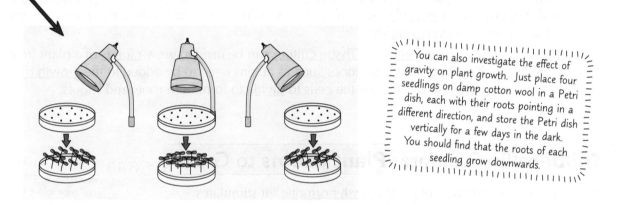

You can also investigate the effect of gravity on plant growth. Just place four seedlings on damp cotton wool in a Petri dish, each with their roots pointing in a different direction, and store the Petri dish vertically for a few days in the dark. You should find that the roots of each seedling grow downwards.

Make Sure You **Control** the **Variables**

1) You know that the <u>growth response</u> of the cress seeds is due to <u>light</u> only, if you <u>control</u> all other variables.

2) Examples of variables that could <u>affect the experiment</u> and so need to be <u>controlled</u> are:

Variable	How to control it
number of seeds	use the same number of seeds in each dish
type of seed	use seeds that all come from the same packet
temperature	keep your Petri dishes in a place where the temperature is stable (i.e. away from heat sources and draughts)
water	use a measuring cylinder to add the same amount of water
light intensity	keep the distance between the bulb and dish the same

Record your results using scientific drawings

<u>Labelled diagrams</u> are a really good way to show the results of experiments like this. There's more about scientific drawings on page 20. Make sure your drawings are <u>neat</u> and <u>useful</u> — remember, <u>don't</u> do any sketching or shading and <u>label</u> your drawing using <u>straight</u>, <u>uncrossed</u> lines.

Commercial Uses of Plant Hormones

*Plant hormones can be **extracted**, or **artificial copies** can be made. This comes in pretty handy...*

Auxins Have Many Uses

Auxins are useful for controlling <u>plant growth</u>. Here are some of the ways they come in handy:

1) <u>Killing weeds</u> — Most <u>weeds</u> growing in fields of crops or in a lawn are <u>broad-leaved</u>, in contrast to <u>grasses</u> and <u>cereals</u> which have very <u>narrow leaves</u>. <u>Selective weedkillers</u> have been developed using auxins, which only affect the <u>broad-leaved plants</u>. They totally <u>disrupt</u> their normal growth patterns, which soon <u>kills</u> them, whilst leaving the grass and crops <u>untouched</u>.

2) <u>Growing from cuttings with rooting powder</u> — A <u>cutting</u> is part of a plant that has been <u>cut off it</u>, like the end of a branch with a few leaves on it. Normally, if you stick cuttings in the soil they <u>won't grow</u>, but if you add <u>rooting powder</u>, which contains <u>auxins</u>, they will <u>produce roots</u> rapidly and start growing as <u>new plants</u>. This enables growers to produce lots of <u>clones</u> (exact copies) of a really good plant <u>very quickly</u>.

3) <u>Growing cells in tissue culture</u> — <u>Tissue culture</u> can be used to grow <u>clones</u> of a plant from a few of its cells. To do this, hormones such as auxins need to be added to the <u>growth medium</u> (along with <u>nutrients</u>) to stimulate the cells to <u>divide</u> to form both roots and shoots.

Gibberellin Stimulates Plant Stems to Grow

Gibberellin is another type of <u>plant growth hormone</u>. It stimulates <u>seed germination</u>, <u>stem growth</u> and <u>flowering</u>. Its uses include:

Seed germination is when a seed starts to grow into a plant.

1) <u>Controlling dormancy</u> — Lots of seeds <u>won't germinate</u> until they've been through <u>certain conditions</u> (e.g. a period of <u>cold</u> or of <u>dryness</u>). This is called <u>dormancy</u>. Seeds can be treated with <u>gibberellin</u> to <u>alter dormancy</u> and make them germinate at <u>times of year</u> that they <u>wouldn't</u> normally. It also helps to make sure <u>all</u> the seeds in a batch germinate at the <u>same time</u>.

2) <u>Inducing flowering</u> — Some plants require <u>certain conditions</u> to <u>flower</u>, such as <u>longer days</u> or <u>low temperatures</u>. If these plants are treated with <u>gibberellin</u>, they will flower <u>without</u> any change in their environment. Gibberellin can also be used to grow <u>bigger flowers</u>.

3) <u>Growing larger fruit</u> — <u>Seedless varieties</u> of fruit (e.g. seedless grapes) often <u>do not grow as large</u> as seeded fruit. However, if <u>gibberellin</u> is added to these fruit, they will grow <u>larger</u> to match the normal types.

Ethene Stimulates Ripening of Fruit

Some fruit will produce more ethene as it ripens.

1) Ethene is a <u>gas</u> produced by <u>aging</u> parts of a plant. It influences the <u>growth</u> of the plant by controlling <u>cell division</u>. It also <u>stimulates enzymes</u> that cause <u>fruit to ripen</u>.

2) Commercially, it can be used to <u>speed up the ripening</u> of fruits — either while they are still on the plant, or during <u>transport</u> to the shops.

3) This means that fruit, such as bananas, can be picked while still <u>unripe</u> (and therefore firmer and <u>less easily damaged</u>). The gas is then added to the fruit on the way to the supermarket so that it will be <u>perfect</u> just as it reaches the shelves.

4) <u>Ripening</u> can also be <u>delayed</u> while the fruit is in <u>storage</u> by adding chemicals that <u>block</u> ethene's effect on the fruit or reduce the amount of ethene that the fruit can <u>produce</u>. Alternatively, some chemicals can be used that <u>react with ethene</u> to remove it from the air.

Warm-Up & Exam Questions

You could skim through this page in a few minutes, but there's no point unless you check over any bits you don't know and make sure you understand everything. It's not quick but it's the only way.

Warm-Up Questions

1) Name the plant hormone responsible for both phototropism and gravitropism.
2) Explain what causes plant shoots to grow towards the light.
3) Give one way that gibberellin is used commercially.
4) Give one way that ethene is used commercially.

Exam Questions

1 A gardener frequently uses products containing plant hormones in her garden. **[Grade 4-6]**

1.1 The gardener has a problem with weeds in her lawn.
She uses a weedkiller that targets the weeds without affecting the growth of the lawn.
Name the hormone likely to be present in the weedkiller.

[1 mark]

1.2 The gardener has a cutting of a plant she would like to grow more of.
Explain how a plant hormone could help the gardener to grow a new plant from the cutting.

[2 marks]

1.3 The gardener is entering some flowering plants into a competition. It is important that the plants all flower in time for the competition. What plant hormone could the gardener use to achieve this?

[1 mark]

PRACTICAL

2 A student placed some germinating beans on the surface of some damp soil and left them in the dark for five days. The appearance of the beans before and after the five day period is shown in **Figure 1**. **[Grade 6-7]**

Figure 1

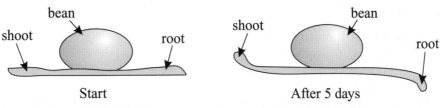

Start   After 5 days

Both the shoot and the root have undergone a gravitropic response after 5 days.

2.1 Describe the gravitropic response of the shoot.

[1 mark]

2.2 Explain the mechanism behind this response.

[2 marks]

2.3 The student wants to compare his findings with beans grown in the light.
He puts some new germinating beans on damp soil and shines a light on them.
Give **two** variables that the student should control in this second experiment.

[2 marks]

Revision Summary for Topic 5

Congratulations, you've made it to the end of Topic 5 — now for some questions to make sure you've been paying attention...
- Try these questions and tick off each one when you get it right.
- When you're completely happy with a sub-topic, tick it off.

For even more practice, try the Retrieval Quiz for Topic 5 — just scan this QR code!

Topic 5 Quiz

Homeostasis and the Nervous System (p.116-120) ☑

1) What is a stimulus?
2) Explain how negative feedback helps to maintain a stable internal environment.
3) What makes up the central nervous system and what does it do?
4) What is a synapse?
5) What is the purpose of a reflex action?
6) What is a reaction time?

The Brain, the Eye and Body Temperature (p.122-127) ☑

7) Give one thing the medulla in the brain is responsible for.
8) Give three methods used by scientists to study the brain.
9) Explain the roles of the following parts of the eye:
   a) cornea   b) retina   c) lens
10) What is the medical term for short-sightedness?
11) Explain why we shiver when we get cold.

Hormones in Humans (p.130-144) ☑

12) What is a hormone?
13) Give two differences between nervous and hormonal responses.
14) Where is excess glucose stored in the body?
15) What effect does the hormone glucagon have on blood glucose level?
16) What is the difference between how Type 1 and Type 2 diabetes are usually controlled?
17) Name three things that are reabsorbed by kidneys.
18) Describe how dialysis works.
19) Draw a timeline of the 28 day menstrual cycle.
    Label the four stages of the cycle and label when the egg is released.
20) Describe two effects of FSH on the body.
21) Which of the following is a hormonal contraceptive — condom, plastic IUD or diaphragm?
22) Briefly describe how IVF is carried out.
23) What is the role of thyroxine in the body?

Plant Hormones (p.146-148) ☑

24) What is auxin?
25) What is: a) phototropism? b) gravitropism?
26) Explain how auxin causes plant roots to grow downwards.
27) Give three ways that auxin can be used commercially.
28) Which plant hormone is responsible for fruit ripening?

DNA

*The first step in understanding **genetics** is getting to grips with **DNA**.*

Chromosomes Are Really Long Molecules of DNA

1) DNA stands for <u>d</u>eoxyribo<u>n</u>ucleic <u>a</u>cid. It's the <u>chemical</u> that all of the <u>genetic material</u> in a cell is <u>made</u> up from.

Head to page 153 for more on the structure of DNA.

2) It contains <u>coded information</u> — basically all the <u>instructions</u> to put an organism together and <u>make it work</u>.

3) So it's <u>what's in your DNA</u> that determines <u>what inherited characteristics</u> you have.

4) DNA is found in the <u>nucleus</u> of animal and plant cells, in really long structures called <u>chromosomes</u>.

5) <u>Chromosomes</u> normally come in <u>pairs</u>.

6) DNA is a <u>polymer</u>. It's made up of <u>two strands</u> coiled together in the shape of a <u>double helix</u>.

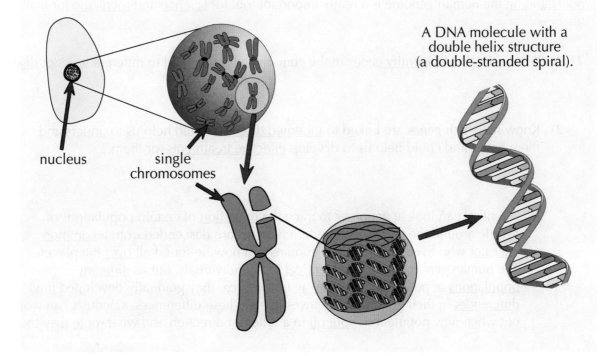

A DNA molecule with a double helix structure (a double-stranded spiral).

nucleus

single chromosomes

Every living organism has DNA

Remember, DNA contains all the <u>instructions</u> to 'build' an organism. The instructions are <u>different</u> for each type of organism on Earth (otherwise all living things would be the same). There's a lot more about <u>DNA</u> and <u>chromosomes</u> coming up in this topic so make sure you understand this page before you move on.

DNA

*DNA determines what **characteristics** an organism has — it's a **very important** molecule.
It's not surprising then that scientists are **super keen** on understanding more about it.*

A **Gene** Codes for a **Specific Protein**

1) A gene is a small section of DNA found on a chromosome.

2) Each gene codes for (tells the cells to make) a particular sequence of amino acids which are put together to make a specific protein.

3) Only 20 amino acids are used, but they make up thousands of different proteins.

4) Genes simply tell cells in what order to put the amino acids together (more on this on the next page).

5) DNA also determines what proteins the cell produces, e.g. haemoglobin, keratin.

6) That in turn determines what type of cell it is, e.g. red blood cell, skin cell.

Every Organism Has a **Genome**

1) Genome is just the fancy term for the entire set of genetic material in an organism.

2) Scientists have worked out the complete human genome.

3) Understanding the human genome is a really important tool for science and medicine for many reasons.

    1) It allows scientists to identify genes in the genome that are linked to different types of disease.

    2) Knowing which genes are linked to inherited diseases could help us to understand them better and could help us to develop effective treatments for them.

    3) Scientists can look at genomes to trace the migration of certain populations of people around the world. All modern humans are descended from a common ancestor who lived in Africa, but humans can now be found all over the planet. The human genome is mostly identical in all individuals, but as different populations of people migrated away from Africa, they gradually developed tiny differences in their genomes. By investigating these differences, scientists can work out when new populations split off in a different direction and what route they took.

Your genes make you different from everyone else

Working out the human genome was a massive project — it involved scientists from many different parts of the world and took more than ten years to complete. Still, if scientists can use the information to help us understand more about diseases and how to fight them, then I reckon it was well worth all the effort.

The Structure of DNA and Protein Synthesis

*So here's how life works — DNA molecules contain a **genetic code** that determines which **proteins** are built.*

DNA is Made Up of Nucleotides

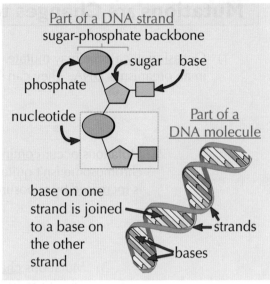

Part of a DNA strand

1) DNA strands are <u>polymers</u> made up of lots of repeating units called <u>nucleotides</u>.

2) Each nucleotide consists of a <u>sugar</u>, a <u>phosphate group</u> and <u>one 'base'</u>.

3) The <u>sugar</u> and <u>phosphate</u> groups in the nucleotides form a '<u>backbone</u>' to the DNA strands. The sugar and phosphate groups <u>alternate</u>. One of <u>four</u> different bases — A, T, C or G — <u>joins</u> to each <u>sugar</u>.

4) Each base <u>links</u> to a base on the opposite strand in the helix.

5) A always pairs up with T, and C always pairs up with G. This is called <u>complementary base pairing</u>.

6) It's the <u>order</u> of <u>bases</u> in a <u>gene</u> that decides the order of <u>amino acids</u> in a <u>protein</u>.

7) Each amino acid is <u>coded for</u> by a sequence of <u>three bases</u> in the gene.

8) The amino acids are <u>joined together</u> to make various proteins, depending on the <u>order</u> of the gene's <u>bases</u>.

9) There are parts of DNA that <u>don't code for proteins</u>. Some of these <u>non-coding</u> parts switch genes on and off, so they <u>control</u> whether or not a gene is <u>expressed</u> (used to make a protein).

mRNA Carries The Code to The Ribosomes

1) Proteins are made in the cell <u>cytoplasm</u> on tiny structures called <u>ribosomes</u>.

2) To make proteins, ribosomes <u>use</u> the <u>code</u> in the <u>DNA</u>. DNA is found in the cell <u>nucleus</u> and can't move out of it because it's really big. So the cell needs to get the code <u>from</u> the DNA <u>to</u> the ribosome.

3) This is done using a molecule called <u>mRNA</u> — which is made by <u>copying</u> the code from DNA. The mRNA acts as a <u>messenger</u> between the DNA and the ribosome — it carries the code between the two.

4) The correct <u>amino acids</u> are brought to the ribosomes in the <u>correct order</u> by <u>carrier molecules</u>.

Proteins Have Many Different Functions

When a chain of amino acids has been assembled, it <u>folds</u> into a <u>unique shape</u> which allows the protein to <u>perform</u> the task it's meant to do. Here are a few examples of types of protein:

1) ENZYMES — act as <u>biological catalysts</u> to <u>speed up</u> chemical reactions in the body (see page 47).

2) HORMONES — used to <u>carry messages</u> around the body. E.g. <u>insulin</u> is a hormone released into the blood by the pancreas to <u>regulate</u> the <u>blood sugar level</u>.

3) STRUCTURAL PROTEINS — are physically <u>strong</u>. E.g. <u>collagen</u> is a structural protein that strengthens <u>connective tissues</u> (like ligaments and cartilage).

<u>A</u>pple <u>T</u>urnover and <u>G</u>loopy <u>C</u>ustard...

Don't forget that in a DNA molecule <u>A always pairs with T</u>, and <u>C always pairs with G</u>.

Q1 The diagram on the right shows a short sequence of DNA bases. C T C C T A C G T G A T

Q1 Video Solution

a) The sequence is from a coding region of DNA.
How many amino acids does it code for? [1 mark]

b) Give the sequence of bases for the complementary strand. [1 mark]

Mutations

*Sometimes the **sequence** of **DNA bases** can change. These changes are called **mutations**. Read on...*

Mutations are Changes to the Genetic Code

1) Occasionally a gene may mutate. A mutation is a random change in an organism's DNA. They can sometimes be inherited.

2) Mutations occur continuously. They can occur spontaneously, e.g. when a chromosome isn't quite replicated properly. However, the chance of mutation is increased by exposure to certain substances or some types of radiation.

3) Mutations change the sequence of the DNA bases in a gene, which produces a genetic variant (a different form of the gene). As the sequence of DNA bases codes for the sequence of amino acids that make up a protein (see page 152), mutations to a gene sometimes lead to changes in the protein that it codes for.

4) Most mutations have very little or no effect on the protein. Some will change it to such a small extent that its function or appearance is unaffected.

5) However, some mutations can seriously affect a protein. Sometimes, the mutation will code for an altered protein with a change in its shape. This could affect its ability to perform its function. For example:

1) If the shape of an enzyme's active site is changed, its substrate may no longer be able to bind to it.

Enzymes are proteins — see page 47.

2) Structural proteins like collagen could lose their strength if their shape is changed, making them pretty useless at providing structure and support.

6) If there's a mutation in non-coding DNA, it can alter how genes are expressed.

There's more on non-coding DNA and gene expression on the previous page.

Mutations are very common, but are rarely noticeable

Mutations sound pretty scary (especially if you're thinking about all those mutant creatures in sci-fi movies). But in reality, mutations occur all the time and hardly ever affect the structure or function of a protein. So we can usually carry on happily with our lives, without knowing anything about how our DNA is mutating.

Mutations

There Are **Different Types** of Mutation

There are <u>different ways</u> that mutations can <u>change</u> the DNA base sequence. For example:

Insertions

1) <u>Insertions</u> are where a <u>new base</u> is <u>inserted</u> into the DNA base sequence where it shouldn't be.

2) You should remember from page 153 that every <u>three bases</u> in a DNA base sequence <u>codes</u> for a particular <u>amino acid</u>.

3) An insertion <u>changes</u> the way the groups of <u>three bases</u> are 'read', which can change the <u>amino acids</u> that they code for.

4) Insertions can change <u>more than one</u> amino acid as they have a <u>knock-on effect</u> on the bases further on in the sequence. E.g.

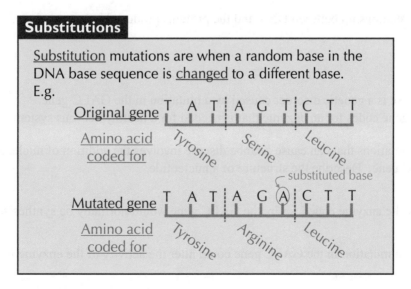

Deletions

1) <u>Deletions</u> are when a random base is <u>deleted</u> from the DNA base sequence.

2) Like insertions, they <u>change</u> the way that the <u>base sequence</u> is 'read' and have <u>knock-on effects</u> further down the sequence.

Substitutions

<u>Substitution</u> mutations are when a random base in the DNA base sequence is <u>changed</u> to a different base. E.g.

In, out, swap it all about...

The main thing to remember about mutations is that they change the <u>sequence of bases</u> in DNA — changes in bases can affect the <u>amino acid sequence</u>, and therefore the <u>protein</u> coded for.

Warm-Up & Exam Questions

Take a deep breath and go through these Warm-Up Questions one by one. Then onto the Exam Questions. Don't panic if you get something wrong — as they say, practice makes perfect...

Warm-Up Questions

1) Name the structures that contain DNA in the nucleus of a cell.
2) What is a gene?
3) Give three reasons why understanding the human genome is important for science and medicine.
4) Which DNA bases pair up according to complementary base pairing?
5) What is a mutation?
6) Explain why the function of a protein may be affected by a gene mutation.

Exam Questions

1 An organism's genetic material is made up of a chemical called DNA. (Grade 4-6)

1.1 Which of the following describes the structure of DNA?
Tick **one** box.

☐ A protein made up of two strands.   ☐ A polymer made up of two strands.

☐ A protein made up of four strands.   ☐ A polymer made up of four strands.

[1 mark]

1.2 Which of the following contains the largest amount of an organism's DNA?
Tick **one** box.

☐ A gene   ☐ Its genome   ☐ A chromosome

[1 mark]

1.3 Explain the relationship between DNA and the proteins produced by an organism.

[3 marks]

2 Krabbe disease is a genetic disorder caused by a mutation in the GALC gene. (Grade 7-9)
The GALC gene codes for an enzyme that is needed for a healthy nervous system.

2.1 One of the mutations that can cause Krabbe disease involves the addition of nucleotides to the GALC gene. Describe the structure of a nucleotide.

[1 mark]

2.2 Outline how the enzyme coded for by the GALC gene would normally be synthesised within a cell.

[4 marks]

2.3 Explain how a mutation in the GALC gene could alter the activity of the enzyme it codes for.

[4 marks]

2.4 Mutations happen continuously, although genetic disorders such as Krabbe disease are rare.
Explain why this is the case.

[1 mark]

Reproduction

*Reproduction is important for all species. It can happen in **two** different ways...*

Sexual Reproduction Produces **Genetically Different Cells**

1) Sexual reproduction is where genetic information from two organisms (a father and a mother) is combined to produce offspring which are genetically different to either parent.

2) In sexual reproduction, the mother and father produce gametes by meiosis (see next page) — e.g. egg and sperm cells in animals.

3) In humans, each gamete contains 23 chromosomes — half the number of chromosomes in a normal cell. (Instead of having two of each chromosome, a gamete has just one of each.)

4) The egg (from the mother) and the sperm cell (from the father) then fuse together (fertilisation) to form a cell with the full number of chromosomes (half from the father, half from the mother).

SEXUAL REPRODUCTION involves the fusion of male and female gametes.
Because there are TWO parents, the offspring contain a mixture of their parents' genes.

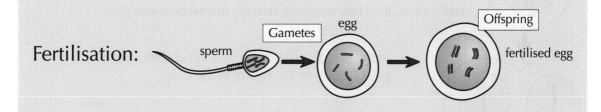

Fertilisation: sperm — Gametes — egg — Offspring — fertilised egg

5) This is why the offspring inherits features from both parents — it's received a mixture of chromosomes from its mum and its dad (and it's the chromosomes that decide how you turn out).

6) This mixture of genetic information produces variation in the offspring.

7) Flowering plants can reproduce in this way too. They also have egg cells, but their version of sperm is known as pollen.

Asexual Reproduction Produces **Genetically Identical Cells**

1) In asexual reproduction there's only one parent so the offspring are genetically identical to that parent.

2) Asexual reproduction happens by mitosis — an ordinary cell makes a new cell by dividing in two (see page 27).

3) The new cell has exactly the same genetic information (i.e. genes) as the parent cell — it's called a clone.

In ASEXUAL REPRODUCTION there's only ONE parent. There's no fusion of gametes,
no mixing of chromosomes and no genetic variation between parent and offspring.
The offspring are genetically identical to the parent — they're clones.

4) Bacteria, some plants and some animals reproduce asexually.

You might need to reproduce these facts in the exam...

The main messages on this page are that: 1) sexual reproduction needs two parents and forms cells that are genetically different to the parents, so there's lots of genetic variation. And 2) asexual reproduction needs just one parent to make genetically identical cells, so there's no genetic variation in the offspring.

158

Meiosis

*If you're wondering how gametes end up with **half** the number of **chromosomes** of a normal cell, read on...*

Gametes Are Produced by Meiosis

1) As you know from the previous page, <u>gametes</u> only have <u>one copy</u> of each <u>chromosome</u>, so that when <u>gamete fusion</u> takes place, you get the <u>right amount</u> of <u>chromosomes</u> again (two copies of each).

2) To make gametes which only have <u>half</u> the original number of chromosomes, cells divide by <u>meiosis</u>. This process involves <u>two cell divisions</u>. In humans, it <u>only</u> happens in the <u>reproductive organs</u> (the ovaries in females and testes in males).

Meiosis Produces Cells Which Have **Half** the **Normal Number** of **Chromosomes**

Before the cell starts to divide, it <u>duplicates</u> its <u>genetic information</u>, forming two armed chromosomes — one arm of each chromosome is an <u>exact copy</u> of the other arm. After replication, the chromosomes arrange themselves into <u>pairs</u>.

The genetic information is stored in DNA — see p.151.

In the <u>first division</u> in meiosis the chromosome pairs <u>line up</u> in the centre of the cell.

The pairs are then <u>pulled apart</u> so each new cell only has one copy of each chromosome. <u>Some</u> of the father's chromosomes (shown in blue) and <u>some</u> of the mother's chromosomes (shown in red) go into each new cell.

In the <u>second division</u>, the chromosomes <u>line up</u> again in the centre of the cell. The arms of the chromosomes are <u>pulled apart</u>.

You get four gametes, each with only a <u>single set</u> of chromosomes in it. Each of the gametes is <u>genetically different</u> from the others because the chromosomes all get <u>shuffled up</u> during meiosis and each gamete only gets <u>half</u> of them, at random.

The **Cell** Produced by **Gamete Fusion Replicates Itself**

1) After two <u>gametes</u> have fused during fertilisation, the resulting new cell <u>divides</u> by <u>mitosis</u> to make a <u>copy</u> of itself.

There's loads on mitosis on page 27.

2) Mitosis <u>repeats many times</u> to produce <u>lots</u> of new cells in an embryo.

3) As the embryo develops, these cells then start to <u>differentiate</u> (see page 22) into the <u>different types</u> of <u>specialised cell</u> that make up a <u>whole organism</u>.

Now that I have your undivided attention...

Remember, in humans, meiosis only occurs in <u>reproductive organs</u>.

Q1   Human body cells contain 46 chromosomes each. The graph on the right shows how the mass of DNA per cell changed as some cells divided by meiosis in a human ovary. How many chromosomes were present in each cell when they reached stage 6?   [1 mark]

Q1 Video Solution

More on Reproduction

*You know that there are **two different types** of reproduction (take a look back at page 157 if you need a reminder). Now it's time to find out the **advantages** of each type...*

Sexual Reproduction Has **Advantages** Over Asexual Reproduction

1) Offspring from sexual reproduction have a <u>mixture</u> of two sets of chromosomes. The organism inherits genes (and therefore features) from <u>both</u> parents, which produces <u>variation</u> in the offspring (see p.157).

2) Variation <u>increases</u> the chance of a species <u>surviving</u> a <u>change in the environment</u>. While a change in the environment could <u>kill</u> some <u>individuals</u>, it's likely that <u>variation</u> will have led to <u>some</u> of the offspring being able to <u>survive</u> in the new environment. They have a <u>survival advantage</u>.

3) Because individuals with characteristics that make them <u>better adapted</u> to the environment have a <u>better</u> chance of <u>survival</u>, they are <u>more likely</u> to breed <u>successfully</u> and pass the genes for the characteristics on. This is known as <u>natural selection</u> (see p.176).

4) We can use <u>selective breeding</u> to <u>speed up</u> natural selection. This allows us to produce animals with <u>desirable characteristics</u>. Selective breeding is where individuals with a desirable characteristic are bred to produce <u>offspring</u> that have the desirable characteristic too (see p.180). This means that we can <u>increase food production</u>, e.g. by breeding animals that produce a lot of meat.

Asexual Reproduction Has **Advantages** Over Sexual Reproduction

1) There only needs to be <u>one parent</u>.

2) This means that asexual reproduction uses <u>less energy</u> than sexual reproduction, because organisms <u>don't</u> have to <u>find a mate</u>.

3) This also means that asexual reproduction is <u>faster</u> than sexual reproduction.

4) <u>Many</u> identical offspring can be produced in <u>favourable conditions</u>.

Each type of reproduction has its advantages

<u>Asexual</u> reproduction is a <u>faster</u> method than sexual reproduction, but it might be more <u>risky</u> for the survival of the species in the long-run — if there's an unfavourable change in the environment that causes one of the organisms to die, there's a chance they could <u>all die</u> (because they're all genetically identical).

More on Reproduction

Some Organisms Can Reproduce by Both Methods

Some organisms can reproduce sexually or asexually depending on their circumstances.
Here are some examples:

Malarial parasites

1) Malaria is caused by a parasite that's spread by mosquitoes — see page 84.

2) When a mosquito carrying the parasite bites a human, the parasite can be transferred to the human.

3) The parasite reproduces sexually when it's in the mosquito and asexually when it's in the human host.

Fungi

1) Many species of fungus can reproduce both sexually and asexually.

2) These species release spores, which can become new fungi when they land in a suitable place.

3) Spores can be produced sexually and asexually.

4) Asexually-produced spores form fungi that are genetically identical to the parent fungus.

5) Sexually-produced spores introduce variation and are often produced in response to an unfavourable change in the environment, increasing the chance that the population will survive the change.

Plants

1) Loads of species of plant produce seeds sexually, but can also reproduce asexually.

2) Asexual reproduction can take place in different ways.

3) For example, strawberry plants produce 'runners'. These are stems that grow horizontally on the surface of the soil away from a plant. At various points along the runner, a new strawberry plant forms that is identical to the original plant.

4) Another example is in plants that grow from bulbs (e.g. daffodils). New bulbs can form from the main bulb and divide off. Each new bulb can grow into a new identical plant.

Strawberry plants can reproduce asexually by producing 'runners' and sexually by flowers that produce seeds.

Well that's reproduction sorted...

It's generally a good thing if organisms can reproduce by both sexual and asexual reproduction — it increases their chances of being able to produce offspring, which keeps the species in existence.

X and Y Chromosomes

*Now for a couple of **very important** little chromosomes...*

Your **Chromosomes** Control Whether You're **Male** or **Female**

1) There are <u>23 pairs</u> of chromosomes in every human body cell (page 26).
2) Of these, <u>22</u> are <u>matched pairs</u> of chromosomes that just control <u>characteristics</u>.
3) The <u>23rd pair</u> are labelled <u>XX</u> or <u>XY</u>.
4) They're the two chromosomes that <u>decide</u> your <u>sex</u> — whether you turn out <u>male</u> or <u>female</u>.

<u>Males</u> have an <u>X</u> and a <u>Y</u> chromosome: XY
The <u>Y chromosome</u> causes <u>male characteristics</u>.

<u>Females</u> have <u>two X chromosomes</u>:   XX
The <u>XX combination</u> allows
<u>female characteristics</u> to develop.

X-chromosome   Y-chromosome

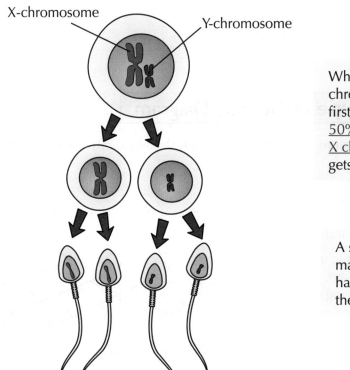

When making sperm, the X and Y chromosomes are drawn apart in the first division in meiosis. There's a <u>50% chance</u> each sperm cell gets an <u>X chromosome</u> and a <u>50% chance</u> it gets a <u>Y chromosome</u>.

A similar thing happens when making eggs. But the original cell has two X-chromosomes, so all the eggs have one X-chromosome.

The Y chromosome is physically smaller than the X chromosome

It's possible for people to have one X and two Y chromosomes, or even three X chromosomes, in their cells. But you just need to remember that <u>XX</u> gives female characteristics and <u>XY</u> gives male characteristics.

X and Y Chromosomes

*You can work out the **probability** of offspring being male or female by using a **genetic diagram**.*

Genetic Diagrams Show the Possible Combinations of Gametes

1) To find the <u>probability</u> of getting a boy or a girl, you can draw a <u>genetic diagram</u>.

2) Genetic diagrams are just <u>models</u> that are used to show all the possible genetic <u>outcomes</u> when you <u>cross together</u> different genes or chromosomes.

3) Put the <u>possible gametes</u> (eggs or sperm) from <u>one</u> parent down the side, and those from the <u>other</u> parent along the top.

4) Then in each middle square you <u>fill in</u> the letters from the top and side that line up with that square. The <u>pairs of letters</u> in the middle show the possible combinations of the gametes.

5) There are <u>two XX results</u> and <u>two XY results</u>, so there's the same probability of getting a boy or a girl.

6) Don't forget that this <u>50:50 ratio</u> is only a <u>probability</u> at each pregnancy.

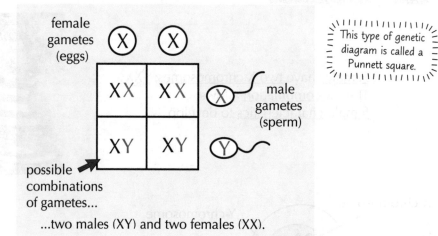

female gametes (eggs)

male gametes (sperm)

This type of genetic diagram is called a Punnett square.

possible combinations of gametes...

...two males (XY) and two females (XX).

There's More Than One Type of Genetic Diagram

The other type of genetic diagram looks a bit more complicated, but it shows exactly the same thing.

1) At the top are the <u>parents</u>.

2) The middle circles show the <u>possible gametes</u> that are formed. One gamete from the female combines with one gamete from the male (during fertilisation).

3) The criss-cross lines show <u>all</u> the <u>possible</u> ways the X and Y chromosomes <u>could</u> combine. The <u>possible combinations</u> of the offspring are shown in the bottom circles.

4) Remember, only <u>one</u> of these possibilities would <u>actually happen</u> for any one offspring.

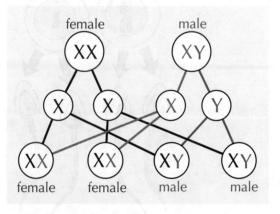

female   male

female   female   male   male

These diagrams aren't as scary as they look...

Most genetic diagrams you'll see in exams concentrate on a <u>gene</u>, instead of a <u>chromosome</u>. But the principle's the same. Don't worry — there are loads of other examples on pages 165-168.

Warm-Up & Exam Questions

It's time to see how much you picked up about meiosis, reproduction and sex chromosomes...

Warm-Up Questions

1) Suggest why there is variation in the offspring of sexual reproduction.
2) How many cell divisions take place in meiosis?
3) Which type of reproduction, sexual or asexual, produces offspring most quickly?
4) What combination of sex chromosomes do human females have?

Exam Questions

1 Some species of worm can produce offspring through a process called fragmentation. In this process, fragments of the parent's body break off and undergo cell division by mitosis to develop into mature, complete organisms.

1.1 What term is used to describe this form of reproduction?

[1 mark]

1.2 Suggest how the chromosomes in the offspring will compare to those of the parent worm.

[1 mark]

2 Mosquitoes have three pairs of chromosomes in their body cells. **Figure 1** shows a mosquito cell which is about to divide by meiosis.

Figure 1

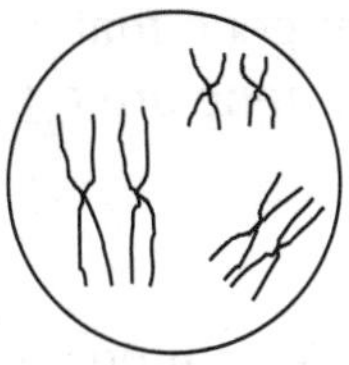

2.1 The cell in **Figure 1** undergoes meiosis. State how many chromosomes will be present in each new cell produced.

[1 mark]

2.2 How many cells will be produced in total when the cell in **Figure 1** undergoes meiosis?

[1 mark]

2.3 Explain how the processes of meiosis and fertilisation lead to genetic variation in the mosquito's offspring.

[3 marks]

When a mosquito infected with malarial parasites bites a human, parasites present in the mosquito's saliva pass into the human's bloodstream.

2.4 Malarial parasites reproduce asexually whilst in a human host. Give **three** advantages of this method of reproduction compared to sexual reproduction.

[3 marks]

2.5 Genetic variation within the malarial parasite population increases whilst in the mosquito. Explain why.

[1 mark]

Genetic Diagrams

*For those of you expecting to see a **diagram** or two on a page called 'Genetic Diagrams', prepare to be disappointed. You need to understand a bit more about what genetic diagrams **show** to start with...*

Some **Characteristics** are **Controlled** by **Single Genes**

1) What genes you inherit control what characteristics you develop.

2) Different genes control different characteristics. Some characteristics are controlled by a single gene, e.g. mouse fur colour and red-green colour blindness in humans.

3) However, most characteristics are controlled by several genes interacting.

4) All genes exist in different versions called alleles (which are represented by letters in genetic diagrams).

5) You have two versions (alleles) of every gene in your body — one on each chromosome in a pair.

6) If an organism has two alleles for a particular gene that are the same, then it's homozygous for that trait. If its two alleles for a particular gene are different, then it's heterozygous.

7) If the two alleles are different, only one can determine what characteristic is present. The allele for the characteristic that's shown is called the dominant allele (use a capital letter for dominant alleles — e.g. 'C'). The other one is called recessive (and you show these with small letters — e.g. 'c').

8) For an organism to display a recessive characteristic, both its alleles must be recessive (e.g. cc). But to display a dominant characteristic the organism can be either CC or Cc, because the dominant allele overrules the recessive one if the plant/animal/other organism is heterozygous.

9) Your genotype is the combination of alleles you have. Your alleles work at a molecular level to determine what characteristics you have — your phenotype.

EXAM TIP

There are lots of fancy words to learn on this page...

Make sure you fully understand what all the different terms on this page mean (i.e. genes, alleles, homozygous, heterozygous, dominant, recessive, genotype and phenotype). You'll feel much more comfortable going into the exam knowing that these words aren't going to trip you up.

Genetic Diagrams

Genetic Diagrams Show the **Possible Alleles** of **Offspring**

Suppose you start breeding <u>hamsters</u> with <u>superpowers</u>. The allele which causes hamsters to have superpowers is <u>recessive</u> ("b"), whilst <u>normal</u> (boring) behaviour is due to a <u>dominant</u> allele ("B").

1) A <u>superpowered</u> hamster <u>must</u> have the <u>genotype bb</u>. But a <u>normal</u> hamster could be <u>BB or Bb</u>.

2) Here's what happens if you breed from two <u>homozygous</u> hamsters:

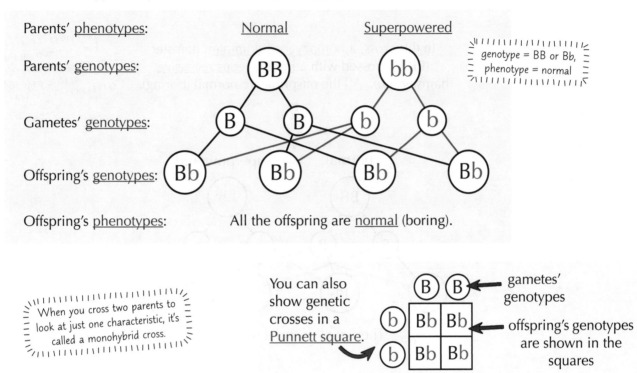

When you cross two parents to look at just one characteristic, it's called a monohybrid cross.

You can also show genetic crosses in a <u>Punnett square</u>.

gametes' genotypes

offspring's genotypes are shown in the squares

3) If two of these <u>offspring</u> now <u>breed</u>, you'll get the next generation:

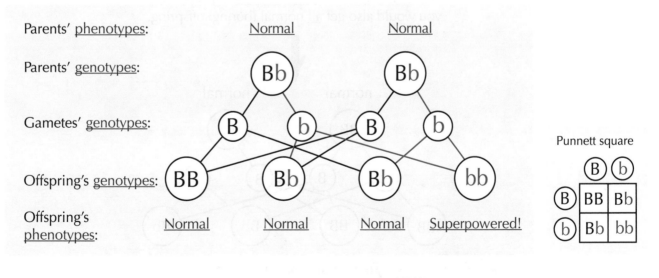

Punnett square

4) That's a <u>3:1 ratio</u> of normal to superpowered offspring in this generation (a <u>1 in 4</u> or <u>25%</u> probability of superpowers).

But remember — genetic diagrams only tell you probabilities. They don't say definitely what'll happen.

Genetic diagrams aren't that scary — you just need to practise them...

You should know how to <u>produce</u> and <u>interpret</u> both of these types of genetic diagram before exam day.

More Genetic Diagrams

*In the exam, you could be asked to **predict** and **explain** the outcomes of crosses between individuals for each **possible combination** of **dominant** and **recessive alleles** of a gene. You should be able to draw a **genetic diagram** and **work it out** — but it'll be easier if you've seen them all before. So here are some more examples.*

All the Offspring are Normal

Let's take another look at the <u>superpowered hamster</u> example from page 165:

In this cross, a <u>homozygous dominant</u> hamster (BB) is crossed with a <u>homozygous recessive</u> hamster (bb). <u>All</u> the offspring are normal (boring).

For a reminder on the terms homozygous and heterozygous, head to page 164.

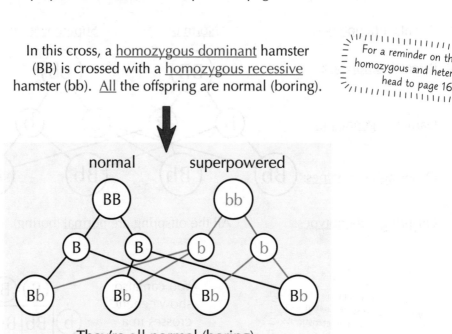

They're <u>all</u> normal (boring).

But, if you crossed a <u>homozygous dominant</u> hamster (BB) with a <u>heterozygous</u> hamster (Bb), you would also get <u>all</u> normal (boring) offspring.

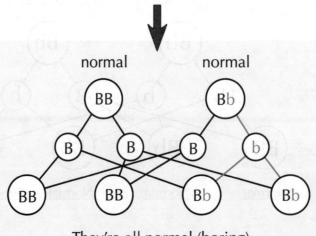

They're <u>all</u> normal (boring).

To find out <u>which</u> it was you'd have to <u>breed the offspring together</u> and see what kind of <u>ratio</u> you got that time — then you'd have a good idea. If it was <u>3:1</u>, it's likely that you originally had BB and bb.

More Genetic Diagrams

One more example of a genetic cross diagram coming up on this page.
*Then a little bit about another type of genetic diagram called a **family tree**...*

There's a **1:1 Ratio** in the Offspring

1) A cat with <u>long hair</u> was bred with another cat with <u>short hair</u>.

2) The long hair is caused by a <u>dominant</u> allele 'H', and the short hair by a <u>recessive</u> allele 'h'.

3) The cats had 8 kittens — 4 with long hair and 4 with short hair.

4) This is a <u>1:1</u> ratio — it's what you'd expect when a parent with only <u>one dominant allele</u> (heterozygous — Hh) is crossed with a parent with <u>two recessive alleles</u> (homozygous recessive — hh).

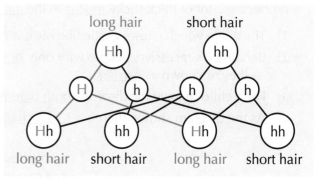

Family Trees Can Show How Characteristics Are Inherited

1) Knowing how inheritance works can help you to interpret a <u>family tree</u> — this is one for <u>cystic fibrosis</u> (p.168).

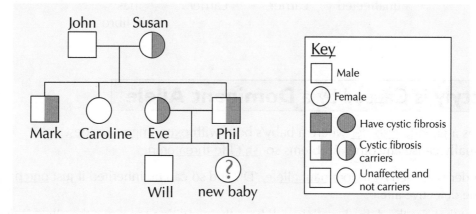

Key
- □ Male
- ○ Female
- ◼ ⬤ Have cystic fibrosis
- ◧ ◑ Cystic fibrosis carriers
- □ ○ Unaffected and not carriers

2) From the family tree, you can tell that the allele for cystic fibrosis <u>isn't</u> dominant because plenty of the family <u>carry</u> the allele but <u>don't</u> have the disorder.

3) There is a <u>25%</u> chance that the new baby will have the disorder and a <u>50%</u> chance that it will be a carrier, as both of its parents are carriers but are unaffected. The case of the new baby is just the same as in the genetic diagram on page 168 — so the baby could be <u>unaffected</u> (FF), a <u>carrier</u> (Ff) or <u>have</u> cystic fibrosis (ff).

It's enough to make you go cross-eyed...

Now, here's a fascinating practice question about <u>peas</u>...

Q1 Round peas are caused by the dominant allele, R. The allele for wrinkly peas, r, is recessive. Using a Punnett square, predict the ratio of plants with round peas to plants with wrinkly peas for a cross between a heterozygous pea plant and a pea plant that is homozygous recessive.

[3 marks]

Q1 Video Solution

Inherited Disorders

*Some disorders can be **inherited** from your parents. Many of these can be **screened** for in embryos.*

Cystic Fibrosis is Caused by a **Recessive Allele**

Cystic fibrosis is a genetic disorder of the cell membranes. It results in the body producing a lot of thick sticky mucus in the air passages and in the pancreas.

1) The allele which causes cystic fibrosis is a recessive allele, 'f', carried by about 1 person in 25.
2) Because it's recessive, people with only one copy of the allele won't have the disorder — they're known as carriers.
3) For a child to have the disorder, both parents must be either carriers or have the disorder themselves.
4) As the diagram shows, there's a 1 in 4 chance of a child having the disorder if both parents are carriers.

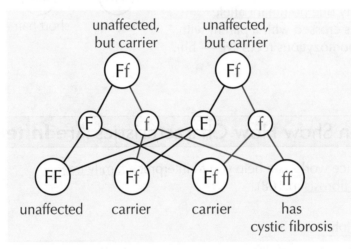

Polydactyly is Caused by a **Dominant Allele**

Polydactyly is a genetic disorder where a baby's born with extra fingers or toes. It doesn't usually cause any other problems so isn't life-threatening.

1) The disorder is caused by a dominant allele, 'D', and so can be inherited if just one parent carries the defective allele.
2) The parent that has the defective allele will have the condition too since the allele is dominant.
3) As the genetic diagram shows, there's a 50% chance of a child having the disorder if one parent has one D allele.

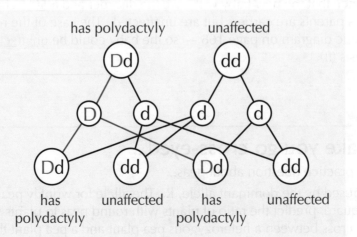

Inherited Disorders

Embryos Can Be Screened for Genetic Disorders

1) During *in vitro* fertilisation (IVF), embryos are fertilised in a laboratory, and then implanted into the mother's womb.

2) Before being implanted, it's possible to remove a cell from each embryo and analyse its genes.

3) Many genetic disorders can be detected in this way, such as cystic fibrosis.

4) It's also possible to get DNA from an embryo in the womb and test that for disorders.

5) There are lots of ethical, social and economic concerns surrounding embryo screening.

6) Embryonic screening is quite controversial because of the decisions it can lead to.

7) For embryos produced by IVF — after screening, embryos with 'bad' alleles would be destroyed.

8) For embryos in the womb — screening could lead to the decision to terminate the pregnancy.

9) Here are some more arguments for and against screening:

For Embryonic Screening

1) It will help to stop people suffering.

2) Treating disorders costs the Government (and the taxpayers) a lot of money.

3) There are laws to stop it going too far. At the moment parents cannot even select the sex of their baby (unless it's for health reasons).

Against Embryonic Screening

1) It implies that people with genetic problems are 'undesirable' — this could increase prejudice.

2) There may come a point where everyone wants to screen their embryos so they can pick the most 'desirable' one, e.g. they want a blue-eyed, blond-haired, intelligent boy.

3) Screening is expensive.

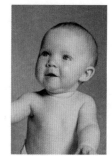

Embryo screening — it's a tricky one...

It's great to think that we might be able to stop people from having inherited disorders that cause suffering, but there are many concerns to think about too. Try writing a balanced argument for and against embryo screening — it's good practice.

The Work of Mendel

*Mendel's discoveries about **inheritance** were really important. Here's a whole page on him...*

Mendel Did Genetic Experiments with Pea Plants

1) Gregor Mendel was an Austrian monk who trained in mathematics and natural history at the University of Vienna.

2) On his garden plot at the monastery in the mid 19th century, Mendel noted how characteristics in plants were passed on from one generation to the next.

3) The results of his research were published in 1866 and eventually became the foundation of modern genetics.

4) The diagrams show two crosses for height in pea plants that Mendel carried out...

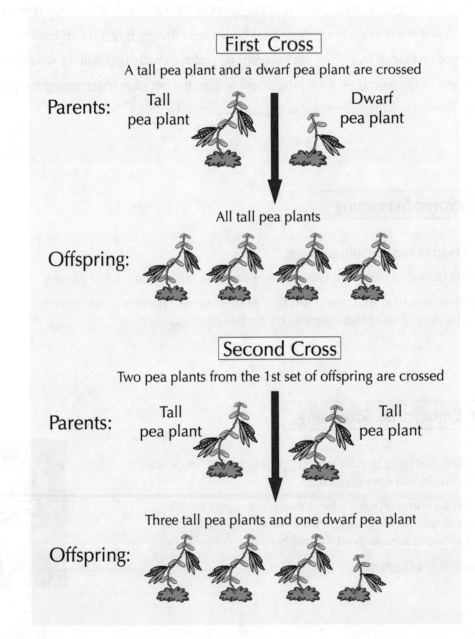

First Cross

A tall pea plant and a dwarf pea plant are crossed

Parents: Tall pea plant   Dwarf pea plant

All tall pea plants

Offspring:

Second Cross

Two pea plants from the 1st set of offspring are crossed

Parents: Tall pea plant   Tall pea plant

Three tall pea plants and one dwarf pea plant

Offspring:

Mendel had shown that the height characteristic in pea plants was determined by separately inherited "hereditary units" passed on from each parent. The ratios of tall and dwarf plants in the offspring showed that the unit for tall plants, T, was dominant over the unit for dwarf plants, t.

The Work of Mendel

*People **didn't understand** the importance of what Mendel had discovered until after he'd died...*

Mendel Reached **Three Important Conclusions**

Mendel reached these three important conclusions about <u>heredity in plants</u>:

1) Characteristics in plants are determined by "<u>hereditary units</u>".

2) Hereditary units are passed on to offspring <u>unchanged</u> from both parents, <u>one unit</u> from <u>each parent</u>.

3) Hereditary units can be <u>dominant</u> or <u>recessive</u> — if an individual has <u>both</u> the dominant and the recessive unit for a characteristic, the <u>dominant</u> characteristic will be expressed.

It Took a **While** For People to **Understand** His Work

1) Mendel's work was <u>cutting edge</u> and <u>new</u> to the scientists of the day.
They didn't have the background knowledge to <u>properly understand</u> his findings —
they had <u>no idea</u> about <u>genes</u>, <u>DNA</u> and <u>chromosomes</u>.

2) It wasn't until <u>after his death</u> that people realised how <u>significant</u> his work was.

3) Using Mendel's work as a starting point, the observations of <u>many</u> different scientists
have contributed to the <u>understanding</u> of genes that we have <u>today</u>. For example:

1) In the <u>late 1800s</u>, scientists became familiar with <u>chromosomes</u>.
They were able to observe how they <u>behaved</u> during <u>cell division</u>.

2) Then in the <u>early 20th century</u>, scientists realised that there were striking <u>similarities</u> in
the way that <u>chromosomes</u> and <u>Mendel's "units"</u> acted. Based on this, it was proposed
that the "units" were <u>found</u> on the <u>chromosomes</u>. We now know these "units" as <u>genes</u>.

3) In <u>1953</u>, the <u>structure</u> of <u>DNA</u> was determined (see page 153).
This allowed scientists to go on and find out exactly how <u>genes work</u>.

Mendel looked at more than just the height of the pea plants...

For example, he also looked at the <u>colour</u> of the <u>pea plant flowers</u> and the <u>shape</u> of the <u>peas</u>.
The results of his experiments contributed to what we understand about <u>genetics</u> and <u>inheritance</u>
today — it's a good example of how scientific theories <u>develop over time</u>.

Warm-Up & Exam Questions

There's no better preparation for exam questions than doing... err... practice exam questions.
Hang on, what's this I see...

Warm-Up Questions

1) What are alleles?
2) What does genotype mean?
3) Why won't someone heterozygous for the cystic fibrosis allele have the disorder?
4) What is polydactyly?
5) Outline what embryo screening involves.
6) Suggest why the importance of Mendel's work wasn't realised straight away.

Exam Questions

1 Cystic fibrosis is a genetic disorder caused by recessive alleles. **(Grade 4-6)**

F = the normal allele **f** = the faulty allele that leads to cystic fibrosis

Figure 1 is an incomplete Punnett square showing the possible inheritance of cystic fibrosis from one couple.

Figure 1

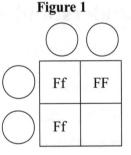

1.1 Complete the Punnett square to show the missing offspring's genotype and the genotypes of the gametes.

[2 marks]

1.2 What proportion of the possible offspring are homozygous?

[1 mark]

1.3 State the phenotypes of the parents.

[2 marks]

2 Fruit flies usually have red eyes. However, there are a small number of white-eyed fruit flies. Having white eyes is a recessive characteristic. **(Grade 6-7)**

Two fruit flies with red eyes have the heterozygous genotype for this characteristic. They are crossed to produce offspring.

2.1 Draw a genetic diagram to show the possible phenotypes of the offspring.
Use **R** to represent the dominant allele and **r** to represent the recessive allele.

[3 marks]

2.2 State the probability that one of the fruit flies' offspring will have white eyes.

[1 mark]

Exam Questions

3 Polydactyly is a genetic disorder transmitted by the dominant allele **D**.
The corresponding recessive allele is **d**.
Figure 2 shows the family pedigree of a family with a history of polydactyly.

Grade 6-7

Figure 2

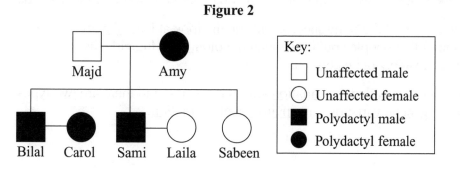

Key:
☐ Unaffected male
○ Unaffected female
■ Polydactyl male
● Polydactyl female

Using the information given above, state what Amy's genotype must be.
Explain your answer.

[2 marks]

4 Colour blindness in humans is caused by a recessive allele located on the X chromosome.
It is more common in men because men carry only one X chromosome.

Grade 6-7

A man who is colour blind has a child with a woman who does not have the recessive allele.

4.1 Draw a genetic diagram to show the possible sex of the offspring.

[3 marks]

4.2 The child is a boy. Explain why the boy will not be colour blind.

[1 mark]

4.3 State the probability that a daughter of this couple would be colour blind.

[1 mark]

5 Albinism is a condition characterised by the lack of pigment in the hair and skin.
It is caused by the recessive allele **a**. The dominant allele **A** results in normal pigmentation.

Grade 7-9

5.1 State the possible genotypes of a rabbit that shows no symptoms of albinism.

[1 mark]

A rabbit with albinism mated with a rabbit that showed no symptoms of the condition.
56% of the offspring had albinism.

5.2 Deduce the genotypes of the parent rabbits and the possible genotypes of their offspring.
Use a genetic diagram to explain your answer.

[3 marks]

5.3 From your genetic diagram, what percentage of offspring are likely to have albinism?

[1 mark]

5.4 Explain why the percentage of offspring which were born with albinism was not the same as that
suggested by your genetic diagram.

[1 mark]

Topic 6 — Inheritance, Variation and Evolution

Variation

*You'll probably have noticed that not all people are **identical**. There are reasons for this.*

Organisms of the **Same Species** Have **Differences**

1) Different species look... well... different — my dog definitely doesn't look like a daisy.

2) But even organisms of the <u>same species</u> will usually look at least <u>slightly</u> different — e.g. in a room full of people you'll see different <u>colour hair</u>, individually <u>shaped noses</u>, a variety of <u>heights</u>, etc.

3) These differences are called the <u>variation</u> within a species, and there are <u>two</u> types of variation — <u>genetic variation</u> and <u>environmental variation</u>.

Different Genes Cause **Genetic** Variation

1) All plants and animals have <u>characteristics</u> that are in some ways similar to their <u>parents'</u> (e.g. I've got my dad's nose, apparently).

2) This is because an organism's <u>characteristics</u> are determined by the <u>genes inherited</u> from their <u>parents</u>. (Genes are the <u>codes</u> inside your cells that <u>control</u> how you're made — more about these on page 152.)

3) These genes are passed on in <u>sex cells</u> (<u>gametes</u>), from which the offspring develop (see page 157).

4) Most animals (and quite a lot of plants) get <u>some</u> genes from the <u>mother</u> and <u>some</u> from the <u>father</u>.

5) This combining of genes from two parents causes <u>genetic variation</u> — no two of the species are <u>genetically identical</u> (other than identical twins).

6) <u>Some</u> characteristics are determined <u>only</u> by genes (e.g. violet flower colour). In <u>animals</u> these include:

- <u>eye colour</u>,
- <u>blood group</u>,
- <u>inherited disorders</u> (e.g. haemophilia or cystic fibrosis).

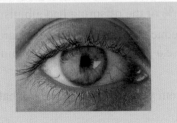

Variation

Characteristics are also Influenced by the Environment

1) The environment, including the conditions that organisms live and grow in, also causes differences between members of the same species — this is called environmental variation.

2) For example:

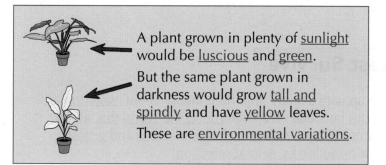

A plant grown in plenty of sunlight would be luscious and green.

But the same plant grown in darkness would grow tall and spindly and have yellow leaves.

These are environmental variations.

3) Environmental variation covers a wide range of differences — from losing your toes in a piranha attack, to getting a suntan, to having yellow leaves, and so on.

Most Characteristics are Due to Genes AND the Environment

1) Most characteristics (e.g. body weight, height, skin colour, condition of teeth, academic or athletic prowess, etc.) are determined by a mixture of genetic and environmental factors.

2) For example, the maximum height that an animal or plant could grow to is determined by its genes. But whether it actually grows that tall depends on its environment (e.g. how much food it gets).

Mutations Introduce Variation

Mutations are covered in loads more detail on pages 154-155.

1) Mutations are changes to the sequence of bases in DNA.

2) As you saw on page 154, mutations can lead to changes in the protein that a gene codes for.

3) Most mutations have no effect on the protein the gene codes for, so most mutations have no effect on the organism's phenotype. Some have a small influence on phenotype, and so only alter characteristics slightly. However, although it's very rare, mutations can result in a new phenotype (characteristic — see page 164) being seen in a species.

4) If the environment changes, and the new phenotype makes an individual more suited to the new environment, it can become common throughout the species relatively quickly by natural selection — see the next page.

You can't blame all of your faults on your parents...

Although the genes that you inherit from your parents are really important at determining what characteristics you have, the conditions in which you live usually play a role too.

Evolution

*Evolution is very important. Without it we wouldn't have the great **variety of life** we have on Earth today.*

> THEORY OF EVOLUTION: All of today's species have evolved from simple life forms that first started to develop over three billion years ago.

Only the **Fittest Survive**

Charles Darwin came up with a really important theory about evolution. He used the observations he made on a huge round-the-world trip, along with experiments, discussions and new knowledge of fossils and geology, to suggest the theory of evolution by natural selection.

1) Darwin knew that organisms in a species show wide variation in their characteristics (phenotypic variation). He also knew that organisms have to compete for limited resources in an ecosystem.

2) Darwin concluded that the organisms with the most suitable characteristics for the environment would be more successful competitors and would be more likely to survive. This idea is called the 'survival of the fittest'.

3) The successful organisms that survive are more likely to reproduce and pass on the genes for the characteristics that made them successful to their offspring.

4) The organisms that are less well adapted would be less likely to survive and reproduce, so they are less likely to pass on their genes to the next generation.

5) Over time, beneficial characteristics become more common in the population and the species changes — it evolves.

New Discoveries Have Helped to **Develop** the Theory

1) Darwin's theory wasn't perfect. Because the relevant scientific knowledge wasn't available at the time, he couldn't give a good explanation for why new characteristics appeared or exactly how individual organisms passed on beneficial adaptations to their offspring.

2) We now know that phenotype is controlled by genes. New phenotypic variations arise because of genetic variants produced by mutations (changes in DNA — see page 154). Beneficial variations are passed on to future generations in the genes that parents contribute to their offspring.

Natural selection — the fittest pass on their genes...

Q1 Video Solution

Natural selection's all about the organisms with the best characteristics surviving to pass on their genes so that the whole species ends up adapted to its environment.

Q1 The sugary nectar in some orchid flowers is found at the end of a long tube behind the flower. There are moth species with long tongues that can reach the nectar. Explain how natural selection could have led to the moths developing long tongues. [4 marks]

Evolution

*Species need to **continue evolving** in order to **survive**. Sometimes this evolution creates a whole **new species**, but if a species can't evolve fast enough it might **die out** completely.*

The Development of a **New Species** is Called **Speciation**

1) Over a long period of time, the phenotype of organisms can change <u>so much</u> because of natural selection that a completely <u>new species</u> is formed. This is called <u>speciation</u>.

2) Speciation happens when populations of the same species change enough to become <u>reproductively isolated</u> — this means that they <u>can't interbreed</u> to produce <u>fertile offspring</u>.

There's more on speciation on page 187.

Extinction is When **No Individuals** of a Species **Remain**

The fossil record contains many species that <u>don't exist any more</u> — these species are said to be <u>extinct</u>. Species become extinct for these reasons:

1) The <u>environment changes</u> too quickly (e.g. destruction of habitat).

2) A <u>new predator</u> kills them all (e.g. humans hunting them).

3) A <u>new disease</u> kills them all.

4) They can't <u>compete</u> with another (new) species for <u>food</u>.

5) A <u>catastrophic event</u> happens that kills them all (e.g. a volcanic eruption or a collision with an asteroid).

Example — Dodos

1) <u>Dodos</u> are now extinct.

2) Humans not only <u>hunted</u> them, but introduced <u>other animals</u> which ate all their eggs, and we <u>destroyed</u> the forest where they <u>lived</u> — they really didn't stand a chance...

Evolution's happening all the time...

Many species evolve so <u>slowly</u> that there are <u>no significant changes</u> in them within our lifetime. However, some species <u>reproduce really quickly</u>, so we're able to watch <u>evolution in action</u>. A good example is species of <u>bacteria</u> which evolve to become <u>resistant</u> to the <u>antibiotics</u> we make to kill them (see p.189).

More About Evolution

Not Everyone Agreed with Darwin...

When Darwin proposed his theory in his book "On the Origin of Species" in 1859, his idea was very <u>controversial</u> for various reasons...

1) It went against common <u>religious beliefs</u> about how life on Earth developed — it was the first plausible explanation for the existence of life on earth <u>without</u> the need for a "Creator" (God).

2) Darwin couldn't explain why these new, useful characteristics <u>appeared</u> or <u>how</u> they were <u>passed on</u> from individual organisms to their offspring. But then he didn't know anything about <u>genes</u> or <u>mutations</u> — they weren't discovered 'til 50 years after his theory was published.

3) There wasn't enough <u>evidence</u> to convince many <u>scientists</u>, because not many <u>other studies</u> had been done into how organisms change over time.

...and Lamarck had Different Ideas

There were <u>different scientific hypotheses</u> about evolution around at the same time, such as Lamarck's:

1) <u>Jean-Baptiste Lamarck</u> (1744-1829) argued that <u>changes</u> that an organism acquires <u>during</u> its lifetime will be <u>passed on</u> to its offspring — e.g. he thought that if a <u>characteristic</u> was <u>used a lot</u> by an organism, then it would become <u>more developed</u> during its <u>lifetime</u>, and the organism's offspring would inherit the <u>acquired characteristic</u>.

2) For example, using this theory, if a rabbit <u>used</u> its legs to run a lot (to escape predators), then its legs would get <u>longer</u>. The offspring of that rabbit would then be <u>born</u> with <u>longer legs</u>.

Scientists Develop Different Hypotheses from Observations

1) Often scientists come up with <u>different hypotheses</u> to explain <u>similar observations</u>.

2) Scientists might develop different hypotheses because they have different <u>beliefs</u> (e.g. religious) or they have been <u>influenced</u> by different people (e.g. other scientists and their way of thinking)... or they just darn well <u>think differently</u>.

There's more about making hypotheses on page 1.

3) The only way to <u>find out</u> whose hypothesis is right is to find evidence to <u>support</u> or <u>disprove</u> each one.

4) For example, Lamarck and Darwin both had different hypotheses to explain how evolution happens. In the end...

- Lamarck's hypothesis was eventually <u>rejected</u> because experiments <u>didn't support his hypothesis</u>. You can see it for yourself, e.g. if you dye a hamster's fur <u>bright pink</u> (not recommended), its offspring will still be born with the <u>normal</u> fur colour because the new characteristic <u>won't</u> have been passed on.

- The discovery of genetics <u>supported</u> Darwin's idea because it provided an <u>explanation</u> of how organisms born with beneficial characteristics can <u>pass them on</u> (i.e. via their genes). Other evidence was also found by looking at <u>fossils</u> of <u>different ages</u> (the <u>fossil record</u>) — this allows you to see how <u>changes</u> in organisms <u>developed slowly over time</u>. The relatively recent discovery of how <u>bacteria</u> are able to evolve to become <u>resistant to antibiotics</u> also further supports <u>evolution</u> by <u>natural selection</u>.

5) There's so much evidence for Darwin's idea that it's now an <u>accepted hypothesis</u> (a <u>theory</u>).

WORKING SCIENTIFICALLY

Here's to crazy new ideas...

Science is fuelled by new ideas. These new ideas need to be <u>well tested</u> though before they can become an <u>accepted theory</u>. If there's <u>not enough evidence</u> to support them, they'll be <u>rejected</u>.

Warm-Up & Exam Questions

You need to test your knowledge with a few Warm-Up Questions, followed by some Exam Questions...

Warm-Up Questions

1) Explain what is meant by environmental variation.
2) According to the theory of evolution, what have all of today's species evolved from?
3) Give three factors that can lead to a species becoming extinct.
4) Explain why Darwin's theory of evolution was considered controversial when it was first proposed.

Exam Questions

1   Helen and Stephanie are identical twins. This means they have identical DNA. **Grade 4-6**

1.1   Helen weighs 7 kg more than Stephanie.
Explain whether this is due to genes, environmental factors or both.

[2 marks]

1.2   Stephanie has a birthmark on her shoulder. Helen doesn't.
State whether birthmarks are caused by genes and explain your answer.

[1 mark]

2   Genetic variation in a population arises partly due to mutations. **Grade 6-7**

2.1   Give **one** cause of genetic variation in a population, other than mutations.

[1 mark]

2.2   Explain how mutations can increase variation in a species.

[3 marks]

2.3   Some mutations are neutral, having no effect on an organism, but some do have an impact.
Suggest how some mutations may be beneficial.

[2 marks]

3*   **Figure 1** shows a type of stingray. The stingray's appearance mimics a flat rock. **Grade 7-9**
It spends most of its time on a rocky sea bed.

Figure 1

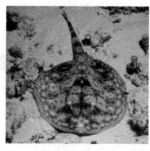

Describe and explain how the stingray might have evolved to look like this.

[4 marks]

Selective Breeding

'Selective breeding' sounds like it has the potential to be a tricky topic, but it's actually dead simple.
You take the **best** plants or animals and breed them together to get the best possible **offspring**. That's it.

Selective Breeding is Very Simple

Selective breeding is when humans <u>artificially select</u> the plants or animals that are going to <u>breed</u> so that the genes for particular characteristics <u>remain</u> in the population. Organisms are <u>selectively bred</u> to develop features that are <u>useful</u> or <u>attractive</u>, for example:

- Animals that produce more <u>meat</u> or <u>milk</u>.
- Crops with <u>disease resistance</u>.
- Dogs with a <u>good</u>, <u>gentle temperament</u>.
- Decorative plants with <u>big</u> or <u>unusual flowers</u>.

This is the basic process involved in <u>selective breeding</u>:

Selective breeding is also known as 'artificial selection'.

1) From your <u>existing stock</u>, select the ones which have the <u>characteristics</u> you're after.
2) <u>Breed them</u> with each other.
3) Select the <u>best</u> of the <u>offspring</u>, and <u>breed them together</u>.
4) Continue this process over <u>several generations</u>, and the desirable trait gets <u>stronger</u> and <u>stronger</u>. Eventually, <u>all</u> the offspring will have the characteristic.

In <u>agriculture</u> (farming), selective breeding can be used to <u>improve yields</u>. E.g. to improve <u>meat yields</u>, a farmer could breed together the <u>cows</u> and <u>bulls</u> with the <u>best characteristics</u> for producing <u>meat</u>, e.g. large size. After doing this for <u>several generations</u> the farmer would get cows with a <u>very high meat yield</u>.

Selective breeding is <u>nothing new</u> — people have been doing it for <u>thousands</u> of years. It's how we ended up with <u>edible crops</u> from <u>wild plants</u> and how we got <u>domesticated animals</u> like cows and dogs.

The **Main Drawback** is a **Reduction** in the **Gene Pool**

1) The main problem with selective breeding is that it reduces the <u>gene pool</u> — the <u>number of different alleles</u> (forms of a gene) in a population. This is because the farmer keeps breeding from the "<u>best</u>" animals or plants — which are all <u>closely related</u>. This is known as <u>inbreeding</u>.

2) Inbreeding can cause <u>health problems</u> because there's more chance of the organisms inheriting <u>harmful genetic defects</u> when the <u>gene pool</u> is <u>limited</u>. Some <u>dog breeds</u> are particularly susceptible to <u>certain defects</u> because of inbreeding — e.g. pugs often have breathing problems.

3) There can also be serious problems if a <u>new disease appears</u>, because there's <u>not much variation</u> in the population. All the stock are <u>closely related</u> to each other, so if one of them is going to be killed by a new disease, the others are <u>also</u> likely to succumb to it.

Selective Breeding Reduction in the number of different alleles (forms of a gene) Less chance of any resistant alleles being present in the population

Selective breeding is just breeding the best to get the best...

Different breeds of <u>dog</u> came from <u>selective breeding</u>. E.g., somebody thought 'I like this small, yappy wolf — I'll breed it with this other one'. After thousands of generations, we got <u>poodles</u>.

Q1 Explain how you could selectively breed for floppy ears in rabbits. [4 marks]

Genetic Engineering

*Genetic engineering is a relatively new area of science (well, it began in the 1970s). We've already put the technology to **good use** and it has many more **exciting possibilities** too...*

Genetic Engineering Transfers Genes Between Organisms

The basic idea of genetic engineering is to <u>transfer</u> a <u>gene</u> responsible for a <u>desirable characteristic</u> from one organism's genome into <u>another</u> organism, so that it also has the <u>desired characteristic</u>.

1) A useful gene is <u>isolated</u> (cut) from one organism's genome using <u>enzymes</u> and is inserted into a <u>vector</u>.

2) The vector is usually a <u>virus</u> or a <u>bacterial plasmid</u> (a fancy piece of circular DNA found in bacterial cells), depending on the type of organism that the gene is being transferred to.

3) When the vector is <u>introduced</u> to the target organism, the <u>useful gene</u> is <u>inserted</u> into its cell(s).

4) Scientists use this method to do <u>all sorts</u> of things. For example:

1) <u>Bacteria</u> have been genetically modified to produce <u>human insulin</u> that can be used to treat <u>diabetes</u>.

2) <u>Genetically modified</u> (<u>GM</u>) <u>crops</u> have had their genes modified, e.g. to improve the size and quality of their fruit, or make them <u>resistant</u> to <u>disease</u>, <u>insects</u> and <u>herbicides</u> (chemicals used to kill weeds).

3) <u>Sheep</u> have been genetically engineered to produce substances, like drugs, in their <u>milk</u> that can be used to treat <u>human diseases</u>.

4) Scientists are researching genetic modification treatments for <u>inherited diseases</u> caused by faulty genes, e.g. by <u>inserting working genes</u> into people with the disease. This is called <u>gene therapy</u>.

5) In some cases, the transfer of the gene is carried out when the organism receiving the gene is at an <u>early stage</u> of <u>development</u> (e.g. egg or embryo). This means that the organism <u>develops</u> with the <u>characteristic</u> coded for by the gene.

Genetic engineering has huge potential benefits...

Scientists are creating all sorts of <u>weird and wonderful creatures</u> with their genetic engineering sets. E.g. they have made cats that glow in the dark thanks to a gene taken from a jellyfish. But of course they don't just do it for fun — they're usually aiming to make organisms that <u>benefit humans</u> in some way.

Genetic Engineering

*On the face of it, **genetic engineering** is great.*
*But like most other things, there are **benefits** and **risks** that you need to consider.*

Genetic Engineering is a **Controversial Topic**

1) Genetic engineering is an <u>exciting new area of science</u>, which has the <u>potential</u> for solving many of our problems (e.g. treating diseases, more efficient food production etc.) but not everyone thinks it's a great idea.

2) There are <u>worries</u> about the long-term effects of genetic engineering — that changing an organism's genes might <u>accidentally</u> create unplanned <u>problems</u>, which could get passed on to <u>future generations</u>.

There Are **Pros** and **Cons** of **GM Crops**

Pros:

1) On the plus side, the characteristics chosen for GM crops can <u>increase the yield</u>, making more food.

2) People living in developing nations often lack <u>nutrients</u> in their diets. GM crops could be <u>engineered</u> to contain the nutrient that's <u>missing</u>. For example, 'golden rice' is a GM rice crop that contains beta-carotene — lack of this substance causes <u>blindness</u>.

3) GM crops are already being grown in some places, often <u>without any problems</u>.

Cons:

1) Some people say that growing GM crops will affect the number of <u>wild flowers</u> (and so the population of <u>insects</u>) that live in and around the crops — <u>reducing</u> farmland <u>biodiversity</u>.

2) Not everyone is convinced that GM crops are <u>safe</u> and some people are concerned that we might not <u>fully understand</u> the effects of eating them on <u>human health</u>. E.g. people are worried they may develop <u>allergies</u> to the food — although there's probably no more risk for this than for eating usual foods.

3) A big concern is that <u>transplanted genes</u> may get out into the <u>natural environment</u>. For example, the <u>herbicide resistance</u> gene may be picked up by weeds, creating a new '<u>superweed</u>' variety.

If only there was a gene to make revision easier...

At the end of the day, it's down to the <u>Government</u> to weigh up all the <u>evidence</u> for the pros and cons before <u>making a decision</u> on how this scientific knowledge is used. All that the scientists can do is make sure the Government has all the information that it needs to make the decision.

Cloning

*We can clone **plants** and **animals** in several different ways. Cool.*

Plants Can Be Cloned by Tissue Culture and from Cuttings

Tissue Culture

1) This is where <u>a few plant cells</u> are put in a <u>growth medium</u> with <u>hormones</u>, and they grow into <u>new plants</u> — <u>clones</u> of the parent plant.

2) These plants can be made very <u>quickly</u>, in very little <u>space</u>, and be <u>grown all year</u>.

3) Tissue culture is used by <u>scientists</u> to preserve <u>rare plants</u> that are hard to reproduce naturally and by <u>plant nurseries</u> to produce lots of <u>stock</u> quickly.

Cuttings

1) Gardeners can take <u>cuttings</u> from good parent plants, and then plant them to produce <u>genetically identical copies</u> (clones) of the parent plant.

2) These plants can be produced <u>quickly and cheaply</u>.

3) This is an <u>older</u>, <u>simpler</u> method than tissue culture.

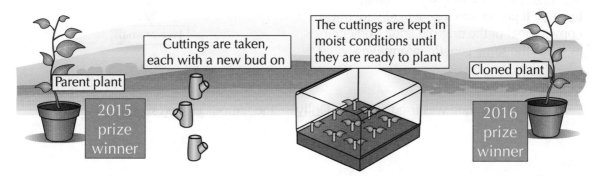

You Can Make Animal Clones Using Embryo Transplants

Farmers can produce <u>cloned offspring</u> from their best bull and cow using <u>embryo transplants</u>.

1) <u>Sperm cells</u> are taken from a prize bull and <u>egg cells</u> are taken from a prize cow. The sperm are then used to <u>artificially fertilise</u> an egg cell. The <u>embryo</u> that develops is then <u>split</u> many times (to form <u>clones</u>) before any cells become specialised.

2) These <u>cloned embryos</u> can then be <u>implanted</u> into lots of other cows where they grow into <u>baby calves</u> (which will all be <u>genetically identical</u> to each other).

3) <u>Hundreds</u> of "ideal" offspring can be produced <u>every year</u> from the best bull and cow.

Cloning produces genetically identical organisms

Cloning can come in pretty handy if you're a gardener or a farmer. If you've spent ages trying to get an <u>ideal</u> plant or animal (like a prize cow) then you can use <u>cloning</u> to produce plenty more just like it.

Cloning

*There's another way to **clone animals** and it's a bit **controversial**...*

Adult Cell Cloning is Another Way to Make a Clone

1) Adult cell cloning involves taking an unfertilised egg cell and removing its nucleus.

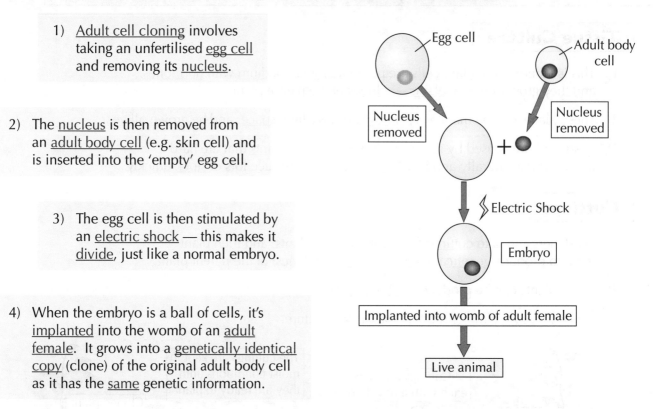

2) The nucleus is then removed from an adult body cell (e.g. skin cell) and is inserted into the 'empty' egg cell.

3) The egg cell is then stimulated by an electric shock — this makes it divide, just like a normal embryo.

4) When the embryo is a ball of cells, it's implanted into the womb of an adult female. It grows into a genetically identical copy (clone) of the original adult body cell as it has the same genetic information.

5) This technique was used to create Dolly — the famous cloned sheep.

There are Many Issues Surrounding Cloning

1) Cloning quickly gets you lots of "ideal" offspring. But you also get a "reduced gene pool" — this means there are fewer different alleles in a population. If a population are all closely related and a new disease appears, they could all be wiped out — there may be no allele in the population giving resistance to it.

2) But the study of animal clones could lead to greater understanding of the development of the embryo, and of ageing and age-related disorders.

3) Cloning could also be used to help preserve endangered species.

4) However, it's possible that cloned animals might not be as healthy as normal ones, e.g. Dolly the sheep had arthritis, which tends to occur in older sheep (but the jury's still out on if this was due to cloning).

5) Some people worry that humans might be cloned in the future. If it was allowed, any success may follow many unsuccessful attempts, e.g. children born severely disabled.

Cloning can be a pretty controversial topic...

...especially when it's to do with cloning animals (and especially humans). Is it healthy scientific progress, or are we trying to 'play God'? It's one of those questions science can't answer (see p.3).

Warm-Up & Exam Questions

By doing these Warm-Up Questions, you'll soon find out if you've got the basic facts straight.

Warm-Up Questions

1) Why might a plant nursery use selective breeding?
2) What potential issues can selective breeding cause?
3) Name one useful product that humans have genetically modified bacteria to produce.
4) Briefly outline how plant clones can be produced using tissue culture.

Exam Questions

1   Organisms can be genetically modified.
    This means an organism's genes can be altered to alter its characteristics.
    Grade 4-6

1.1 Give **one** function of the enzymes used in genetic engineering.

[1 mark]

1.2 Suggest **one** useful way that plants can be genetically modified.

[1 mark]

1.3 Some people think that it is wrong to genetically modify crop plants.
    Give **two** different objections that people might have.

[2 marks]

2   The characteristics of two varieties of wheat plants are shown in **Table 1**.
    Grade 6-7

Table 1

Variety	Grain yield	Resistance to bad weather
Tall stems	High	Low
Dwarf stems	Low	High

Describe how selective breeding could be used to create a wheat plant with a high grain yield and high resistance to bad weather.

[3 marks]

3   In 1997 scientists at the Roslin Institute announced the birth of Dolly the sheep, the first mammal to be cloned using adult cell cloning.

    Grade 6-7

3.1 Explain how a sheep can be cloned using adult cell cloning.

[4 marks]

3.2 Dolly was a female sheep. What would have been the gender
    of the sheep that Dolly was created from? Explain your answer.

[1 mark]

3.3 Give **one** potential problem with adult cell cloning.

[1 mark]

3.4 Give **one** reason why cloning may be beneficial in the field of medicine.

[1 mark]

Fossils

*Fossils are great. If they're **well-preserved**, you can see what oldy-worldy creatures **looked** like.*
*They also show how living things have **evolved**. Although we're not sure how life started in the first place...*

Fossils are the Remains of Plants and Animals

Fossils are the <u>remains</u> of organisms from <u>many thousands of years ago</u>, which are found in <u>rocks</u>. They provide the <u>evidence</u> that organisms lived ages ago. Fossils can tell us a lot about <u>how much</u> or <u>how little</u> organisms have <u>changed</u> (<u>evolved</u>) over time. Fossils form in rocks in one of <u>three</u> ways:

1) From gradual replacement by minerals

1) Things like <u>teeth</u>, <u>shells</u>, <u>bones</u> etc., which <u>don't decay</u> easily, can last a long time when <u>buried</u>.

2) They're eventually <u>replaced by minerals</u> as they decay, forming a <u>rock-like substance</u> shaped like the original hard part.

3) The surrounding sediments also turn to rock, but the fossil stays <u>distinct</u> inside the rock and eventually someone <u>digs it up</u>.

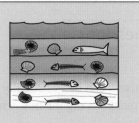

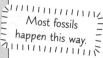
Most fossils happen this way.

2) From casts and impressions

1) Sometimes, fossils are formed when an organism is <u>buried</u> in a <u>soft</u> material like clay. The clay later <u>hardens</u> around it and the organism decays, leaving a <u>cast</u> of itself. An animal's <u>burrow</u> or a plant's <u>roots</u> (<u>rootlet traces</u>) can be preserved as casts.

2) Things like footprints can also be <u>pressed</u> into these materials when soft, leaving an <u>impression</u> when it hardens.

3) From preservation in places where no decay happens

1) In <u>amber</u> (a clear yellow 'stone' made from fossilised resin) and <u>tar pits</u> there's no <u>oxygen</u> or <u>moisture</u> so <u>decay microbes</u> can't survive.

2) In <u>glaciers</u> it's too <u>cold</u> for the <u>decay microbes</u> to work.

3) <u>Peat bogs</u> are too <u>acidic</u> for <u>decay microbes</u>.

A fully preserved man they named 'Pete Marsh' was found in a bog.

But No One Knows How Life Began

Fossils show how much or how little different organisms have changed (<u>evolved</u>) as life has developed on Earth over millions of years. But where did the <u>first</u> living thing come from...

1) There are various <u>hypotheses</u> suggesting how life first came into being, but no one really <u>knows</u>.

2) Maybe the first life forms came into existence in a primordial <u>swamp</u> (or under the <u>sea</u>) here on <u>Earth</u>. Maybe simple organic molecules were brought to Earth on <u>comets</u> — these could have then become more <u>complex</u> organic molecules, and eventually very simple <u>life forms</u>.

3) These hypotheses can't be supported or disproved because there's a <u>lack</u> of good, <u>valid</u> evidence:

• Many early forms of life were <u>soft-bodied</u>, and soft tissue tends to decay away <u>completely</u> — so the fossil record is <u>incomplete</u>.

• Fossils that did form millions of years ago may have been <u>destroyed</u> by <u>geological activity</u>, e.g. the movement of tectonic plates may have crushed fossils already formed in the rock.

Don't get bogged down by all this information...

It's a bit mind-boggling really how fossils can still exist even <u>millions of years</u> after the organism died. They really are fascinating things, and scientists have learned a whole lot from studying them in detail.

Speciation

*If you've been wanting to know more about how a **new species** can spring up, this is the page for you.*

Speciation is the Development of a New Species

1) A species is a group of <u>similar organisms</u> that can <u>reproduce</u> to give <u>fertile offspring</u>.

2) <u>Speciation</u> is the development of a <u>new species</u>.

3) Speciation occurs when <u>populations</u> of the <u>same species</u> become so <u>different</u> that they can <u>no longer successfully interbreed</u> to produce <u>fertile offspring</u>.

Isolation and Natural Selection Lead to Speciation

1) <u>Isolation</u> is where <u>populations</u> of a species are <u>separated</u>.

2) Isolation can happen due to a <u>physical barrier</u>. E.g. floods and earthquakes can cause barriers that <u>geographically isolate</u> some individuals from the main population.

3) <u>Conditions</u> on either side of the barrier will be <u>slightly different</u>, e.g. they may have <u>different climates</u>.

4) Because the environment is <u>different</u> on each side, <u>different characteristics</u> will become more common in each population due to <u>natural selection</u> operating <u>differently</u> on the populations:

   - Each population shows <u>genetic variation</u> because they have a wide range of <u>alleles</u>.
   - In each population, individuals with characteristics that make them better adapted to their environment have a <u>better chance of survival</u> and so are more likely to <u>breed</u> successfully.
   - So the <u>alleles</u> that control the <u>beneficial characteristics</u> are more likely to be <u>passed on</u> to the <u>next generation</u>.

5) Eventually, individuals from the different populations will have <u>changed</u> so much that they <u>won't</u> be able to <u>breed</u> with one another to produce fertile offspring.

6) The two groups will have become <u>separate species</u>:

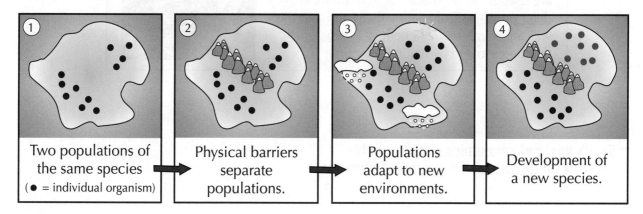

| Two populations of the same species (● = individual organism) | Physical barriers separate populations. | Populations adapt to new environments. | Development of a new species. |

New species can develop when populations become isolated

<u>Speciation</u> happens if two or more populations of the same species change so much that they can <u>no longer breed together</u> to produce <u>fertile offspring</u>. It can occur when populations are <u>separated</u> from each other.

Speciation

*Our understanding of how **different species** come to exist didn't just happen over night. It was one of Charles Darwin's mates back in the **1800s** who started to develop the theory.*

Wallace Was a **Pioneer** of the **Theory of Speciation**

1) <u>Alfred Russel Wallace</u> was a scientist working at the <u>same time</u> as Charles Darwin.

There's more on Darwin and natural selection on page 176.

2) Wallace was one of the <u>early</u> scientists working on the idea of <u>speciation</u> (see previous page). His observations greatly <u>contributed</u> to how we understand speciation <u>today</u>. Our current understanding <u>developed</u> as <u>more evidence</u> became available over time.

3) During his career, Wallace <u>independently</u> came up with the idea of <u>natural selection</u> and published work on the subject <u>together</u> with Darwin in <u>1858</u>. This then prompted Darwin to publish '<u>On the Origin of Species</u>' in <u>1859</u>.

4) <u>Observations</u> made by Wallace as he travelled the world provided lots of <u>evidence</u> to support the theory of evolution by natural selection.

> For example, he realised that <u>warning colours</u> are used by some species (e.g. butterflies) to <u>deter predators</u> from eating them and that this was an example of a <u>beneficial characteristic</u> that had evolved by natural selection.

5) It's this work on <u>warning colours</u> and his work on <u>speciation</u> that he's <u>most famous</u> for.

Darwin and Wallace both helped us to understand evolution

Darwin and Wallace worked on their evolutionary theories around the same time. They shared a lot of the same ideas on <u>natural selection</u>, but <u>Darwin</u> tends to be more well-remembered because it was <u>his book</u> that became famous. <u>Wallace</u> is still well-remembered for his work on <u>speciation</u> and <u>warning colours</u> though.

Antibiotic-Resistant Bacteria

*The discovery of **antibiotics** was a huge benefit to medicine — but they might **not** be a **permanent solution**.*

Bacteria can Evolve and Become Antibiotic-Resistant

1) Like all organisms, bacteria sometimes develop <u>random mutations</u> (see p.154) in their DNA. These can lead to <u>changes</u> in the bacteria's characteristics, e.g. being less affected by a particular antibiotic. This can lead to <u>antibiotic-resistant strains</u> forming as the <u>gene</u> for antibiotic resistance becomes <u>more common</u> in the population.

2) To make matters worse, because bacteria are so <u>rapid</u> at <u>reproducing</u>, they can <u>evolve</u> quite <u>quickly</u>.

The gene for antibiotic resistance becomes more common in the population because of natural selection — see page 176 for more.

3) For the bacterium, the ability to resist antibiotics is a big <u>advantage</u>. It's better able to survive, even in a host who's being treated to get rid of the infection, and so it lives for longer and <u>reproduces</u> many more times. This <u>increases</u> the <u>population size</u> of the antibiotic-resistant strain.

4) Antibiotic-resistant strains are a problem for people who become <u>infected</u> with these bacteria because they aren't immune to the new strain and there is no effective treatment. This means that the infection <u>easily spreads</u> between people. Sometimes drug companies can come up with a <u>new</u> antibiotic that's effective, but '<u>superbugs</u>' that are resistant to most known antibiotics are becoming more common.

5) <u>MRSA</u> is a relatively common '<u>superbug</u>' that's really hard to get rid of. It often affects people in <u>hospitals</u> and can be <u>fatal</u> if it enters their bloodstream.

Antibiotic Resistance is Becoming More Common

1) For the last few decades, we've been able to deal with <u>bacterial infections</u> pretty easily using <u>antibiotics</u>. The <u>death rate</u> from infectious bacterial diseases (e.g. pneumonia) has <u>fallen</u> dramatically.

2) But the problem of <u>antibiotic resistance</u> is getting <u>worse</u> — partly because of the <u>overuse</u> and <u>inappropriate use</u> of antibiotics, e.g. doctors prescribing them for <u>non-serious conditions</u> or infections caused by <u>viruses</u>.

Antibiotics don't kill viruses — see p.90.

3) The more <u>often</u> antibiotics are used, the <u>bigger</u> the problem of <u>antibiotic resistance</u> becomes, so it's important that doctors <u>only</u> prescribe antibiotics when they <u>really need</u> to:

It's not that antibiotics actually <u>cause</u> resistance — they create a situation where naturally resistant bacteria have an <u>advantage</u> and so increase in numbers.

4) It's also important that you take <u>all</u> the antibiotics a doctor prescribes for you:

Taking the <u>full course</u> makes sure that <u>all</u> the bacteria are <u>destroyed</u>, which means that there are <u>none</u> left to mutate and develop into <u>antibiotic-resistant strains</u>.

5) In <u>farming</u>, antibiotics can be given to animals to <u>prevent</u> them becoming <u>ill</u> and to make them <u>grow faster</u>. This can lead to the development of <u>antibiotic-resistant bacteria</u> in the animals which can then spread to humans, e.g. during meat preparation and consumption. Increasing concern about the <u>overuse</u> of antibiotics in agriculture has led to some countries <u>restricting their use</u>.

6) The increase in antibiotic resistance has encouraged drug companies to work on developing <u>new</u> antibiotics that are <u>effective</u> against the resistant strains. Unfortunately, the <u>rate of development</u> is <u>slow</u>, which means we're <u>unlikely</u> to be able to keep up with the <u>demand</u> for new drugs as <u>more</u> antibiotic-resistant strains develop and spread. It's also a very <u>costly</u> process.

Classification

*It seems to be a basic human urge to want to **classify** things — that's the case in **biology** anyway...*

Classification is Organising **Living Organisms** into Groups

1) Traditionally, organisms have been <u>classified</u> according to a system first proposed in the 1700's by <u>Carl Linnaeus</u>, which <u>groups</u> living things according to their <u>characteristics</u> and the <u>structures</u> that make them up.

2) In this system (known as the <u>Linnaean system</u>), living things are first divided into <u>kingdoms</u> (e.g. the plant kingdom).

3) The kingdoms are then <u>subdivided</u> into smaller and smaller groups — <u>phylum</u>, <u>class</u>, <u>order</u>, <u>family</u>, <u>genus</u>, <u>species</u>.

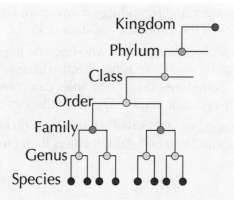

Classification Systems **Change** Over Time

1) As knowledge of the <u>biochemical processes</u> taking place inside organisms developed and <u>microscopes improved</u> (which allowed us to find out more about the <u>internal structures</u> of organisms), scientists put forward <u>new</u> models of classification.

2) In 1990, Carl Woese proposed the <u>three-domain system</u>. Using evidence gathered from <u>new chemical analysis techniques</u> such as RNA sequence analysis, he found that in some cases, species thought to be <u>closely related</u> in traditional classification systems are in fact <u>not</u> as closely related as first thought.

3) In the three-domain system, organisms are first of all split into <u>three large groups</u> called <u>domains</u>:

1) ARCHAEA — Organisms in this domain are <u>primitive bacteria</u>. They're often found in <u>extreme places</u> such as hot springs and salt lakes.

2) BACTERIA — This domain contains <u>true bacteria</u> like *E. coli* and *Staphylococcus*. Although they often look similar to Archaea, there are lots of <u>biochemical differences</u> between them.

3) EUKARYOTA — This domain includes a <u>broad range</u> of organisms including <u>fungi</u> (page 82), <u>plants</u>, <u>animals</u> and <u>protists</u> (page 82).

4) These are then <u>subdivided</u> into smaller groups — kingdom, phylum, class, order, family, genus, species.

Classification

*A bit of a **Latin** lesson for you now. And a diagram of a **funny looking tree**.*

Organisms Are **Named** According to the **Binomial System**

1) In the binomial system, every organism is given its own two-part Latin name.

2) The first part refers to the genus that the organism belongs to. This gives you information on the organism's ancestry. The second part refers to the species. E.g. humans are known as *Homo sapiens*. '*Homo*' is the genus and '*sapiens*' is the species.

3) The binomial system is used worldwide and means that scientists in different countries or who speak different languages all refer to a particular species by the same name — avoiding potential confusion.

Evolutionary Trees Show **Evolutionary Relationships**

1) Evolutionary trees show how scientists think different species are related to each other.

2) They show common ancestors and relationships between species. The more recent the common ancestor, the more closely related the two species — and the more characteristics they're likely to share.

3) Scientists analyse lots of different types of data to work out evolutionary relationships. For living organisms, they use the current classification data (e.g. DNA analysis and structural similarities). For extinct species, they use information from the fossil record (see page 177).

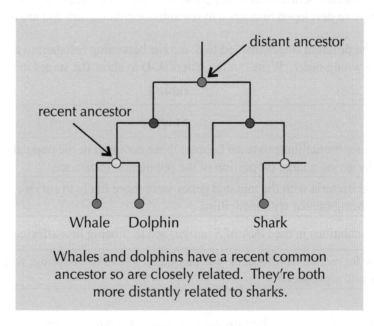

Whales and dolphins have a recent common ancestor so are closely related. They're both more distantly related to sharks.

Binomial system — uh oh, sounds like maths...

In the binomial system the genus comes first, then the species. Sometimes, the genus in a binomial name is abbreviated to a capital letter with a full stop after it.

Q1 The evolutionary tree on the right shows the relationship between four species, A-D.
Which two species shown in the tree are the most closely related? [1 mark]

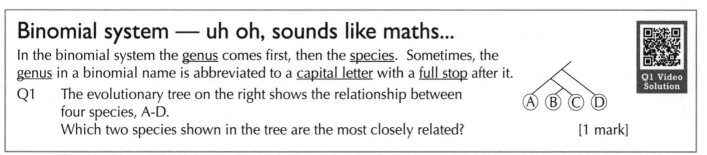

Warm-Up & Exam Questions

The end of the topic is in sight now — just a few more questions to check you've been paying attention.

Warm-Up Questions

1) Suggest what makes low-oxygen environments suitable for the formation of fossils.
2) Why might natural selection work differently on two isolated populations of a species?
3) Suggest a situation where antibiotics could be prescribed inappropriately.
4) Explain why it's important that people take the full course of antibiotics they are prescribed.
5) What species does the Eurasian beaver, *Castor fiber*, belong to?

Exam Questions

1 **Figure 1** shows a section of an evolutionary tree. (Grade 4-6)

Figure 1

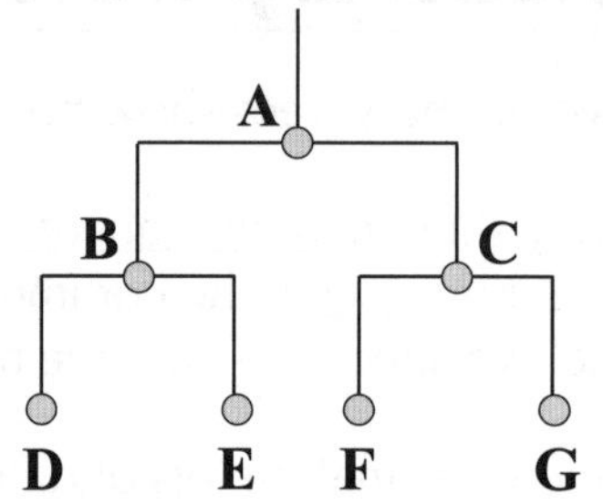

1.1 Which species is the most recent common ancestor of Species **F** and Species **G**?

[1 mark]

1.2 Would you expect Species **D** to look similar to Species **E**?
Give a reason for your answer.

[1 mark]

2 *Staphylococcus aureus* (*S. aureus*) is a common bacterium that is found on the skin and mucous membranes. It can cause serious illness in people with weakened immune systems. Some strains of the bacterium have developed resistance to the antibiotic meticillin, and are known as MRSA. (Grade 6-7)

2.1 **Table 1** shows the different stages that led to *S. aureus* becoming resistant to meticillin. The stages are shown in the wrong order. Write out the letters **A-D** to show the stages in the correct order.

Table 1

	Stage
A	The gene for meticillin resistance became more common in the population over time, eventually giving a large proportion of the population resistance.
B	Individual bacteria with the mutated genes were more likely to survive and reproduce in a host being treated with meticillin.
C	Random mutations in the DNA of *S. aureus* led to it being less affected by meticillin.
D	The gene for meticillin resistance was passed on to lots of offspring, which also survived and reproduced.

[2 marks]

2.2 Suggest why MRSA is a more serious problem in hospitals than in wider society.

[2 marks]

2.3 Explain why antibiotic resistance in bacteria is a concern for humans.

[1 mark]

2.4 Suggest why the National Health Service (NHS) is trying to reduce the use of antibiotics.

[3 marks]

Revision Summary for Topic 6

So you've finished Topic 6 — hoorah. Now here's a page full of questions to test your knowledge.

- Try these questions and tick off each one when you get it right.
- When you're completely happy with a sub-topic, tick it off.

For even more practice, try the Retrieval Quiz for Topic 6 — just scan this QR code!

Topic 6 Quiz

DNA, Genes and Mutations (p.151-155) ☐

1) What do genes code for? ☑
2) How many bases in a DNA sequence code for one amino acid? ☑
3) Give a function of the non-coding parts of DNA. ☑
4) True or False: "Most mutations have little or no effect on the protein coded for by a gene". ☑

Reproduction and Meiosis (p.157-160) ☐

5) Name the male and female gametes of animals. ☑
6) Which type of reproduction produces genetically identical cells? ☑
7) State the type of cell division used to make gametes in humans. ☑
8) How does variation in a population increase its chance of surviving environmental change? ☑
9) Describe the methods of sexual and asexual reproduction used by strawberry plants. ☑

Sex Chromosomes, Genetic Diagrams and Inherited Disorders (p.161-169) ☐

10) What is the probability that offspring will have the XX combination of sex chromosomes? ☑
11) How many genes are responsible for controlling fur colour in mice? ☑
12) What does it mean if someone is heterozygous for a gene? ☑
13) What is the chance of a child being born with polydactyly if one parent has a single dominant allele for the gene that controls it? ☑
14) Give two arguments for and two arguments against screening embryos for genetic disorders. ☑

Mendel, Variation and Evolution (p.170-178) ☐

15) What do we now know Mendel's "units" as? ☑
16) What is variation? ☑
17) Explain how beneficial characteristics can become more common in a population over time. ☑
18) What was Jean-Baptiste Lamarck's theory about evolution? ☑

Selective Breeding, Genetic Engineering and Cloning (p.180-184) ☐

19) What is selective breeding? ☑
20) How might farmers use selective breeding? ☑
21) What is genetic engineering? ☑
22) How can embryo transplants be used to create animal clones? ☑

Fossils, Speciation, Antibiotic-Resistant Bacteria and Classification (p.186-191) ☐

23) Give two ways that fossils can be formed. ☑
24) What leads to the formation of antibiotic-resistant strains of bacteria? ☑
25) Name the groups that organisms are classified into in the Linnaean system. ☑
26) Who proposed the 'three-domain system' of classification in 1990? ☑

Competition

Ecology is all about organisms and the environment they live in, and how the two interact. Simple.

First Learn Some Words to Help You Understand Ecology...

This topic will make a lot more sense if you become familiar with these terms first:

1) <u>Habitat</u> — the place where an organism <u>lives</u>.
2) <u>Population</u> — <u>all</u> the organisms of <u>one species</u> living in a <u>habitat</u>.
3) <u>Community</u> — the <u>populations</u> of <u>different species</u> living in a habitat.
4) <u>Abiotic</u> factors — <u>non-living</u> factors of the environment, e.g. temperature.
5) <u>Biotic</u> factors — <u>living</u> factors of the environment, e.g. food.
6) <u>Ecosystem</u> — the <u>interaction</u> of a <u>community</u> of <u>living</u> organisms (biotic) with the non-living (<u>abiotic</u>) parts of their environment.

There's more about abiotic and biotic factors on the next two pages.

Organisms Compete for Resources to Survive

Organisms need things from their <u>environment</u> and from <u>other organisms</u> in order to <u>survive</u> and <u>reproduce</u>:

1) <u>Plants</u> need <u>light</u> and <u>space</u>, as well as <u>water</u> and <u>mineral ions (nutrients)</u> from the soil.
2) <u>Animals</u> need <u>space (territory)</u>, <u>food</u>, <u>water</u> and <u>mates</u>.

Organisms <u>compete with other species</u> (and members of their <u>own species</u>) for the <u>same resources</u>.

Any Change in Any Environment can Have Knock-on Effects

1) In a community, each species <u>depends</u> on other species for things such as <u>food</u>, <u>shelter</u>, <u>pollination</u> and <u>seed dispersal</u> — this is called <u>interdependence</u>.

2) The <u>interdependence</u> of all the living things in an ecosystem means that any major <u>change</u> in the ecosystem (such as one species being removed) can have <u>far-reaching effects</u>.

3) The diagram on the right shows part of a <u>food web</u> (a diagram of what eats what) from a <u>stream</u>.

4) <u>Stonefly larvae</u> are particularly sensitive to <u>pollution</u>. Suppose pollution <u>killed</u> them in this stream. The table below shows some of the <u>effects</u> this might have on some of the other organisms in the food web.

Organism	Effect of loss of stonefly larvae	Effect on population
Blackfly larvae	Less competition for algae	Increase
	More likely to be eaten by predators	Decrease
Water spider	Less food	Decrease
Stickleback	Less food (if water spider or mayfly larvae numbers decrease)	Decrease

Remember that food webs are very complex and that these effects are difficult to predict accurately.

5) In some communities, all the species and environmental factors are in <u>balance</u> so that the <u>population sizes</u> are <u>roughly constant</u> (they may go up and down in cycles — see p.198). These are called <u>stable communities</u>. Stable communities include <u>tropical rainforests</u> and <u>ancient oak woodlands</u>.

Survival — the prize for being a winner

Q1   Give three things plants compete for in an ecosystem.   [3 marks]

Q2   Using the food web above, suggest what might happen to the frog population if the stickleback population decreased.   [2 marks]

Q2 Video Solution

Abiotic and Biotic Factors

*The environment in which organisms live **changes** all the time. The things that change are either **abiotic** (non-living) or **biotic** (living) factors. These can have a big **effect** on a community...*

Abiotic Factors Can **Vary** in an **Ecosystem**...

Abiotic factors are <u>non-living</u> factors. For example:

1) <u>Moisture level</u>
2) <u>Light intensity</u>
3) <u>Temperature</u>
4) <u>Carbon dioxide level</u> (for plants)
5) <u>Wind intensity</u> and <u>direction</u>
6) <u>Oxygen level</u> (for aquatic animals)
7) <u>Soil pH</u> and <u>mineral content</u>

Light intensity can vary within an ecosystem because of shading caused by, e.g. tree cover.

Different organisms are <u>adapted</u> (see page 197) to different abiotic <u>conditions</u>.

Changes in Abiotic Factors Can **Affect Populations**

1) A <u>change</u> in the environment could be an <u>increase</u> or <u>decrease</u> in an abiotic factor, e.g. an increase in temperature. These changes can affect the <u>sizes</u> of <u>populations</u> in a <u>community</u>.

2) This means they can also affect the <u>population sizes</u> of other organisms that <u>depend</u> on them (see previous page).

3) For example, animals depend on <u>plants</u> for food, so a decrease in a <u>plant population</u> could affect the <u>animal species</u> in a community.

4) Here are <u>two examples</u> of changes in <u>abiotic factors</u> which may affect <u>plant populations</u>:

- A <u>decrease</u> in light intensity, temperature or level of carbon dioxide could <u>decrease</u> the <u>rate of photosynthesis</u> in a plant species (see p.102-103).
- This could affect <u>plant growth</u> and cause a <u>decrease</u> in the <u>population size</u>.

- A <u>decrease</u> in the <u>mineral content</u> of the soil (e.g. a lack of nitrates) could cause <u>nutrient deficiencies</u> (see p.98).
- This could also affect <u>plant growth</u> and cause a <u>decrease</u> in the <u>population size</u>.

A = not, biotic = living, so abiotic means non-living

Some <u>human activities</u> can affect the <u>abiotic factors</u> of ecosystems, see pages 213, 216 and 217 for more. As you can see from this page, this can affect some organisms <u>directly</u> and other organisms <u>indirectly</u>.

Abiotic and Biotic Factors

*The previous page shows how abiotic factors can affect the **populations** in an ecosystem, but changes in **biotic factors** can also have big consequences. This page has a few examples to show you how.*

Biotic Factors Can Also Vary in an Ecosystem

Biotic factors are <u>living</u> factors.
Here are some examples of biotic factors that might affect organisms in an ecosystem:

1) <u>New predators</u> arriving
2) <u>Competition</u> — one species may outcompete another so that numbers are too low to breed
3) <u>New pathogens</u>
4) <u>Availability of food</u>

Changes in Biotic Factors Can have Knock-On Effects

1) A <u>change</u> in the environment could be the introduction of a <u>new</u> biotic factor, e.g. a new predator or pathogen.

2) These changes can affect the <u>sizes</u> of <u>populations</u> in a <u>community</u>, which can have <u>knock-on effects</u> because of interdependence (see page 194). Here are a few examples:

> A new predator could cause a decrease in the <u>prey</u> population. There's more about predator-prey populations on p.198.

> Red and grey <u>squirrels</u> live in the same habitat and eat the same food. Grey squirrels outcompete the red squirrels — so the <u>population</u> of red squirrels is <u>decreasing</u>.

1) The following graph shows the effect of a <u>new pathogen</u> on <u>Species A</u>.
2) The population size of Species A was <u>increasing</u> up until 1985, when it <u>decreased rapidly</u> until 1990 — suggesting that <u>1985</u> was the year that the new pathogen arrived.
3) The population started to <u>rise</u> again after 1990.

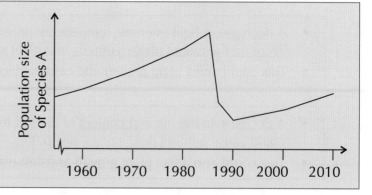

Changing biotic factors — it's like dominoes...

<u>Learn</u> the list of factors here, as well as on the previous page. I reckon this is a prime time for shutting the book, <u>scribbling</u> them all down and then <u>checking</u> how you did.

Adaptations

*Life exists in so many **different environments** because the **organisms** that live in them have **adapted** to them.*

Adaptations Allow Organisms to Survive

Organisms, including microorganisms, are adapted to live in different environmental conditions.
The features or characteristics that allow them to do this are called adaptations. Adaptations can be:

1. Structural

These are features of an organism's body structure — such as shape or colour. For example:

Arctic animals like the Arctic fox have white fur so they're camouflaged against the snow. This helps them avoid predators and sneak up on prey.

Animals that live in cold places (like whales) have a thick layer of blubber (fat) and a low surface area to volume ratio to help them retain heat.

Animals that live in hot places (like camels) have a thin layer of fat and a large surface area to volume ratio to help them lose heat.

2. Behavioural

These are ways that organisms behave. Many species (e.g. swallows) migrate
to warmer climates during the winter to avoid the problems of living in cold conditions.

3. Functional

These are things that go on inside an organism's body that can be related to processes like
reproduction and metabolism (all the chemical reactions happening in the body). For example:

Desert animals conserve water by producing very little sweat and small amounts of concentrated urine.

Brown bears hibernate over winter.
They lower their metabolism, which conserves energy, so they don't have to hunt when there's not much food about.

Microorganisms Have a Huge Variety of Adaptations...

...so that they can live in a wide range of environments:

- Some microorganisms (e.g. bacteria) are known as extremophiles
  — they're adapted to live in very extreme conditions.

- For example, some can live at high temperatures (e.g. in super hot volcanic
  vents), and others can live in places with a high salt concentration (e.g.
  very salty lakes) or at high pressure (e.g. deep sea vents).

Organisms can adapt to life in the most extreme environments

Q1 The diagram on the right shows a penguin. Penguins live in the cold, icy
    environment of the Antarctic. They swim in the sea to hunt for fish to eat.
    Some penguins also huddle together in large groups to keep warm.
    a) What type of adaptation is being described when penguins
       'huddle together'?   [1 mark]
    b) Explain one structural adaptation a penguin has to its environment. [2 marks]

Q1 Video
Solution

Food Chains

*You might remember **food webs** from page 194. Well, **food chains** are a similar idea — except that you only really show one part of a food web in a food chain. Read on to find out more...*

Food Chains Show **What's Eaten by What** in an Ecosystem

1) <u>Food chains</u> always start with a <u>producer</u>.
   Producers <u>make</u> (produce) <u>their own food</u> using energy from the Sun.

2) Producers are usually <u>green plants</u> or <u>algae</u> — they make <u>glucose</u> by <u>photosynthesis</u> (see page 101).

3) When a green plant produces glucose, some of it is used to make <u>other biological molecules</u> in the plant.

4) These biological molecules are the plant's <u>biomass</u> — the <u>mass</u> of <u>living material</u>.

5) Biomass can be thought of as <u>energy stored</u> in a plant.

6) <u>Energy</u> is <u>transferred</u> through living organisms in an ecosystem when organisms <u>eat</u> other organisms.

7) Producers are eaten by <u>primary consumers</u>. Primary consumers are then eaten by <u>secondary consumers</u> and secondary consumers are eaten by <u>tertiary consumers</u>. Here's an example of a food chain:

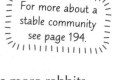

Consumers are organisms that eat other organisms. 'Primary' means 'first', so primary consumers are the first consumers in a food chain. Secondary consumers are second and tertiary consumers are third.

Producers   Primary consumers   Secondary consumer

<u>5000</u> dandelions... feed... <u>100</u> rabbits... which feed... <u>1</u> fox.

Populations of **Prey** and **Predators** Go in **Cycles**

Consumers that <u>hunt and kill</u> other animals are called <u>predators</u>, and their <u>prey</u> are what they eat.
In a <u>stable community</u> containing <u>prey</u> and <u>predators</u> (as most of them do of course):

1) The <u>population</u> of any species is usually <u>limited</u> by the amount of <u>food</u> available.

2) If the population of the <u>prey</u> increases, then so will the population of the <u>predators</u>.

3) However as the population of predators <u>increases</u>, the number of prey will <u>decrease</u>.

For more about a stable community see page 194.

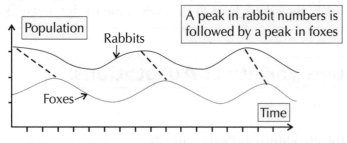

A peak in rabbit numbers is followed by a peak in foxes

- E.g. <u>more grass</u> means <u>more rabbits</u>.
- More rabbits means <u>more foxes</u>.
- But more foxes means <u>fewer rabbits</u>.
- Eventually fewer rabbits will mean <u>fewer foxes again</u>.
- This <u>up and down pattern</u> continues...

4) Predator-prey cycles are always <u>out of phase</u> with each other. This is because it <u>takes a while</u> for one population to <u>respond</u> to changes in the other population.

E.g. when the number of rabbits goes up, the number of foxes doesn't increase immediately because it takes time for them to reproduce.

A food chain shows part of a food web

Q1   Look at the following food chain for a particular area: grass → grasshopper → rat → snake

     a) Name the producer in the food chain.   [1 mark]

     b) How many consumers are there in the food chain?   [1 mark]

     c) Name the primary consumer in the food chain.   [1 mark]

     d) All the rats in the area are killed.
        Explain two effects that this could have on the food chain.   [4 marks]

 Q1 Video Solution

Warm-Up & Exam Questions

This ecology topic's a long one — so make sure you've really got these first few pages stuck in your head before moving on and learning the rest. These questions should help you out.

Warm-Up Questions

1) What is the correct scientific term for all the different species in a habitat?
2) What is an ecosystem?
3) Give four examples of abiotic factors that could affect a land-based plant species.
4) What is meant by a structural adaptation?
5) What is meant by a producer in a food chain?

Exam Questions

1 **Figure 1** shows a food chain for a particular area: **Grade 4-6**

Figure 1

| algae → shrimp → sea turtle → tiger shark |

1.1 What term is used to describe the tiger shark in **Figure 1**? Tick **one** box.

☐ producer ☐ primary consumer ☐ secondary consumer ☐ tertiary consumer

[1 mark]

1.2 Explain the importance of the algae in **Figure 1**.

[2 marks]

2 The Harris's antelope squirrel lives in hot deserts in parts of the USA and Mexico. It has grey fur, small ears and does not sweat. It has sharp claws which enable it to dig burrows, in which it lives. Above ground, during the hottest parts of the day it often holds its large tail over its head, or lies in the shade with its limbs spread out wide. **Grade 6-7**

2.1 Give **one** functional adaptation the Harris's antelope squirrel has to its environment.

[1 mark]

2.2 Explain **one** behavioural adaptation the Harris's antelope squirrel has to its environment.

[2 marks]

3 Cutthroat trout are present in lakes in Yellowstone National Park. In the last few decades, lake trout have been introduced to the lakes. However, lake trout have emerged as predators of the cutthroat trout. **Grade 6-7**

3.1 Explain how the introduction of the lake trout might cause the population sizes of both species of fish to fluctuate over time.

[5 marks]

3.2 Give **two** other biotic factors that could affect the size of the cutthroat trout population.

[2 marks]

Using Quadrats

*This is where the **fun** starts. Studying **ecology** gives you the chance to **rummage around** in bushes, get your hands **dirty** and look at some **real organisms**, living in the **wild**.*

Environmental Variation Affects the Distribution of Organisms

1) As you know from page 194, a <u>habitat</u> is the place where an organism <u>lives</u>, e.g. a playing field.
2) The <u>distribution</u> of an organism is <u>where</u> an organism is <u>found</u>, e.g. in a part of the playing field.
3) Where an organism is found is affected by <u>environmental factors</u> (see pages 195-196). An organism might be <u>more common</u> in <u>one area</u> than another due to <u>differences</u> in environmental factors between the two areas. For example, in the playing field, you might find that daisies are <u>more common</u> in the open than under trees, because there's <u>more light</u> available in the open.
4) There are a couple of ways to <u>study</u> the distribution of an organism. You can:
   • <u>measure</u> how common an organism is in <u>two sample areas</u> (e.g. using <u>quadrats</u>) and compare them.
   • study how the distribution <u>changes</u> across an area, e.g. by placing quadrats along a <u>transect</u> (p.201). Both of these methods give <u>quantitative</u> data (numbers) about the distribution.

Use Quadrats to Study The Distribution of Small Organisms

A <u>quadrat</u> is a <u>square</u> frame enclosing a <u>known area</u>, e.g. 1 m². To compare <u>how common</u> an organism is in <u>two sample areas</u> (e.g. shady and sunny spots in that playing field) just follow these simple steps:

1) Place a <u>1 m² quadrat</u> on the ground at a <u>random point</u> within the <u>first</u> sample area. E.g. divide the area into a grid and use a random number generator to pick coordinates.
2) <u>Count</u> all the organisms <u>within</u> the quadrat.
3) <u>Repeat</u> steps 1 and 2 as many times as you can.
4) <u>Work out</u> the <u>mean</u> number of organisms per quadrat within the first sample area.

A quadrat

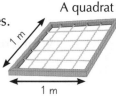

1 m

1 m

EXAMPLE **Anna counted the number of daisies in 7 quadrats within her first sample area and recorded the following results: 18, 20, 22, 23, 23, 23, 25.**

Here the MEAN is: $\dfrac{\text{TOTAL number of organisms}}{\text{NUMBER of quadrats}} = \dfrac{154}{7}$ = 22 daisies per quadrat

5) <u>Repeat</u> steps 1 to 4 in the <u>second</u> sample area.
6) Finally <u>compare</u> the two means. E.g. you might find 2 daisies per m² in the shade, and 22 daisies per m² (lots more) in the open field.

You Can Also Work Out the Population Size of an Organism in One Area

EXAMPLE **Students used a quadrat with an area of 0.5 m² to randomly sample daisies on an open field. The students found a mean of 10.5 daisies per quadrat. The field had an area of 800 m². Estimate the population of daisies on the field.**

1) Work out the <u>mean number of organisms per m²</u>.

$1 \div 0.5 = 2$
$2 \times 10.5 = 21$ daisies per m²

2) Then multiply the <u>mean</u> by the <u>total area</u> (in m²) of the habitat.

$800 \times 21 = 16\,800$
daisies on the open field

The population size of an organism is sometimes called its abundance.

If your quadrat has an area of 1 m², the mean number of organisms per m² is just the same as the mean number per quadrat.

Don't try to study elephants using a quadrat

Q1 A 1200 m² field was randomly sampled for buttercups using a quadrat with an area of 0.25 m². A mean of 0.75 buttercups were found per quadrat. Estimate the total population of buttercups. [2 marks]

Q1 Video Solution

Using Transects

*So, now you think you've learnt **all about** distribution. Well **hold on** — there's more **ecology fun** to be had.*

Use **Transects** to **Study** The **Distribution** of Organisms

You can use lines called <u>transects</u> to help find out how organisms (like plants) are <u>distributed</u> across an area — e.g. if an organism becomes <u>more or less common</u> as you move from a hedge towards the middle of a field. Here's what to do:

1) <u>Mark out a line</u> in the area you want to study using a tape measure.

2) Then <u>collect data</u> along the line.

3) You can do this by just <u>counting</u> all the organisms you're interested in that <u>touch</u> the line.

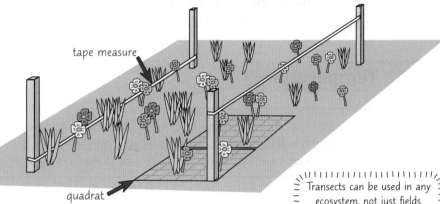

tape measure

quadrat

Transects can be used in any ecosystem, not just fields. For example, along a beach.

4) Or, you can collect data by using <u>quadrats</u> (see previous page). These can be placed <u>next to</u> each other along the line or <u>at intervals</u>, for example, every 2 m.

You Can **Estimate** the **Percentage Cover** of a **Quadrat**

If it's difficult to count all the individual organisms in the quadrat (e.g. if they're grass) you can calculate the <u>percentage cover</u>. This means estimating the percentage <u>area</u> of the quadrat covered by a particular type of organism, e.g. by <u>counting</u> the number of little squares covered by the organisms.

EXAMPLE

Some students were measuring the distribution of organisms from one corner of a school playing field to another, using quadrats placed at regular intervals along a transect. Below is a picture of one of the quadrats. Calculate the percentage cover of each organism, A and B.

Measuring % cover

☐ Organism Type A

☐ Organism Type B

You count a square if it's more than half covered.

1) <u>Count</u> the <u>number of squares</u> covered by organism A.

2) Make this into a <u>percentage</u> — divide the number of squares covered by the organism by the total number of squares in the quadrat (100), then multiply the result by 100.

3) Do the same for <u>organism B</u>.

Type A = 42 squares

(42/100) × 100
= 0.42 × 100 = **42%**

Type B = 47 squares

(47/100) × 100
= 0.47 × 100 = **47%**

PRACTICAL TIP

You don't need fancy kit to study the distribution of organisms

So if you want to measure the distribution of a organism <u>across</u> an area, you could use a <u>transect</u>. You can use them <u>alone</u> or along with <u>quadrats</u>. Using <u>percentage cover</u> instead of <u>number</u> of organisms is a good way of studying the distribution of plants, as there may be <u>too many</u> to count.

Environmental Change

*Now you know how to **measure** the **distribution** of **organisms** (see pages 200-201), it's time to learn why their distribution may **change** over time.*

Environmental Changes Affect The Distribution of Organisms

1) Environmental changes can cause the distribution of organisms to change.
2) A change in distribution means a change in where an organism lives.
3) Environmental changes that can affect organisms in this way include:

1. Temperature

> The distribution of bird species in Germany is changing because of a rise in average temperature. E.g. the European bee-eater bird is a Mediterranean species but it's now present in parts of Germany.

2. Availability of Water

The distribution of some animal and plant species in the tropics changes between the wet and the dry seasons — i.e. the times of year where there is more or less rainfall, and so more or less water available.

> Each year in Africa, large numbers of giant wildebeest migrate, moving north and then back south as the rainfall patterns change.

3. Composition of Atmospheric Gases

The distribution of some species changes in areas where there is more air pollution.

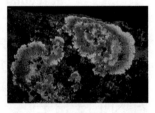

> Some species of lichen can't grow in areas where sulfur dioxide is given out by certain industrial processes.

These environmental changes can be caused by seasonal factors, geographic factors or human interaction.

For example, the rise in average temperature (see above) is due to global warming, which has been caused by human activity (see pages 216-217).

The distribution of organisms doesn't just stay the same all the time

Organisms rely on biotic and abiotic factors in the environment (see pages 195-196), so it's no wonder that when the factors change, it affects where organisms live. Some of the non-living (abiotic) factors that affect organisms are in a constant cycle — read about the water and carbon cycles on the next couple of pages.

The Water Cycle

*The **amount** of water on Earth is pretty much **constant** — but **where** it is changes.*
*Water moves between **rivers, lakes, oceans** and the **atmosphere** in what's known as the **water cycle**.*

The **Water Cycle** Means Water is **Endlessly Recycled**

The water here on planet Earth is constantly <u>recycled</u>.
There are four key steps you should understand:

1) <u>Energy</u> from the <u>Sun</u> makes water <u>evaporate</u> from the land and sea, turning it into <u>water vapour</u>. Water also evaporates from plants — this is known as <u>transpiration</u> (see p.75).

As warm water vapour rises it cools down and forms clouds.

2) The warm water vapour is <u>carried upwards</u> (as warm air rises). When it gets higher up it <u>cools</u> and <u>condenses</u> to form <u>clouds</u>.

3) Water falls from the clouds as <u>precipitation</u> (usually rain, but sometimes snow or hail) onto <u>land</u>, where it provides <u>fresh water</u> for <u>plants</u> and <u>animals</u>.

4) It then <u>drains</u> into the <u>sea</u>, before the whole process starts again.

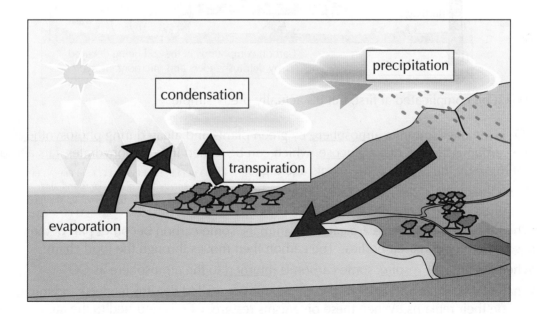

Evaporation, transpiration, condensation, precipitation

The water cycle is really easy — there are <u>four main stages</u> and they're all pretty straightforward.
So there's absolutely no excuse not to learn it inside out. The most important thing to remember is
that it's a <u>cycle</u> — a <u>continuous</u> process with no beginning or end. Water that falls to the ground as rain
(or any other kind of precipitation for that matter) will eventually end up back in the clouds again.

The Carbon Cycle

Recycling may be a buzz word for us but it's old school for nature. All the **nutrients** in our environment are constantly being **recycled** — there's a nice balance between what **goes in** and what **goes out** again.

Elements are Cycled Back to the Start of the Food Chain by Decay

1) Living things are made of materials they take from the world around them. E.g. plants turn elements like carbon, oxygen, hydrogen and nitrogen from the soil and the air into the complex compounds (carbohydrates, proteins and fats) that make up living organisms. These get passed up the food chain.

2) These materials are returned to the environment in waste products, or when the organisms die and decay.

3) Materials decay because they're broken down (digested) by microorganisms. This happens faster in warm, moist, aerobic (oxygen rich) conditions because microorganisms are more active in these conditions.

4) Decay puts the stuff that plants need to grow (e.g. mineral ions) back into the soil.

5) In a stable community, the materials that are taken out of the soil and used by plants etc. are balanced by those that are put back in. There's a constant cycle happening.

The Constant Cycling of Carbon is called the Carbon Cycle

CO$_2$ in the air

Burning Photosynthesis plant respiration animal respiration CO$_2$ released from decay

Products made from plants and animals Carbon compounds in plants Eating Carbon compounds in animals Death and waste

Fossil fuels are made of decayed plant and animal matter.

Burning

Fossil fuels

Carbon compounds in the soil being decayed by detritus feeders and microorganisms

That can look a bit complicated at first, but it's actually pretty simple:

1) CO$_2$ is removed from the atmosphere by green plants and algae during photosynthesis. The carbon is used to make glucose, which can be turned into carbohydrates, fats and proteins that make up the bodies of the plants and algae.

2) When the plants and algae respire, some carbon is returned to the atmosphere as CO$_2$.

The energy that green plants and algae get from photosynthesis is transferred up the food chain.

3) When the plants and algae are eaten by animals, some carbon becomes part of the fats and proteins in their bodies. The carbon then moves through the food chain.

4) When the animals respire, some carbon is returned to the atmosphere as CO$_2$.

5) When plants, algae and animals die, other animals (called detritus feeders) and microorganisms feed on their remains. When these organisms respire, CO$_2$ is returned to the atmosphere.

6) Animals also produce waste that is broken down by detritus feeders and microorganisms.

7) The combustion (burning) of wood and fossil fuels also releases CO$_2$ back into the air.

8) So the carbon (and energy) is constantly being cycled — from the air, through food chains (via plants, algae and animals, and detritus feeders and microorganisms) and eventually back out into the air again.

Warm-Up & Exam Questions

You can't just stare at these pages and expect all of the information to go in. Especially the practical pages with the maths examples. Do these questions to see how well you really know the stuff.

Warm-Up Questions

1) What is a transect?
2) A student counted the number of daises in five quadrats and recorded the following results: 14, 11, 11, 12, 12. What is the mean number of daises per quadrat?
3) Give three reasons why environmental factors in an area may change.
4) What is the role of microorganisms in the carbon cycle?
5) How is the carbon in fossil fuels returned to the atmosphere?

Exam Questions

1   **Figure 1** shows a simplified version of the carbon cycle.   Grade 4-6

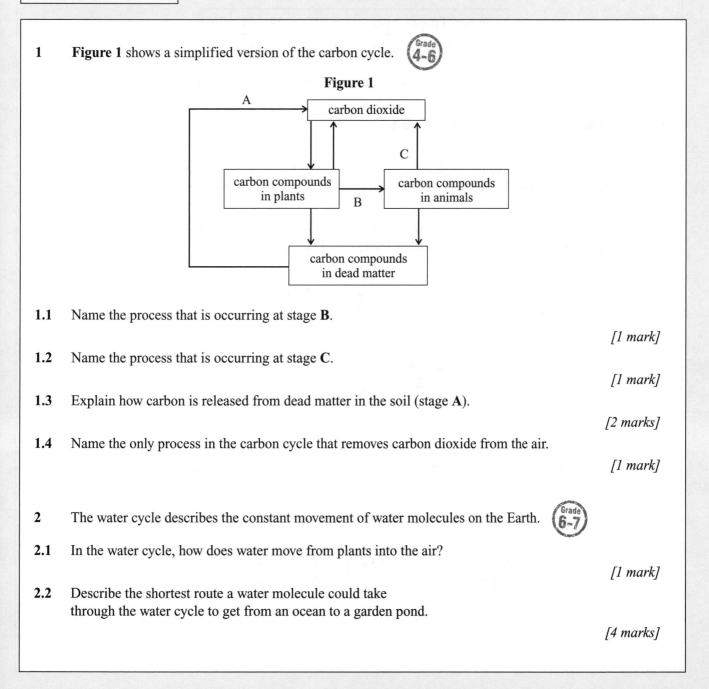

Figure 1

1.1   Name the process that is occurring at stage **B**.

[1 mark]

1.2   Name the process that is occurring at stage **C**.

[1 mark]

1.3   Explain how carbon is released from dead matter in the soil (stage **A**).

[2 marks]

1.4   Name the only process in the carbon cycle that removes carbon dioxide from the air.

[1 mark]

2   The water cycle describes the constant movement of water molecules on the Earth.   Grade 6-7

2.1   In the water cycle, how does water move from plants into the air?

[1 mark]

2.2   Describe the shortest route a water molecule could take through the water cycle to get from an ocean to a garden pond.

[4 marks]

Exam Questions

3   Some students investigated the distribution of poppies across a
     field next to a wood. A sketch of the area is shown in **Figure 2**.

(Grade 6-7)

Figure 2

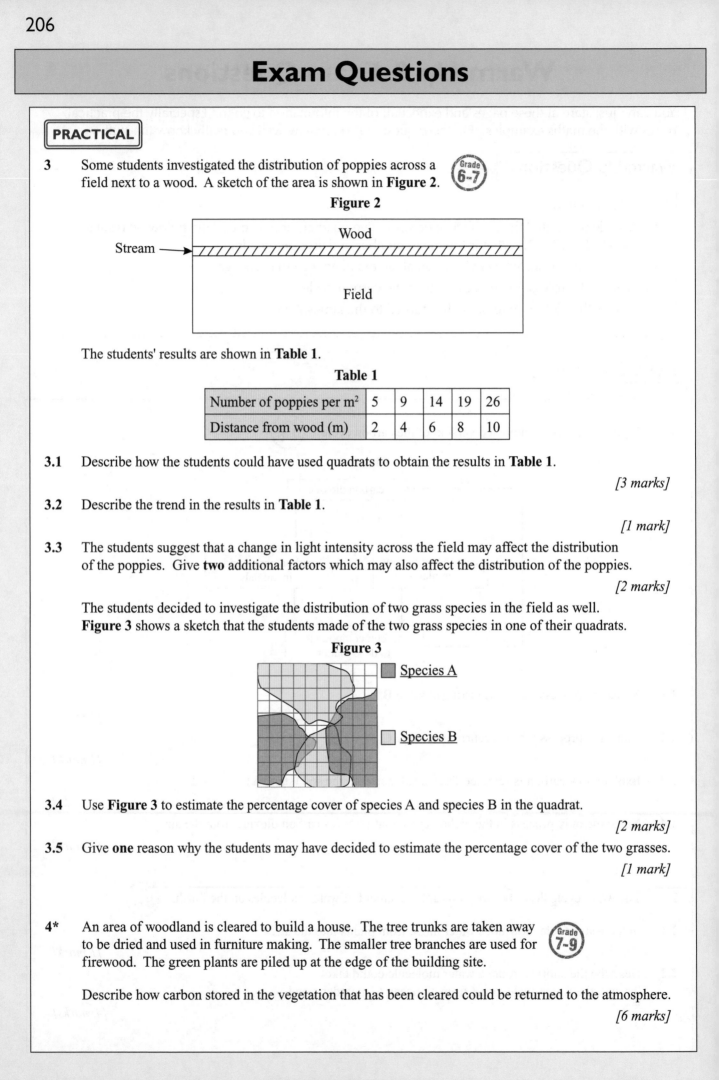

The students' results are shown in **Table 1**.

Table 1

Number of poppies per m^2	5	9	14	19	26
Distance from wood (m)	2	4	6	8	10

3.1 Describe how the students could have used quadrats to obtain the results in **Table 1**.

[3 marks]

3.2 Describe the trend in the results in **Table 1**.

[1 mark]

3.3 The students suggest that a change in light intensity across the field may affect the distribution
of the poppies. Give **two** additional factors which may also affect the distribution of the poppies.

[2 marks]

The students decided to investigate the distribution of two grass species in the field as well.
Figure 3 shows a sketch that the students made of the two grass species in one of their quadrats.

Figure 3

3.4 Use **Figure 3** to estimate the percentage cover of species A and species B in the quadrat.

[2 marks]

3.5 Give **one** reason why the students may have decided to estimate the percentage cover of the two grasses.

[1 mark]

4*   An area of woodland is cleared to build a house. The tree trunks are taken away
     to be dried and used in furniture making. The smaller tree branches are used for
     firewood. The green plants are piled up at the edge of the building site.

(Grade 7-9)

Describe how carbon stored in the vegetation that has been cleared could be returned to the atmosphere.

[6 marks]

Decay

*Microorganisms **break down** plant and animal material and waste to get **energy**. This process of **decay** allows the material contained within the organisms to be released, so that it can cycle through the ecosystem.*

Decomposition Can Produce Compost

1) Compost is <u>decomposed organic matter</u> (e.g. food waste) that is used as a <u>natural fertiliser</u> for crops and garden plants.

2) Farmers and gardeners try to provide the <u>ideal conditions</u> for quick decay to make <u>compost</u>.

The Rate of Decay is Affected by Several Factors

1) <u>Microorganisms</u> such as <u>bacteria</u> and <u>fungi</u>, as well as <u>detritus feeders</u> (p.204) are responsible for <u>decomposition</u> (decay).

2) You'd think that organisms that feed on dead stuff wouldn't be that <u>picky</u>, but they're a bit like Goldilocks — everything has to be <u>just right</u> for them to work at their best.

Temperature

<u>Warmer</u> temperatures make things decompose <u>quicker</u> because they <u>increase</u> the <u>rate</u> that the <u>enzymes</u> (see p.47) involved in decomposition work at. If it's <u>too hot</u> though, decomposition <u>slows down</u> or <u>stops</u> because the enzymes are <u>destroyed</u> and the <u>organisms die</u>. Really <u>cold</u> temperatures slow the rate of decomposition too.

Water Availability

Decay takes place faster in <u>moist environments</u> because the organisms involved in decay need <u>water</u> to carry out biological processes.

Oxygen Availability

Many organisms need <u>oxygen</u> to <u>respire</u>, which they need to do to <u>survive</u>. The microorganisms involved in <u>anaerobic decay</u> (see next page) don't need oxygen though.

Number of Decay Organisms

The <u>more</u> microorganisms and detritus feeders there are, the <u>faster</u> decomposition happens.

Rainforest ecosystems usually have a very high rate of decay, because they are so hot and wet.

Decomposition helps keep the whole cycle spinning around...

If you think about what's <u>actually needed</u> for decomposition to take place, it makes it much easier to <u>remember</u> the different factors that affect it. Obviously you need <u>decay organisms</u>, then you need all the stuff that decay organisms require in order to <u>survive</u> and carry out the decomposition <u>reactions</u>.

Biogas

*These days, there's a lot of effort being put into finding alternative sources of **fuel**. Here's how we can use the natural process of **decay** to generate **biogas** — a source of fuel. Wonderful.*

Biogas is Made by **Anaerobic Decay** of **Waste Material**

1) Biogas is mainly made up of <u>methane</u>, which can be <u>burned</u> as a <u>fuel</u>.

2) Lots of <u>different microorganisms</u> are used to produce biogas. They decay <u>plant and animal waste anaerobically</u> (without oxygen). This type of decay produces <u>methane gas</u>. <u>Sludge waste</u> from, for example, <u>sewage works</u> or <u>sugar factories</u>, is used to make biogas on a large scale.

3) Biogas is made in a simple fermenter called a <u>digester</u> or <u>generator</u>.

4) Biogas generators need to be kept at a <u>constant temperature</u> to keep the microorganisms <u>respiring</u> away.

5) Biogas <u>can't be stored as a liquid</u> (it needs too high a pressure), so it has to be <u>used straight away</u> — for <u>heating</u>, <u>cooking</u>, <u>lighting</u>, or to <u>power a turbine</u> to <u>generate electricity</u>.

Not All **Biogas Generators** Are the Same

There are two main types of biogas generator — <u>batch generators</u> and <u>continuous generators</u>.

<u>Batch generators</u> make biogas in <u>small batches</u>. They're <u>manually loaded up with waste</u>, which is left to digest, and the by-products are cleared away at the end of each session.

<u>Continuous generators</u> make biogas <u>all the time</u>. Waste is <u>continuously fed in</u>, and biogas is produced at a <u>steady rate</u>. Continuous generators are more suited to <u>large-scale</u> biogas projects.

The diagram below shows a <u>simple biogas generator</u>.

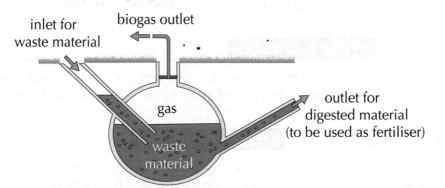

Whether it's a continuous or batch generator, it needs to have the following:

1) an inlet for <u>waste material</u> to be put in,

2) an outlet for the <u>digested material</u> to be removed through,

3) an outlet so that the <u>biogas</u> can be piped to where it is needed.

It might not be pretty, but it is pretty useful...

Biogas generators are quite neat really. The decomposition of waste material is a process that naturally happens <u>anyway</u> — by carrying out the decomposition in <u>generators</u> we can harness the biogas produced and use it to <u>produce energy</u> for different processes. We can also use the process to <u>clean our sewage</u> and other wastes so that they don't <u>pollute</u> our water or land. Win-win-win.

Investigating Decay

*It's time for a **practical**. The following two pages tie in quite nicely with the experiment investigating enzyme activity on page 49 — but this time you'll be looking at the effect of **temperature** on the rate of decay.*

Temperature Affects the Rate of Decay

You can investigate <u>decay</u> by observing the action of the enzyme <u>lipase</u> on a sample of <u>milk</u> that has been made <u>alkaline</u>. When the lipase breaks the milk down, the <u>pH</u> of the milk <u>decreases</u>.

This practical looks at how <u>temperature</u> affects the rate of decay. In it, an indicator dye called <u>phenolphthalein</u> is used — it has a <u>pink</u> colour when the <u>pH</u> is around <u>10</u>, but becomes <u>colourless</u> when the pH falls <u>below 8.3</u>. Here's what you need to do:

1) Measure out <u>5 cm³</u> of <u>lipase solution</u> and add it to a <u>test tube</u>. <u>Label</u> this tube with an 'L' for lipase.

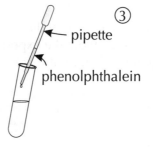

② milk

different test tube

2) Measure out <u>5 cm³</u> of <u>milk</u> and add it to a <u>different test tube</u>.

③ pipette

phenolphthalein

3) Add <u>5 drops</u> of <u>phenolphthalein indicator</u> to the tube containing <u>milk</u>.

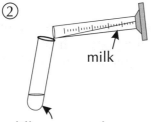

sodium carbonate solution

4) Then measure out <u>7 cm³</u> of <u>sodium carbonate solution</u> and add it to the tube containing <u>milk</u> and <u>phenolphthalein</u>. This makes the solution in the tube <u>alkaline</u>, so it should turn <u>pink</u>.

5) Put <u>both</u> tubes into a <u>water bath</u> set to <u>30 °C</u> and <u>leave them</u> to reach the <u>temperature</u> of the water bath. You could stick a <u>thermometer</u> into the <u>milk tube</u> to check this.

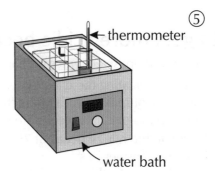

⑤ thermometer

water bath

Turn the page for the rest of the method...

Investigating Decay

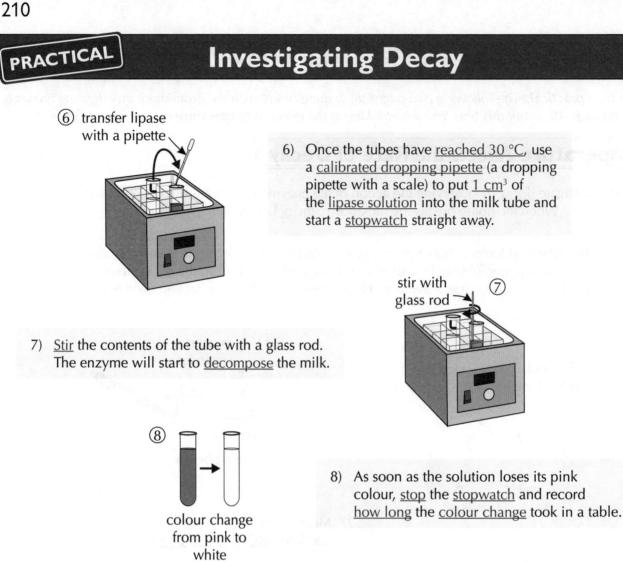

⑥ transfer lipase with a pipette

6) Once the tubes have reached 30 °C, use a calibrated dropping pipette (a dropping pipette with a scale) to put 1 cm³ of the lipase solution into the milk tube and start a stopwatch straight away.

stir with glass rod ⑦

7) Stir the contents of the tube with a glass rod. The enzyme will start to decompose the milk.

⑧

colour change from pink to white

8) As soon as the solution loses its pink colour, stop the stopwatch and record how long the colour change took in a table.

9) Repeat the experiment at a range of different temperatures (e.g. 10 °C, 20 °C, 40 °C, 50 °C). Make sure you carry out the experiment three times at each temperature, then calculate the mean time taken for the colour change to occur at each temperature.

(You can make a water bath capable of temperatures below room temperature by adding ice cubes to a beaker of water and measuring the temperature with a thermometer.)

10) You can use your results to calculate the rate of decay using this formula. The units will be s⁻¹ since rate is given per unit of time.

$$\text{Rate} = \frac{1000}{\text{time}}$$

You've met this formula before, on page 49.

The pH gets more acidic because fatty acids are produced...

...there's more about lipase enzymes on page 50.

Q1 Ted was investigating the effect of temperature on the rate of decay of milk by measuring the time taken for a change in the pH. His results are shown in the table.

Q1 Video Solution

Temperature (°C)	10	20	30	40
Time taken (s)	600	480	350	240

a) Calculate the rate of decay at 20 °C.
   Give your answer in s⁻¹. [1 mark]
b) Describe the trend in rate of decay shown by Ted's results. [1 mark]

Warm-Up & Exam Questions

This material isn't very glamorous, but we need processes like decay so that nutrients and other useful materials don't get locked up in dead organisms. Here are some questions to test your knowledge.

Warm-Up Questions

1) What is compost?
2) Give two types of organism that are responsible for the decomposition of materials.
3) Give three factors that affect the rate of decay.
4) What colour is phenolphthalein indicator in a solution with a pH of 10?
5) Suggest what you could add to milk to turn it alkaline.

Exam Questions

1 Biogas can be made in a generator through the decomposition of food waste. Grade 4-6

1.1 Name the main gas found in biogas.

[1 mark]

1.2 Explain why it is important that little or no oxygen is present in a biogas generator.

[2 marks]

1.3 Suggest **one** possible use of biogas produced in this way.

[1 mark]

PRACTICAL

2 Some students were investigating the effect of temperature on the decay of milk by lipase. Grade 6-7
They added phenolphthalein to alkaline milk, turning it pink, followed by the lipase.
They then started a stopwatch and waited to see a colour change. A water bath was used to control the temperature of the reactants. At the first temperature investigated, it took 280 seconds for the solution to lose its pink colour.

2.1 Calculate the rate of decay. Give your answer in s^{-1}.

[1 mark]

2.2 Give **one** variable the students should have controlled in this experiment
and describe how they should have controlled it.

[2 marks]

2.3 Give **one** possible source of error in this experiment and suggest how it could be reduced.

[2 marks]

3* A gardener wants to increase the rate of decomposition in her compost bin. Grade 7-9

Describe the factors she should consider changing to speed up the rate of
decomposition and explain how each factor affects the rate of decomposition.

[6 marks]

Biodiversity and Waste Management

*Unfortunately, human activity can **negatively affect** the **planet** and its **variety of life**.*

Earth's **Biodiversity** is Important

> Biodiversity is the <u>variety of different species</u>
> of organisms on Earth, or within an ecosystem.

1) <u>High</u> biodiversity is important. It makes sure that <u>ecosystems</u> (see p.194) are <u>stable</u> because different species depend on each other for things like <u>shelter</u> and <u>food</u>. Different species can also help to maintain the right <u>physical environment</u> for each other (e.g. the acidity of the soil).

2) For the human species to <u>survive</u>, it's important that a good level of biodiversity is maintained.

3) Lots of human actions, including <u>waste production</u> (see the next page) and <u>deforestation</u> (see p.217), as well as <u>global warming</u> (see p.214) are reducing biodiversity. However, it's only <u>recently</u> that we've started <u>taking measures</u> to <u>stop</u> this from continuing.

There are Over **Seven Billion People** in the World

1) The <u>population</u> of the world is currently <u>rising</u> very quickly, and it's not slowing down — look at the graph...

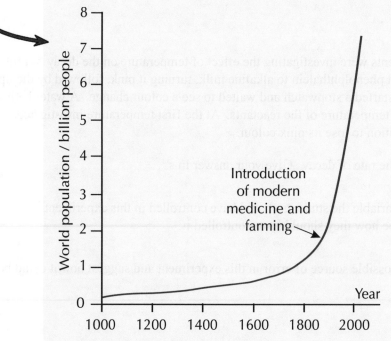

2) This is mostly due to modern <u>medicine</u> and <u>farming</u> methods, which have <u>reduced</u> the number of <u>people dying</u> from <u>disease</u> and <u>hunger</u>.

3) This is great for all of us <u>humans</u>, but it means we're having a <u>bigger effect</u> on the <u>environment</u> we live in.

Biodiversity and Waste Management

We're Making **Increasing Demands** on the **Environment**

When the Earth's population was much smaller, the effects of human activity were usually small and local. Nowadays though, our actions can have a far more widespread effect.

1) Our increasing population puts pressure on the environment, as we take the resources we need to survive.

2) But people around the world are also demanding a higher standard of living (and so demand luxuries to make life more comfortable — cars, computers, etc.). So we use more raw materials (e.g. oil to make plastics), but we also use more energy for the manufacturing processes. This all means we're taking more and more resources from the environment more and more quickly.

3) Unfortunately, many raw materials are being used up quicker than they're being replaced. So if we carry on like we are, one day we're going to run out.

We're Also Producing **More Waste**

As we make more and more things we produce more and more waste, including waste chemicals. And unless this waste is properly handled, more harmful pollution will be caused. Pollution affects water, land and air and kills plants and animals, reducing biodiversity.

Water

- Sewage and toxic chemicals from industry can pollute lakes, rivers and oceans, affecting the plants and animals that rely on them for survival (including humans).
- And the chemicals used on land (e.g. fertilisers, pesticides and herbicides) can be washed into water.

Land

- We use toxic chemicals for farming (e.g. pesticides and herbicides).
- We also bury nuclear waste underground, and we dump a lot of household waste in landfill sites.

Air

Smoke and acidic gases released into the atmosphere can pollute the air, e.g. sulfur dioxide can cause acid rain.

More people, more mess, less space, fewer resources...

...you might call it a recipe for disaster. As you can see, there's a lot of work for us to do in improving our waste management and also finding ways to deal with a growing human population.

Global Warming

*You might remember the **carbon cycle** from p.204. Well, carbon dioxide has an important role in keeping the Earth **warm enough** for life. It's not so good when there's **too much** of it in the atmosphere though...*

Carbon Dioxide and Methane Trap Energy from the Sun

1) The <u>temperature</u> of the Earth is a <u>balance</u> between the energy it gets from the Sun and the energy it radiates back out into space.

2) Gases in the <u>atmosphere</u> naturally act like an <u>insulating layer</u>. They absorb most of the energy that would normally be radiated out into space, and re-radiate it in all directions (including back towards the Earth). This increases the <u>temperature</u> of the planet.

This is what happens in a greenhouse. The Sun shines in, and the glass helps keeps some of the energy in.

3) If this didn't happen, then at night there'd be nothing to keep any energy <u>in</u>, and we'd quickly get <u>very cold</u> indeed. But recently we've started to worry that this effect is getting a bit out of hand.

4) There are several different gases in the atmosphere which help keep the <u>energy in</u>. They're called "<u>greenhouse gases</u>", and the <u>main ones</u> whose levels we worry about are <u>carbon dioxide</u> (CO_2) and <u>methane</u> — because the levels of these two gases are rising quite sharply.

5) The Earth is gradually heating up because of the increasing levels of greenhouse gases — this is <u>global warming</u>. Global warming is a type of <u>climate change</u> and causes other types of climate change, e.g. changing rainfall patterns.

Global Warming

*The Earth is getting **warmer**. Climate scientists are now trying to work out what the **effects** of global warming might be — sadly, it's not as simple as everyone having nicer summers.*

The **Consequences** of **Global Warming** Could be Pretty **Serious**

There are several reasons to be <u>worried</u> about global warming. Here are a few:

Sea levels rising

1) Higher temperatures cause <u>seawater</u> to <u>expand</u> and <u>ice</u> to <u>melt</u>, causing the sea level to <u>rise</u>.
2) It has <u>risen</u> a little bit over the last 100 years.
3) If it keeps rising it'll be <u>bad news</u> for people and animals living in <u>low-lying</u> places.
4) It will lead to <u>flooding</u>, resulting in the loss of <u>habitats</u> (where organisms live).

Changes in species distribution

1) The <u>distribution</u> of many <u>wild animal</u> and <u>plant species</u> may change as <u>temperatures increase</u> and the amount of <u>rainfall changes</u> in different areas.
2) Some species may become <u>more</u> widely distributed, e.g. species that need <u>warmer</u> <u>temperatures</u> may spread <u>further</u> as the conditions they <u>thrive</u> in exist over a <u>wider</u> area.
3) Other species may become <u>less</u> widely distributed, e.g. species that need <u>cooler temperatures</u> may have <u>smaller</u> ranges as the conditions they <u>thrive</u> in exist over a <u>smaller</u> area.

Changes in migration patterns

There could be changes in <u>migration patterns</u>, e.g. some birds may migrate <u>further north</u>, as more northern areas are getting warmer.

Reduction in biodiversity

<u>Biodiversity</u> (see p.212) could be <u>reduced</u> if some species are <u>unable to survive</u> a change in the climate, so become <u>extinct</u>.

WORKING SCIENTIFICALLY

We need to act fast, before the worst effects of climate change

Global warming is rarely out of the news. <u>Most scientists</u> accept that it's happening and that <u>human activity</u> has caused most of the recent warming, based on the evidence that has so far been collected. However, they don't know exactly what the <u>effects</u> will be and scientists will have to collect more data before these questions can really be answered.

Deforestation and Land Use

*Trees and **peat bogs** trap carbon dioxide and **lock it up**. The problems start when it **escapes**...*

Humans Use **Lots of Land** for **Lots of Purposes**

1) We use land for things like building, quarrying, farming and dumping waste.

2) This means that there's less land available for other organisms.

3) Sometimes, the way we use land has a bad effect on the environment — for example, if it requires deforestation (see next page) or the destruction of habitats like peat bogs and other areas of peat (see below).

Destroying Peat Bogs Adds **More CO$_2$** to the Atmosphere

1) Bogs are areas of land that are acidic and waterlogged. Plants that live in bogs don't fully decay when they die, because there's not enough oxygen. The partly-rotted plants gradually build up to form peat.

2) So the carbon in the plants is stored in the peat instead of being released into the atmosphere.

3) However, peat bogs are often drained so that the area can be used as farmland, or the peat is cut up and dried to use as fuel. It's also sold to gardeners as compost. Peat is being used faster than it forms.

4) When peat is drained, it comes into more contact with air and some microorganisms start to decompose it.

5) When these microorganisms respire, they use oxygen and release carbon dioxide, contributing to global warming (see page 214). Carbon dioxide is also released when peat is burned as a fuel.

6) Destroying the bogs also destroys (or reduces the area of) the habitats of some of the animals, plants and microorganisms that live there, so reduces biodiversity.

We need to use land, but we also need a healthy environment

We can't really avoid using land — we've got to if we want to e.g. grow enough food or build enough houses for people. The human population is increasing so it's likely that we'll use even more land in the future — we'll have to find a way to manage land use to reduce the negative effects on the environment.

Deforestation and Land Use

*Many parts of the world have **already** been radically changed by deforestation — for example, much of the **UK** used to be covered in forests. Deforestation can be **bad news** for several reasons.*

Deforestation Means **Chopping Down Trees**

1) <u>Deforestation</u> is the <u>cutting down</u> of <u>forests</u>.
2) This causes big problems when it's done on a <u>large-scale</u>, such as cutting down rainforests in <u>tropical areas</u>.
3) It's done for various reasons, including:

- To <u>clear land</u> for farming (e.g. cattle or rice crops) to provide <u>more food</u>.
- To grow <u>crops</u> from which <u>biofuels</u> based on ethanol can be produced.

Deforestation Can Cause Many **Problems**

Less carbon dioxide taken in

- Cutting down <u>loads of trees</u> means that the amount of carbon dioxide <u>removed</u> from the atmosphere during <u>photosynthesis</u> is <u>reduced</u>.
- Trees '<u>lock up</u>' some of the <u>carbon</u> that they absorb during photosynthesis in their wood, which can <u>remove</u> it from the <u>atmosphere</u> for hundreds of years. Removing trees means that less is locked up.

More CO_2 in the atmosphere causes global warming (see page 214), which leads to climate change.

More carbon dioxide in the atmosphere

- Carbon dioxide is <u>released</u> when trees are <u>burnt</u> to clear land. (Carbon in wood doesn't contribute to atmospheric pollution until it's released by burning.)
- <u>Microorganisms</u> feeding on bits of <u>dead wood</u> release carbon dioxide as a waste product of <u>respiration</u>.

Less biodiversity

- Biodiversity (p.212) is the <u>variety of different species</u> — the more species, the greater the biodiversity.
- Habitats like forests can contain a <u>huge number</u> of different species of <u>plants</u> and <u>animals</u>, so when they are destroyed there is a danger of <u>many species becoming extinct</u> — biodiversity is <u>reduced</u>.

Not a very cheerful page, I know...

Make sure you can link together all the information on pages 214-217 — for example, how <u>deforestation</u> and <u>peat burning</u> can contribute to <u>global warming</u>, and how this might affect <u>biodiversity</u>. In the exam, you might get an extended response question that requires you to draw on several different areas of knowledge like this.

Maintaining Ecosystems and Biodiversity

*It's really important that biodiversity is **maintained** as damage to ecosystems or populations of species can be **hard to undo**. This page is about some of the different **methods** that can be used to maintain biodiversity.*

There are **Programmes** to **Protect Ecosystems** and **Biodiversity**

1) It's important that <u>biodiversity</u> is maintained at a <u>high enough level</u> to make sure that <u>ecosystems</u> are <u>stable</u> (see page 194).

2) In some areas, <u>programmes</u> have been set up by <u>concerned citizens</u> and <u>scientists</u> to <u>minimise damage</u> by <u>human activities</u> (see page 213) to <u>ecosystems</u> and <u>biodiversity</u>. Here are a few examples:

1. Breeding Programmes

1) <u>Breeding programmes</u> have been set up to help prevent <u>endangered species</u> from becoming <u>extinct</u>.

2) These are where animals are bred in <u>captivity</u> to make sure the species survives if it dies out in the wild.

3) Individuals can sometimes be <u>released</u> into the <u>wild</u> to boost or re-establish a population.

Pandas are an endangered species. Many efforts have been made to breed pandas in captivity.

2. Habitat Protection

1) Programmes to <u>protect</u> and <u>regenerate rare habitats</u> like <u>mangroves</u>, <u>heathland</u> and <u>coral reefs</u> have been started. Protecting these habitats helps to <u>protect</u> the species that live there — <u>preserving</u> the <u>ecosystem</u> and <u>biodiversity</u> in the area.

2) There are programmes to <u>reintroduce hedgerows</u> and <u>field margins</u> around fields on farms where only a <u>single type</u> of crop is grown. Field margins are areas of land around the <u>edges</u> of fields where <u>wild flowers</u> and <u>grasses</u> are left to <u>grow</u>. Hedgerows and field margins provide a <u>habitat</u> for a <u>wider variety</u> of organisms than could survive in a single crop habitat.

3. Preventing **Global Warming**

1) Some governments have introduced regulations and programmes to <u>reduce</u> the level of <u>deforestation</u> taking place and the amount of <u>carbon dioxide</u> being released into the atmosphere by businesses.

2) This could reduce the increase of <u>global warming</u> (see page 214).

4. Reducing **Waste**

1) People are encouraged to recycle to <u>reduce</u> the amount of <u>waste</u> that gets dumped in <u>landfill</u> sites.

2) This could <u>reduce</u> the amount of <u>land</u> taken over for landfill, leaving <u>ecosystems</u> in place.

Maintaining Ecosystems and Biodiversity

Conflicting Pressures Affect How Biodiversity is Maintained

Sadly for noble biodiversity warriors, maintaining biodiversity isn't as simple as you would hope.
There are lots of conflicting pressures that have to be taken into account. For example:

1. The Costs of Programmes

1) Protecting biodiversity costs money.
2) For example, governments sometimes pay farmers a subsidy to reintroduce hedgerows and field margins to their land.
3) It can also cost money to keep a watch on whether the programmes and regulations designed to maintain biodiversity are being followed.
4) There can be conflict between protecting biodiversity and saving money — money may be prioritised for other things.

2. The Effect on the Local Economy

1) Protecting biodiversity may come at a cost to local people's livelihoods.
2) For example, reducing the amount of deforestation is great for biodiversity, but the people who were previously employed in the tree-felling industry could be left unemployed.
3) This could affect the local economy if people move away with their family to find work.

3. Protecting Food Security

1) There can be conflict between protecting biodiversity and protecting our food security.
2) Sometimes certain organisms are seen as pests by farmers (e.g. locusts and foxes) and are killed to protect crops and livestock so that more food can be produced.
3) As a result, however, the food chain and biodiversity can be affected.

4. The Development of Society

1) Development is important, but it can affect the environment.
2) Many people want to protect biodiversity in the face of development, but sometimes land is in such high demand that previously untouched land with high biodiversity has to be used for development.
3) For example, for housing developments on the edges of towns, or for new agricultural land in developing countries.

So we should do what we can — within some limits

Like many situations in ecology, maintaining biodiversity isn't black and white. There are lots of factors to take into account before decisions on the best way to go forward can be made.

Warm-Up & Exam Questions

I hope you've got all of that important information in your head. There's a lot to remember here, so have a flick back when you're doing these questions in case you've forgotten any little details.

Warm-Up Questions

1) What is meant by the term 'biodiversity'?
2) Give two greenhouse gases.
3) Give two reasons why an area of forest may be cut down.
4) How are populations of endangered species preserved by breeding programmes?
5) Explain how biodiversity can be increased in areas that farm single crops.

Exam Questions

1   Humans are producing increasing amounts of waste.   `Grade 4-6`
This has negative consequences for biodiversity and the environment.

1.1   Give **two** types of waste that pollute the air.

[2 marks]

1.2   Describe **one** way in which waste produced by humans pollutes water.

[1 mark]

1.3   Give **two** reasons why humans are producing increasingly more waste.

[2 marks]

2   Global warming may lead to a decline in biodiversity in the future.   `Grade 6-7`

2.1   Apart from a decline in biodiversity, suggest **two** possible
biological consequences of global warming.

[2 marks]

2.2   Describe **two** measures being used by some governments
in order to reduce global warming.

[2 marks]

3   Peat bogs can be drained, so that the peat can be cut up and used as a source of fuel.   `Grade 6-7`

3.1   Explain why draining peat bogs and using the peat as a fuel can contribute to global warming.

[4 marks]

3.2   Apart from contributing to global warming, explain **one** other
negative consequence of destroying peat bogs.

[2 marks]

Trophic Levels

*And now for something slightly different... The word 'trophic' comes from the Greek word **trophe** meaning 'nourishment'. This page must contain something about food then. Probably worth reading on I reckon...*

Food Chains Can be Divided into Trophic Levels

1) You might recognise some of this stuff about food chains from page 198. Unfortunately, now you need to learn a bit <u>more</u> about it. Enter the exciting world of <u>trophic levels</u>.

2) <u>Trophic levels</u> are the different <u>stages</u> of a food chain. They consist of one or more organisms that perform a <u>specific role</u> in the food chain.

3) Trophic levels are named after their location in the food chain using <u>numbers</u>. The first level is called <u>trophic level 1</u>. Each level after that is <u>numbered in order</u> based on <u>how far</u> along the food chain the organisms in the trophic level are. For example, the organisms <u>second</u> in line in the food chain belong to <u>trophic level 2</u>, organisms <u>third</u> in line are in <u>trophic level 3</u>, and so on.

Trophic Level 1 Contains Producers

1) Producers are the organisms at the <u>starting point</u> of a food chain, e.g. plants and algae.

2) They're called <u>producers</u> because they <u>make their own food</u> by <u>photosynthesis</u> using energy from the Sun.

Trophic Level 2 Contains Primary Consumers

1) <u>Herbivores</u> that eat the <u>plants</u> and <u>algae</u> are <u>primary consumers</u>.

2) Herbivores eat <u>only</u> plants and algae.

Trophic Level 3 Contains Secondary Consumers

1) <u>Carnivores</u> that <u>eat</u> the <u>primary consumers</u> are <u>secondary consumers</u>.

2) Carnivores are <u>meat eaters</u>.

Trophic Level 4 Contains Tertiary Consumers

1) <u>Carnivores</u> that eat <u>other carnivores</u> (the <u>secondary consumers</u>) are <u>tertiary consumers</u>.

2) Carnivores that have <u>no predators</u> are at the <u>top</u> of the food chain, so they're always in the <u>highest</u> trophic level. They're known as <u>apex predators</u>.

There can be more than four trophic levels in a food chain, but there are only usually 4 or 5 because so much energy is lost from the food chain at each trophic level (see p.224).

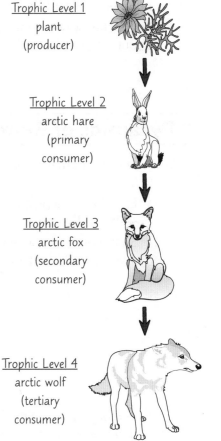

Trophic Level 1
plant
(producer)

Trophic Level 2
arctic hare
(primary consumer)

Trophic Level 3
arctic fox
(secondary consumer)

Trophic Level 4
arctic wolf
(tertiary consumer)

Decomposers Break Down Uneaten Remains and Waste

1) Decomposers such as <u>bacteria</u> and <u>fungi</u> play an <u>important role</u> in ecosystems.

2) They <u>decompose</u> any <u>dead plant</u> or <u>animal</u> material left in an environment.

3) They can do this by <u>secreting</u> (releasing) <u>enzymes</u> that <u>break</u> the dead stuff <u>down</u> into <u>small soluble food molecules</u>. These then <u>diffuse into</u> the microorganisms.

This process also releases nutrients into the environment, which the producers need in order to grow.

Pyramids of Biomass

*Pyramids of biomass are a handy way of illustrating the amount of **biomass** at **each level** in a food chain.*

There's **Less Biomass** Further up a **Food Chain**

1) There's <u>less energy</u> and <u>less biomass</u> every time you move <u>up</u> a stage (<u>trophic level</u>) in a food chain.

2) There are usually <u>fewer organisms</u> every time you move up a level too, as this example shows:

Producers   Primary consumers   Secondary consumer

<u>5000</u> dandelions... feed... <u>100</u> rabbits... which feed... <u>1</u> fox.

Biomass just means the mass of living material.

You might remember this example from p.198.

3) This <u>isn't</u> always true though — for example, if <u>500 fleas</u> are feeding on the fox, the number of organisms has <u>increased</u> as you move up to that stage in the food chain.

4) So a better way to look at the food chain is often to think about <u>biomass</u> instead of number of organisms.

Pyramids of Biomass Show the Relative Masses of Trophic Levels

You can use information about biomass to construct a <u>pyramid of biomass</u> to represent the food chain:

1) Each bar on a <u>pyramid of biomass</u> shows the <u>relative mass of living material</u> at a <u>trophic level</u> — basically how much all the organisms at each level would "<u>weigh</u>" if you put them <u>all together</u>.

2) So the one fox above would have a <u>big biomass</u> and the <u>hundreds of fleas</u> would have a <u>very small biomass</u>. Biomass pyramids are practically <u>always pyramid-shaped</u>:

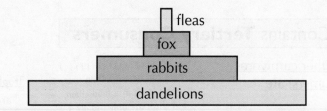

fleas
fox
rabbits
dandelions

3) The big bar along the bottom of the pyramid shows <u>trophic level 1</u>. It always represents the <u>producer</u> (e.g. plants or algae).

4) The next bar will be the <u>primary consumer</u> (the animal that eats the producer), then the <u>secondary consumer</u> (the animal that eats the primary consumer) and so on up the food chain.

Pyramids of biomass are nearly always pyramid shaped

There are actually a couple of <u>exceptions</u> where pyramids of biomass <u>aren't</u> quite <u>pyramid-shaped</u>. It happens when the producer has a very short life but reproduces loads, like with plankton at certain times of year. But it's very <u>rare</u>, so you don't need to worry about it.

Pyramids of Biomass

*More on **pyramids of biomass** — this time, how you can **interpret** pyramids of biomass as well as how you can **draw one accurately** for yourself, if given the right information.*

Pyramids of Biomass Give You Information About Food Chains

It's easy to look at pyramids of biomass and explain what they show about the food chain
— just remember, the biomass at each stage should be drawn to scale. For example:

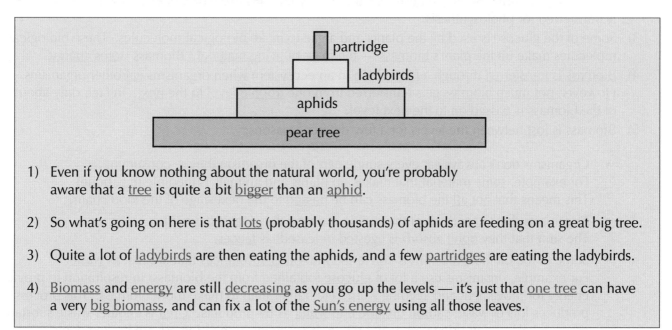

1) Even if you know nothing about the natural world, you're probably
   aware that a tree is quite a bit bigger than an aphid.

2) So what's going on here is that lots (probably thousands) of aphids are feeding on a great big tree.

3) Quite a lot of ladybirds are then eating the aphids, and a few partridges are eating the ladybirds.

4) Biomass and energy are still decreasing as you go up the levels — it's just that one tree can have
   a very big biomass, and can fix a lot of the Sun's energy using all those leaves.

You Can Draw Pyramids of Biomass to the Correct Scale

1) If you're given actual numbers, you can
   use them to draw bars of the correct scale.

2) Don't forget that the order of organisms in the
   pyramid must follow the order of the food chain.

3) Each bar must also be labelled.

Use a sharp pencil and a ruler to draw pyramids of biomass

If you need to draw a pyramid of biomass to scale in the exam, you may be given a grid or some
graph paper to draw it on. You'll need to work out a sensible scale to use — think about how easy
your diagram will be to draw and interpret (something like '5 small squares on the grid = 1 kg'
might work) and make sure that your pyramid takes up at least half of the space available.

Q1   Draw an accurate pyramid of biomass for this food chain.
Include the scale you have used.   **[4 marks]**

	Clover→	Snails→	Thrushes→	Buzzard
Biomass:	96 kg	42 kg	8 kg	1 kg

Biomass Transfer

*So biomass moves between trophic levels in a food chain, but **not all of it** can be transferred.*
*This page shows you how you can make a **rough calculation** to figure out **how much** gets transferred.*

Biomass is **Lost** Between Each **Trophic Level**

1) Energy from the <u>Sun</u> is the source of energy for <u>nearly all</u> life on Earth.

2) <u>Producers</u>, such as <u>green plants</u> and <u>algae</u>, use <u>energy</u> transferred by <u>light</u> from the Sun to make <u>food</u> (<u>glucose</u>) during <u>photosynthesis</u>. Of the energy that hits these producers, <u>only about 1%</u> is transferred for photosynthesis.

3) Some of the glucose is used by the plants and algae to make <u>biological molecules</u>. These biological molecules make up the plant's <u>biomass</u> — the <u>mass</u> of <u>living material</u>. Biomass <u>stores energy</u>.

4) <u>Biomass</u> is <u>transferred</u> through a <u>food chain</u> in an ecosystem when organisms <u>eat</u> other organisms. However, <u>not much biomass</u> gets transferred from one <u>trophic level</u> to the <u>next</u>. In fact, only about <u>10%</u> of the biomass is passed on to the next level.

5) Biomass is <u>lost</u> between the levels for a few different reasons:

- Organisms don't always eat <u>every single part</u> of the organism they're <u>consuming</u>. For example, some material that makes up plants and animals is <u>inedible</u> (e.g. bone). This means that <u>not all</u> the biomass can be <u>passed</u> to the next stage of the food chain.

- Organisms <u>don't absorb</u> all of the stuff in the food they <u>ingest</u> (take in). The stuff that they <u>don't</u> absorb is <u>egested</u> (released) as <u>faeces</u>.

- Some of the biomass taken in is converted into <u>other substances</u> that are lost as <u>waste</u>. For example, organisms use a lot of <u>glucose</u> (obtained from the biomass) in respiration to provide energy for movement and keeping warm, etc. rather than to make more biomass. This process produces lots of waste <u>carbon dioxide</u> and <u>water</u> as by-products. <u>Urea</u> is another waste substance, which is released in <u>urine</u> with <u>water</u> when the <u>proteins</u> in the biomass are <u>broken down</u>.

You Can **Calculate** the **Efficiency** of **Biomass Transfer**

Take a look at this example:

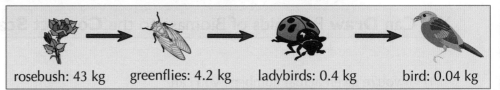

rosebush: 43 kg   greenflies: 4.2 kg   ladybirds: 0.4 kg   bird: 0.04 kg

1) The numbers show the <u>amount of biomass</u> available to the <u>next level</u>. So <u>43 kg</u> is the amount of biomass available to the <u>greenflies</u>, and <u>4.2 kg</u> is the amount available to the <u>ladybirds</u>.

2) You can work out how much biomass has been <u>lost</u> at each level by taking away the biomass that is available at <u>that level</u> from the biomass that was available at the <u>previous level</u>. For example: biomass <u>lost</u> at 2nd trophic level = 43 kg – 4.2 kg = <u>38.8 kg</u>.

3) You can also calculate the <u>efficiency of biomass transfer</u> between trophic levels:

$$\text{efficiency} = \frac{\text{biomass transferred to the next level}}{\text{biomass available at the previous level}} \times 100$$

So, the <u>efficiency</u> of biomass transfer from the 1st trophic level = 4.2 kg ÷ 43 kg × 100 = <u>9.8%</u>.

Hardly any biomass is passed on to the next level

Q1   Give two ways that biomass is lost between trophic levels. [2 marks]

Q2   A shark with 110 kg of available biomass eats some large fish with 995 kg of available biomass.
  a) Calculate the amount of biomass lost between the fish and the shark. [1 mark]
  b) Calculate the percentage efficiency of biomass transfer between the fish and the shark. [1 mark]

Q2 Video Solution

Food Security and Farming

*There are more than **7 billion** people on our planet and they all need **feeding**, so maintaining our **food supply** is important. We need to make sure that we use **sustainable** methods of **food production** wherever we can.*

Lots of Factors Affect Food Security

Food security is having enough food to feed a population.

There's a wide range of things that can threaten food security. For example:

1) The world population keeps increasing, with the birth rate of many developing countries rising quickly.

2) As diets in developed countries change, the demand for certain foods to be imported from developing countries can increase. This means that already scarce food resources can become more scarce.

3) Farming can be affected by new pests and pathogens (e.g. bacteria and viruses) or changes in the environmental conditions (e.g. a lack of rain). This can result in the loss of crops and livestock, and can lead to widespread famine.

4) The high input costs of farming (e.g. the price of seeds, machinery and livestock) can make it too expensive for people in some countries to start or maintain food production, meaning that there sometimes aren't enough people producing food in these areas to feed the people.

5) In some parts of the world, there are conflicts that affect the availability of food and water.

- Sustainable methods of food production are needed so that enough food can be made to feed everyone now and in the future.
- Sustainable production means making enough food without using resources faster than they renew. There's more on this on the next page.

Pests and pathogens keep evolving — so we've got to keep up

Food security is seriously important for our future survival, but there are lots of issues that threaten it. Learning the points on this page should help to improve your exam mark security. Then you can move on to the next page and find out how problems of food security can be reduced.

Food Security and Farming

*This page looks at some of the efforts being made to **improve** food security by increasing the **sustainability** and **efficiency** of food production — but some methods are **more popular** than others...*

Overfishing is Decreasing Fish Stocks

1) <u>Fish stocks</u> are <u>declining</u> in the oceans because we're fishing <u>so much</u>.

2) This means there are <u>fewer fish</u> for us to eat, the ocean's <u>food chains</u> are affected and some species of fish may <u>disappear</u> altogether in some areas — for example, <u>cod</u> are at risk of disappearing from the <u>north west Atlantic</u>.

3) To tackle this problem, we need to <u>maintain</u> fish stocks at a level where the <u>fish continue to breed</u>. This is <u>sustainable food production</u>. Fish stocks can be <u>maintained</u> (<u>conserved</u>) in these ways:

Fishing quotas

1) There are <u>limits</u> on the <u>number</u> and <u>size</u> of fish that can be caught in certain areas.

2) This prevents certain species from being <u>overfished</u>.

Net size

1) There are different limits of the <u>mesh size</u> of the fish net, depending on what's being fished.

2) This is to reduce the number of '<u>unwanted</u>' and <u>discarded</u> fish — the ones that are <u>accidently</u> caught, e.g. shrimp caught along with cod.

3) Using a <u>bigger</u> mesh size will let the 'unwanted' species <u>escape</u>.

4) It also means that <u>younger</u> fish will slip through the net, allowing them to reach <u>breeding age</u>.

Food Production Can be Made More Efficient

1) <u>Limiting</u> the <u>movement</u> of livestock and keeping them in a <u>temperature-controlled environment</u> reduces the <u>transfer</u> of <u>energy</u> from livestock to the environment.

2) This makes farming <u>more efficient</u> as the animals use less energy <u>moving</u> around and <u>controlling</u> their own <u>body temperature</u>.

3) This means that <u>more energy</u> is available for <u>growth</u>, so <u>more food</u> can be produced from the <u>same input</u> of resources.

- Livestock like calves and chickens can be <u>factory farmed</u>. This involves raising them in <u>small pens</u>.
- Fish can also be <u>factory farmed</u> in <u>cages</u> where their movement is restricted.
- Some animals are also fed <u>high-protein food</u> to further increase their growth.

Factory farmed chickens are also called battery chickens.

Some factory farming methods are <u>controversial</u>. Because the animals are kept so close together, <u>disease</u> can <u>spread</u> between them easily. There are also <u>ethical objections</u>, as some people think that making animals live in <u>unnatural</u> and <u>uncomfortable</u> conditions is <u>cruel</u>.

Fishing practices have become 'too' effective

We can actually reduce food security by gathering <u>too much</u> food — this is why there's so much hype about <u>sustainability</u> these days. We need to find methods to produce as much food as we need without damaging <u>future</u> supplies — and preferably methods which aren't also <u>ethically controversial</u>.

Biotechnology

*Biotechnology is where **living things** and **biological processes** are used and manipulated to produce a **useful product**. It's a wide and rapidly expanding field that could be really handy if used to its **full potential**.*

Bacteria can be Engineered to Produce Human Insulin

Genetic engineering is transferring a useful gene from one organism to another (see page 181).
Bacteria can be genetically engineered to make human insulin:

1) A plasmid (a loop of DNA) is removed from a bacterium.

2) The insulin gene is cut out of a human chromosome using a restriction enzyme. Restriction enzymes recognise specific sequences of DNA and cut the DNA at these points. The cut leaves one of the DNA strands with unpaired bases — this is called a 'sticky end'.

3) The plasmid is cut open using the same restriction enzyme — leaving the same sticky ends.

4) The plasmid and the human insulin gene are mixed together.

5) Ligase (an enzyme) is added. This joins the sticky ends together to produce recombinant DNA (two different bits of DNA stuck together).

6) The recombinant DNA is inserted into a bacterium.

7) The modified bacterium is grown in a vat under controlled conditions. You end up with millions of bacteria that produce insulin. The insulin can be harvested and purified to treat people with diabetes.

human insulin gene

Restriction enzymes cut the gene out and cut open the plasmid...

sticky ends

plasmid — sticky ends

...ligase joins the two bits of DNA together...

...and the recombinant DNA is inserted into the bacteria.

The bacteria are grown in a vat.

Insulin

It looks hard, but it's just like a fancy cut and paste...

You might remember from page 181 that bacteria aren't the only organisms that can be genetically engineered for human benefit, but the process can be a bit more complicated in larger organisms. The ability of bacteria to take up plasmids means that they are relatively easy to genetically engineer.

Q1   Rennin is an enzyme used to make cheese. It is naturally produced by stomach cells in cows, which contain the rennin gene. Suggest how a bacterial cell could be genetically engineered to produce rennin.   [3 marks]

Biotechnology

*Biotechnology can be used for all sorts of useful things, including the creation of new **types** of food.*

Mycoprotein — Food from **Fungi**

1) Using <u>modern biotechnology</u> techniques, large amounts of <u>microorganisms</u> can be <u>cultured</u> (grown) industrially under <u>controlled conditions</u> in <u>large vats</u> for use as a <u>food source</u>.

2) <u>Mycoprotein</u> is used to make <u>high-protein meat substitutes</u> for <u>vegetarian</u> meals, e.g. Quorn™.

3) It's made from the fungus *Fusarium*, which is grown in <u>aerobic conditions</u> on <u>glucose syrup</u>, which it uses as food.

> Aerobic conditions are where oxygen is present.

4) The fungal biomass is <u>harvested</u> and <u>purified</u> to produce the <u>mycoprotein</u>.

Crops Can be **Genetically Modified**

Many people in the world today don't have <u>enough</u> food to eat (or the diet they have isn't <u>varied</u>). This mostly happens in <u>developing countries</u> — like those in <u>Africa</u> and parts of <u>Asia</u>.

Biotechnology could help...

1) <u>Genetically modified</u> (GM) <u>crops</u> can be produced that are <u>resistant to pests</u> — improving crop yields.

2) They can be genetically modified to <u>grow better</u> in <u>drought conditions</u> — again improving crop yields.

3) And some crops can be modified to provide <u>more nutritional value</u>, e.g. '<u>Golden Rice</u>' has been <u>genetically engineered</u> to produce a chemical that's converted in the body to <u>vitamin A</u>.

There are some varieties of cotton which have been genetically engineered to be resistant to pests.

...But not everyone agrees

1) Many people argue that people go hungry because they <u>can't afford</u> to buy food, not because there <u>isn't</u> any food about. So they argue that you need to <u>tackle poverty first</u>.

2) There are fears that countries may become <u>dependent</u> on <u>companies</u> who <u>sell</u> GM seeds.

3) Sometimes <u>poor soil</u> is the main reason why <u>crops fail</u>, and even GM crops <u>won't survive</u>.

Scientists have cooked up a few pretty useful things...

Remember, making <u>mycoprotein</u> doesn't involve any <u>genetic engineering</u>, but it is made using another type of <u>biotechnology</u> — culturing microorganisms on an industrial scale.

Warm-Up & Exam Questions

By doing these questions, you'll soon find out if you've got the basic facts straight.

Warm-Up Questions

1) What are trophic levels?
2) What is biomass?
3) How do fishing quotas limit overfishing?
4) The movement of factory farmed animals is often limited. Explain why.
5) What is 'Golden Rice'?

Exam Questions

1 In an ecosystem, a single robin has a mass of 18 g and eats caterpillars.
There are 75 caterpillars available to the robin that each have a mass of 1.5 g. *(Grade 4-6)*
The caterpillars feed on 40 stinging nettles that together have a mass of 1000 g.

1.1 Calculate the total biomass of caterpillars available to the robin.

[1 mark]

1.2 Calculate the efficiency of biomass transfer between the robin and the caterpillars. Use the equation:
efficiency = (biomass transferred to the next level ÷ biomass available at the previous level) × 100

[1 mark]

2 Current methods of fishing and farming may have to be changed in order
to be more sustainable, so that there is greater human food security in the future. *(Grade 6-7)*

2.1 Explain what is meant by the term 'food security'.

[1 mark]

2.2 State **two** threats to global food security and explain why each one is a threat.

[4 marks]

2.3 Explain **one** reason why regulations on the net size used by fishing boats
may help to lessen the impact of overfishing on certain fish species.

[2 marks]

3 **Figure 1** shows a fermenter that could be *(Grade 6-7)*
used to produce mycoprotein.

3.1 Explain the purpose of the
air supply in the fermenter.

[2 marks]

3.2 Suggest and explain why a water-cooled
jacket is used around the fermenter.

[2 marks]

3.3 Give **one** substance not labelled in **Figure 1**
that would also need to be added to the
fermenter in order to produce mycoprotein.
Explain your choice.

[2 marks]

Figure 1

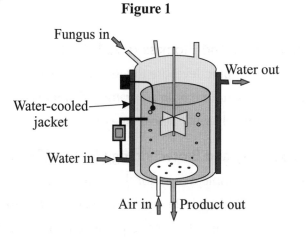

Fungus in

Water out

Water-cooled
jacket

Water in

Air in   Product out

Revision Summary for Topic 7

That's <u>Topic 7</u> done with. I bet you're in the mood for a long list of revision questions now. You're in luck.

- Try these questions and <u>tick off each one</u> when you <u>get it right</u>.
- When you're <u>completely happy</u> with a sub-topic, tick it off.

For even more practice, try the Retrieval Quiz for Topic 7 — just scan this QR code!

Topic 7 Quiz

Competition, Abiotic and Biotic Factors, and Adaptations (p.194-197) ☐

1) Define 'habitat'. ☑
2) What things do animals compete for in an ecosystem? ☑
3) Explain what is meant by a 'stable community'. ☑
4) What are biotic and abiotic factors? ☑
5) What are functional adaptations? ☑

Food Chains (p.198) ☐

6) What do food chains always start with? ☑
7) Explain what happens to the population size of a predator if its prey becomes more common in an ecosystem. ☑

Quadrats and Transects (p.200-201) ☐

8) Explain how a quadrat can be used to investigate the distribution of clover plants in two areas. ☑
9) Suggest why you might use a transect when investigating the distribution of organisms. ☑

Environmental Change and the Water and Carbon Cycles (p.202-204) ☐

10) How might a change in the availability of water affect the distribution of species? ☑
11) When water vapour cools and condenses in the atmosphere, what does it change into? ☑
12) Explain how microorganisms return carbon to the atmosphere. ☑

Decay (p.207-210) ☐

13) Explain why temperature affects the rate of decay. ☑
14) Is biogas produced by aerobic or anaerobic decay? ☑

Human Impacts on the Planet (p.212-219) ☐

15) Suggest why it's important to have high biodiversity in an ecosystem. ☑
16) Give an example of how global warming could reduce biodiversity. ☑
17) How can recycling programmes help to protect ecosystems? ☑

Trophic Levels and Biomass (p.221-224) ☑

18) In which trophic level are the tertiary consumers found? ☑
19) Does the bottom bar on a pyramid of biomass represent the tertiary consumer or the producer? ☑
20) Approximately what percentage of biomass is lost between trophic levels? ☑

Food Security and Biotechnology (p.225-228) ☐

21) Give an example of a factor that can affect food security. ☑
22) How can fish stocks be maintained at a sustainable level? ☑
23) How can bacteria be used to produce human insulin? ☑
24) What is mycoprotein? ☑

Measuring Substances

*Get your lab coats on, it's time to find out about the skills you'll need in **experiments**...*
*First things first — make sure you're using **appropriate equipment** and know **how to use it** correctly.*

Use the **Right Apparatus** to Take **Readings**

1. **Mass**

1) To weigh a solid, start by putting the <u>container</u> you are weighing your substance into on a <u>balance</u>.

2) Set the balance to exactly <u>zero</u> and then weigh out the correct amount of your substance.

0.000

2. **Temperature**

1) You can use a <u>thermometer</u> to measure the temperature of a solution.

2) Make sure that the <u>bulb</u> of the thermometer is <u>completely submerged</u> in the solution and that you wait for the temperature to <u>stabilise</u> before you take your initial reading.

3) Read off the <u>scale</u> on the thermometer at <u>eye level</u> to make sure it's correct.

When you're reading off a scale, write down the value of the graduation that the amount is closest to.

3. **Volume** of a **Liquid**

There's more than one way to measure the volume of a <u>liquid</u>. Whichever method you use, always read the volume from the <u>bottom of the meniscus</u> (the curved upper surface of the liquid) when it's at <u>eye level</u>.

Read volume from here — the bottom of the meniscus.

Using a pipette

1) <u>Pipettes</u> are used to suck up and <u>transfer</u> volumes of liquid between containers.

2) <u>Dropping pipettes</u> are used to transfer <u>drops</u> of liquid.

3) <u>Graduated pipettes</u> are used to transfer <u>accurate</u> volumes.

4) A <u>pipette filler</u> is attached to the end of a graduated pipette, to <u>control</u> the amount of liquid being drawn up.

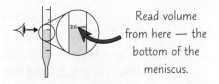

Using a measuring cylinder

1) <u>Measuring cylinders</u> come in all different <u>sizes</u>. Make sure you choose one that's the right size for the measurement you want to make.

2) It's no good using a huge 1 dm³ cylinder to measure out 2 cm³ of a liquid — the graduations will be too big, and you'll end up with <u>massive errors</u>. It'd be much better to use one that measures up to 10 cm³.

Measuring Substances

4. Volume of a Gas

1) To accurately measure the <u>volume</u> of gas, you should use a <u>gas syringe</u>:

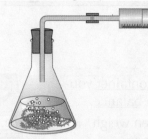

2) Alternatively, you can use an <u>upturned measuring cylinder</u> filled with <u>water</u>. The gas will <u>displace</u> the water so you can <u>read the volume</u> off the <u>scale</u>.

3) Other methods to measure the amount of gas include:

- <u>counting the bubbles</u> produced
- measuring the <u>length</u> of a gas bubble drawn along a tube (see page 105).

These methods are <u>less accurate</u>, but will give you <u>relative</u> amounts of gas to <u>compare results</u>.

4) When you're measuring a gas, you need to make sure that the equipment is set up so that none of the gas can <u>escape</u>, otherwise your results won't be <u>accurate</u>.

5. pH

The method you should use to measure pH depends on what your experiment is.

1) <u>Indicators</u> are dyes that <u>change colour</u> depending on whether they're in an <u>acid</u> or an <u>alkali</u>. You use them by adding a couple of drops of the indicator to the solution you're interested in. <u>Universal indicator</u> is a <u>mixture</u> of indicators that changes colour <u>gradually</u> as pH changes. It's useful for <u>estimating</u> the pH of a solution based on its colour.

2) <u>Indicator paper</u> is useful if you don't want to colour the entire solution that you're testing. It <u>changes colour</u> depending on the pH of the solution it touches. You can also hold a piece of <u>damp indicator paper</u> in a <u>gas sample</u> to test its pH.

> Blue litmus paper turns <u>red</u> in acidic conditions and red litmus paper turns <u>blue</u> in alkaline conditions.

3) <u>pH meters</u> have a <u>digital display</u> that gives an <u>accurate value</u> for the pH of a solution.

Read off the scale carefully when taking readings

Whether you're reading off a thermometer, a pipette or a measuring cylinder, make sure you take all readings at <u>eye level</u>. And, if it's volume you're measuring, read from the <u>bottom of the meniscus</u>.

Safety and Ethics

*There's **danger** all around, particularly in science experiments. But don't let this put you off.
Just be aware of the **hazards** and take **sensible precautions**. Read on to find out more...*

Make Sure You're **Working Safely** in the **Lab**

1) <u>Before</u> you start any experiment, make sure you know about any <u>safety precautions</u> to do with your <u>method</u> or the <u>chemicals</u> you're using. You need to <u>follow</u> any instructions that your teacher gives you <u>carefully</u>. The chemicals you're using may be <u>hazardous</u> — for example, they might be <u>flammable</u> (<u>catch fire easily</u>), or they might <u>irritate</u> or <u>burn</u> your <u>skin</u> if it comes into contact with them.

2) Make sure that you're wearing <u>sensible clothing</u> when you're in the lab (e.g. open shoes won't protect your feet from spillages). When you're doing an experiment, you should wear a <u>lab coat</u> to protect your skin and clothing. Depending on the experiment, you may need to also wear <u>safety goggles</u> and <u>gloves</u>.

3) You also need to be aware of <u>general safety</u> in the lab, e.g. keep anything <u>flammable</u> away from lit Bunsen burners, don't directly touch any <u>hot equipment</u>, handle <u>glassware</u> carefully so it doesn't <u>break</u>, etc.

You Need to Think About **Ethical Issues** In Your Experiments

1) Any <u>organisms</u> involved in your investigations need to be treated <u>safely</u> and <u>ethically</u>.

2) <u>Animals</u> need to be treated <u>humanely</u> — they should be <u>handled carefully</u> and any wild animals captured for studying (e.g. during an investigation of the distribution of an organism) should be <u>returned to their original habitat</u>.

3) Any animals kept in the lab should also be <u>cared for</u> in a humane way, e.g. they should not be kept in <u>overcrowded conditions</u>.

4) If you are carrying out an experiment involving other <u>students</u> (e.g. investigating the effect of caffeine on reaction time), they should not be forced to participate <u>against their will</u> or feel <u>pressured</u> to take part.

BEWARE — hazardous biology experiments about...

<u>Before</u> you carry out an experiment, you must <u>consider all of the hazards</u>. They can be anything from <u>chemicals</u> to <u>sharp objects</u>, <u>pathogens</u> to <u>heating equipment</u>. Whatever the hazard, make sure you know all the <u>safety precautions</u> you should follow to keep yourself, and others, safe.

Sampling

*You need to be able to carry out **sampling** that'll give you **non-biased results**. First up **why**, then **how**...*

Sampling Should be **Random**

1) When you're investigating a population, it's generally <u>not possible</u> to study <u>every single organism</u> in the population. This means that you need to take <u>samples</u> of the population you're interested in.

2) The sample data will be used to <u>draw conclusions</u> about the <u>whole</u> population, so it's important that it <u>accurately</u> represents the <u>whole population</u>.

If a sample doesn't represent the population as a whole, it's said to be biased.

3) To make sure a sample represents the population, it should be <u>random</u>.

Organisms Should Be Sampled At **Random Sites** in an Area

1) If you're interested in the <u>distribution</u> of an organism in an area, or its <u>population size</u>, you can take population samples in the area you're interested in using <u>quadrats</u> or <u>transects</u> (see pages 200-201).

2) If you only take samples from <u>one part</u> of the area, your results will be <u>biased</u> — they may not give an <u>accurate representation</u> of the <u>whole area</u>.

3) To make sure that your sampling isn't biased, you need to use a method of <u>choosing sampling sites</u> in which every site has an <u>equal chance</u> of being chosen. For example:

If you're looking at plant species in a field...
1) <u>Divide</u> the field into a <u>grid</u>.
2) <u>Label the grid</u> along the bottom and up the side with numbers.
3) Use a <u>random number generator</u> (on a computer or calculator) to select coordinates, e.g. (2,6).
4) Take your <u>samples</u> at these coordinates.

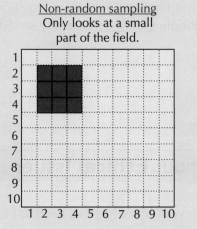

Non-random sampling
Only looks at a small part of the field.

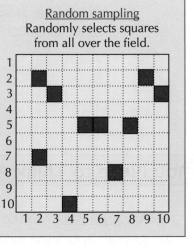

Random sampling
Randomly selects squares from all over the field.

Health Data Should be Taken from **Randomly Selected People**

1) As mentioned above, it's not practical (or even possible) to study an <u>entire human population</u>.

2) You need to use <u>random sampling</u> to choose members of the population you're interested in. For example:

> A <u>health professional</u> is investigating <u>how many</u> people diagnosed with <u>Type 2 diabetes</u> in a particular country <u>also</u> have <u>heart disease</u>:
>
> 1) All the people who have been diagnosed with Type 2 diabetes in the country of interest are identified by <u>hospital records</u>. In total, there are <u>270 196</u> people.
>
> 2) These people are assigned a <u>number</u> between 1 and 270 196.
>
> 3) A <u>random number generator</u> is used to choose the sample group (e.g. it selects the individuals #72 063, #11 822, #193 123, etc.)
>
> 4) The <u>proportion</u> of people in the <u>sample</u> that have heart disease can be used to <u>estimate</u> the <u>total number</u> of people with Type 2 diabetes that also have heart disease.

Heating Substances

*Some more useful lab stuff for you now — a bit about **heating things up**.*

Bunsen Burners Have a **Naked Flame**

Bunsen burners are good for <u>heating things quickly</u>. But you need to make sure you're using them <u>safely</u>:

- You should always use a Bunsen burner on a <u>heat-proof mat</u>.
- If your Bunsen burner is alight but not heating anything, make sure you <u>close</u> the hole so that the flame becomes <u>yellow</u> and <u>clearly visible</u>.
- Use the <u>blue</u> flame to heat things. If you're heating a vessel <u>in</u> the flame, hold it at the <u>top</u> (e.g. with <u>tongs</u>) and point the opening <u>away from</u> yourself (and others).
- If you're heating something <u>over</u> the flame (e.g. a beaker of water), you should put a <u>tripod and gauze</u> over the Bunsen burner before you light it, and place the vessel on this.

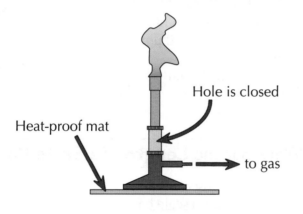

Hole is closed

Heat-proof mat

to gas

The Temperature of **Electric Water Baths** and **Heaters** Can Be **Set**

1) A <u>water bath</u> is a container filled with water that can be heated to a <u>specific temperature</u>.

2) A <u>simple</u> water bath can be made by heating a <u>beaker of water</u> over a <u>Bunsen burner</u> and monitoring the temperature with a <u>thermometer</u>. However, it is difficult to keep the temperature of the water <u>constant</u>.

3) An <u>electric water bath</u> will monitor and adjust the temperature for you. Here's how you use one:

- <u>Set</u> the temperature on the water bath, and allow the water to <u>heat up</u>.
- To make sure it's reached the right temperature, use a <u>thermometer</u>.
- Place the vessel containing your substance in the water bath using test tube holders or tongs. The level of water outside the vessel should be <u>just above</u> the level of the substance in the vessel.
- The substance will then be warmed to the <u>same temperature</u> as the water. As the substance in the vessel is surrounded by water, the heating is very <u>even</u>.

4) <u>Electric heaters</u> are often made up of a metal plate that can be heated to a specified temperature. The vessel containing the substance you want to heat is placed on top of the hot plate. The vessel is only heated from below, so you'll usually have to <u>stir</u> the substance inside to make sure it's <u>heated evenly</u>.

Electric water baths are great for keeping the temperature constant

Make sure you're clear on how to use <u>Bunsen burners</u>, <u>electric water baths</u> and <u>heaters</u>, and more importantly, on how to use them <u>safely</u>. Obviously flames and hot things are <u>very dangerous</u>, so <u>take care</u>.

More on Microscopy and Potometers

*Next up, how to use a **microscope** and a **ruler** to work out the size of a single cell, then on to **potometers**...*

You Can **Measure** the **Size** of a **Single Cell**

When viewing <u>cells</u> under a <u>microscope</u>, you might need to work out their <u>size</u>.
To work out the size of a <u>single cell</u>:

1) Place a <u>clear, plastic ruler</u> on <u>top</u> of your microscope <u>slide</u>. <u>Clip</u> the <u>ruler</u> and <u>slide</u> onto the <u>stage</u>.

2) Select the <u>objective lens</u> that gives an overall magnification of <u>x 100</u>.

3) Adjust the <u>focus</u> to get a <u>clear image</u> of the cells.

4) <u>Move</u> the ruler so that the cells are <u>lined up</u> along <u>1 mm</u>. Then <u>count</u> the <u>number of cells</u> along this <u>1 mm sample</u>.

5) 1 mm = 1000 µm. So to <u>calculate</u> the <u>length</u> of a <u>single cell</u> in µm, you just need to <u>divide</u> 1000 µm by the <u>number of cells</u> in the sample.
E.g. if you counted 4 cells in 1 mm, the length of a single cell would be: 1000 ÷ 4 = <u>250 µm</u>

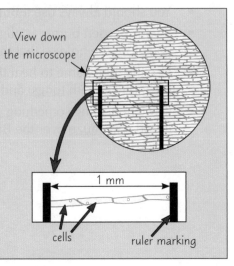

View down the microscope

1 mm

cells   ruler marking

Use the **Cell Size** to Work out the **Length** of a **Scale Bar**

scale bar   drawing of cell

500 µm

1) If you draw a <u>diagram</u> of a cell you've observed under a microscope, you might want to include a <u>scale bar</u>.

2) Once you know the <u>size of one cell</u>, you can use it to calculate how <u>long</u> your scale bar should be.

3) To draw a <u>500 µm scale bar</u>, just use this formula:

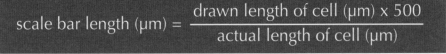

$$\text{scale bar length (µm)} = \frac{\text{drawn length of cell (µm)} \times 500}{\text{actual length of cell (µm)}}$$

Potometers Should Be Set Up **Under Water**

You first met <u>potometers</u> on p.77. It's a special piece of apparatus used to measure the <u>water uptake</u> by a plant. Here's how to set one up:

1) <u>Cut</u> a shoot <u>underwater</u> to prevent air from entering the xylem. Cut it at a <u>slant</u> to increase the surface area available for water uptake.

2) <u>Assemble</u> the potometer <u>in water</u> and insert the shoot <u>under water</u>, so no <u>air</u> can enter.

3) Remove the apparatus from the water but keep the end of the capillary tube <u>submerged</u> in a beaker of water.

4) Check that the apparatus is <u>watertight</u> and <u>airtight</u>.

5) <u>Dry</u> the leaves, allow time for the shoot to <u>acclimatise</u> and then <u>shut</u> the tap.

6) Remove the end of the capillary tube from the beaker of water until <u>one air bubble</u> has formed, then put the end of the tube <u>back into the water</u>.

7) A potometer can be used to estimate the <u>transpiration rate</u> of a plant. There's more about this on page 77.

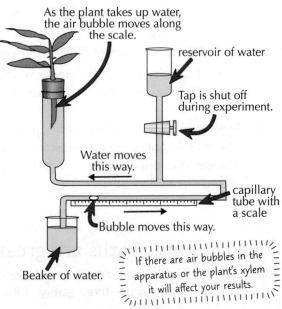

As the plant takes up water, the air bubble moves along the scale.

reservoir of water

Tap is shut off during experiment.

Water moves this way.

capillary tube with a scale

Bubble moves this way.

Beaker of water.

If there are air bubbles in the apparatus or the plant's xylem it will affect your results.

Comparing Results

*Once you've had fun collecting all your data, a few **calculations** might be needed to work out what your data actually shows. Calculating **percentage change** is a great way to **compare results**...*

Percentage Change Allows you to Compare Results

1) When investigating the change in a variable, you may want to compare results that didn't have the same initial value.

> For example, you may want to compare the change in mass of potato cylinders left in different concentrations of sugar solution that had different initial masses (see page 36).

2) One way to do this is to calculate the percentage change. You work it out like this:

$$\text{percentage (\%) change} = \frac{\text{final value} - \text{original value}}{\text{original value}} \times 100$$

EXAMPLE

A student is investigating the effect of the concentration of sugar solution on potato cells. She records the mass of potato cylinders before and after placing them in sugar solutions of different concentrations. The table below shows some of her results. Which potato cylinder had the largest percentage change?

Potato cylinder	Concentration (mol/dm³)	Mass at start (g)	Mass at end (g)
1	0.0	7.5	8.7
2	1.0	8.0	6.8

1) Stick each set of results into the equation:

$$\frac{\%}{\text{change}} = \frac{\text{final value} - \text{original value}}{\text{original value}} \times 100$$

1. $\frac{8.7 - 7.5}{7.5} \times 100 = 16\%$

The mass at the start is the original value and the mass at the end is the final value.

2. $\frac{6.8 - 8.0}{8.0} \times 100 = -15\%$

Here, the mass has decreased so the percentage change is negative.

2) Compare the results.

16% is greater than 15%, so the potato cylinder in the 0.0 mol/dm³ sugar solution had the largest percentage change.

Good practical skills are needed when you're doing an investigation...

...but you also need to know about them for your exams. You're guaranteed to be tested on your practical knowledge, so if you've merrily skipped through this section, you'd better go back and read it through again.

Practice Exams

Once you've been through all the questions in this book, you should feel pretty confident about the exams.
As final preparation, here is a set of **practice exams** to really get you set for the real thing. The time allowed for
each paper is 1 hour 45 minutes. These papers are designed to give you the best possible preparation for your exams.

CGP — Practice Exam Paper GCSE Biology

GCSE Biology

Paper 1

Higher Tier

In addition to this paper you should have:
- A ruler.
- A calculator.

Centre name			
Centre number			
Candidate number			

Time allowed:
- 1 hour 45 minutes

Surname	
Other names	
Candidate signature	

Instructions to candidates
- Write your name and other details in the spaces provided above.
- Answer **all** questions in the spaces provided.
- Do all rough work on the paper.
- Cross out any work you do not want to be marked.

Information for candidates
- The marks available are given in brackets at the end of each question.
- There are 100 marks available for this paper.
- You are allowed to use a calculator.
- You should use good English and present your answers in a clear and organised way.
- For Questions 1.6, 3.2 and 9 ensure that your answers have a clear and logical structure, include the right scientific terms, spelt correctly and include detailed, relevant information.

Advice to candidates
- In calculations show clearly how you worked out your answers.

	For examiner's use						
Q	Attempt Nº			Q	Attempt Nº		
	1	2	3		1	2	3
1				6			
2				7			
3				8			
4				9			
5				10			
			Total				

1   **Figure 1** shows an animal cell.

Figure 1

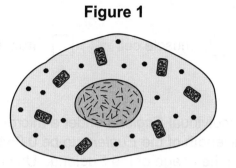

1.1   Give **two** ways in which the cell in **Figure 1** is different from a bacterial cell.

....

....

....
                                                                                      [2 marks]

1.2   Not all animal cells have the same structure as the cell in **Figure 1**.
        Explain why.

....

....
                                                                                       [1 mark]

Figure 2 shows a single-celled organism called *Euglena*, found in pond water.

Figure 2

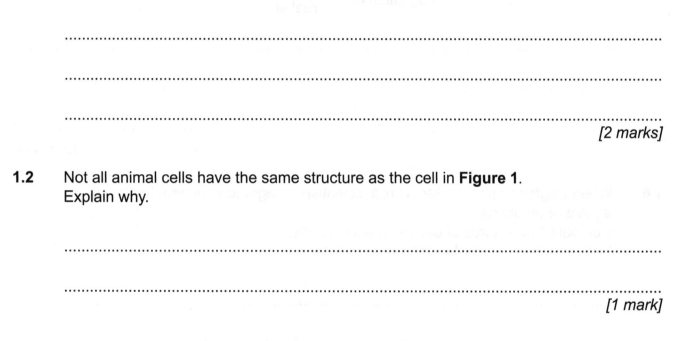

1.3   Name part **X**.

....
                                                                                       [1 mark]

Question 1 continues on the next page

Turn over ▶

1.4 *Euglena* is a eukaryote. Which of the following is **not** a eukaryote?
Tick **one** box.

☐ sperm cell   ☐ muscle cell   ☐ fruit fly   ☐ *E. coli* bacteria

[1 mark]

1.5 A scientist viewed an individual *Euglena* under a microscope with × 150 magnification.
He calculated the real length of the *Euglena* to be 0.054 mm.
Calculate the length of the image of the Euglena. Use the formula:

$$\text{magnification} = \frac{\text{image size}}{\text{real size}}$$

....

....

.... mm

[2 marks]

1.6 When *Euglena* was first discovered, scientists disagreed over whether it was
a plant or an animal.
Compare the features of plant and animal cells.
Include details of their features in your answer.

....

....

....

....

....

....

....

....

....

....

....

[6 marks]

2 Antibiotics can be used to kill bacteria and help a patient fight disease.

Scientists developing antibiotics were comparing the effectiveness of two different antibiotics, X and Y, against a bacterium. They grew the bacteria on agar jelly in 20 Petri dishes — forming an even covering of bacteria on the top of the agar.

They took three identical discs of paper and soaked each of them in one of three different liquids, shown in **Table 1**.

Table 1

Disc	Liquid soaked in
1	Antibiotic X
2	Antibiotic Y
3	Distilled water

The discs were then placed onto the agar in each dish. The dishes were kept in an incubator at 35 °C for two days, and then they were examined.

Figure 3 shows a typical dish.

Figure 3

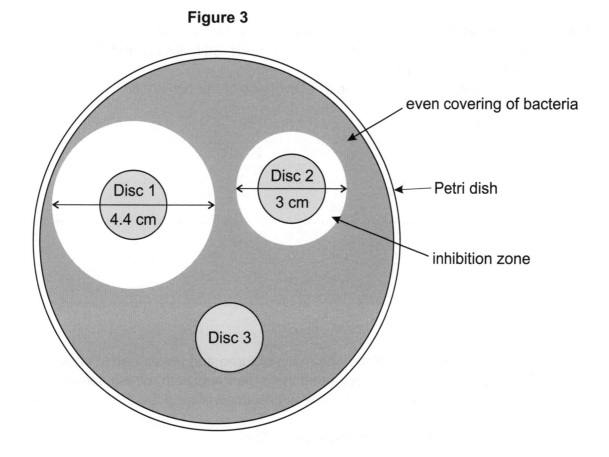

Question 2 continues on the next page

2.1 Explain the purpose of Disc **3**.

....

....

[2 marks]

2.2 Give **two** things that the scientists should have done to avoid contaminating the bacterial cultures.

....

....

[2 marks]

2.3 In school labs, the maximum incubation temperature is 25 °C.
Explain why.

....

[1 mark]

2.4 The diameter of each inhibition zone is shown on **Figure 3**.
Calculate the areas of the inhibition zones for antibiotics **X** and **Y**.
Use the equation area = πr^2.
Use the areas to compare the effectiveness of the two antibiotics.

....

....

....

....

....

[3 marks]

The most effective antibiotic was manufactured and prescribed to patients.
Two years later, scientists repeated the experiment with a fresh sample of the bacteria and found that no inhibition zone was produced around the disc soaked in this antibiotic.

2.5 Suggest an explanation for this observation.

....

[1 mark]

3 Measles, mumps and rubella are all examples of communicable diseases.

3.1 How is measles spread between people?
Tick **one** box.

☐ By droplets from an infected person's sneeze or cough.

☐ By sexual contact.

☐ By eating contaminated food.

☐ By a vector.

[1 mark]

3.2 The MMR vaccine protects against measles, mumps and rubella.
Explain how vaccination helps to protect the body against a disease.

....

....

....

....

....

....
[4 marks]

Zika virus disease is another example of a communicable disease.
Symptoms of infection include fever, skin rashes, muscle and joint pain, and headaches. The virus that causes the disease is spread by a mosquito vector.

3.3 Suggest **two** ways that the spread of the Zika virus disease could be reduced.

....

....

....
[2 marks]

Question 3 continues on the next page

Turn over ▶

3.4 Which of the following communicable diseases is also spread by a vector?
Tick **one** box.

☐ influenza

☐ malaria

☐ HIV

☐ athlete's foot

[1 mark]

3.5 Tuberculosis (TB) is a communicable disease caused by *M. tuberculosis* bacteria.
A strain of this bacteria was observed to have a mean division time of 18 hours.
How many cells would be produced from one bacterium of this strain in 3 days?

....

....

.... cells

[2 marks]

4   Different chemical reagents can be used to test for the presence of certain molecules in samples of food.

4.1   A student prepared a food sample in order to test whether the sample contained protein. What reagent should be used for this test?
Tick **one** box.

☐   Benedict's solution

☐   iodine solution

☐   biuret solution

☐   Sudan III stain solution

[1 mark]

The student tested four different food samples for reducing sugars.
She obtained the results shown in **Table 2**.

Table 2

Sample	Colour of sample
A	blue
B	brick-red
C	yellow
D	green

4.2   Name the reagent that the student would have used to test for reducing sugars.

....

[1 mark]

4.3   Which of the samples in **Table 2** didn't contain reducing sugars?
Tick **one** box.

☐   A

☐   B

☐   C

☐   D

[1 mark]

Question 4 continues on the next page

Turn over ▶

Lactose is a reducing sugar commonly found in dairy products, such as milk and cheese. An enzyme called lactase breaks down lactose during digestion. The resulting products are the sugars glucose and galactose. These are absorbed into the blood from the small intestine.

4.4 Describe how the small intestine is adapted to absorb molecules such as glucose.

....

....

....

....

[3 marks]

4.5 Lactose intolerance is a digestive problem caused by insufficient production of lactase.

To test a person for lactose intolerance, they are given a drink of lactose solution.
A blood sample is then taken from them every 30 minutes for two hours.
The blood is tested to see how much sugar it contains.
Suggest what will happen to the blood sugar level of a person who is lactose intolerant during the test. Explain your answer.

....

....

....

....

[2 marks]

5 The lung is a specialised gas exchange organ.

5.1 What is meant by the term 'organ'?

....

....
[1 mark]

The lung contains millions of air sacs called alveoli.
Figure 4 shows an alveolus and a blood capillary.

Figure 4

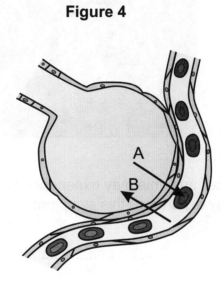

5.2 The arrows in **Figure 4** show the net movement of two gases, **A** and **B**.
Name gases **A** and **B**.

A ....

B ....
[1 mark]

5.3 Alveoli are surrounded by a network of capillaries.
Explain why.

....

....

....
[2 marks]

Question 5 continues on the next page

Turn over ▶

5.4 **Figure 4** shows red blood cells in a capillary. Red blood cells are flexible, which allows them to fit through capillaries.

Sickle cell anaemia is a genetic disorder of the blood where the red blood cells become rigid and sickle-shaped. **Figure 5** shows a sickle-shaped red blood cell and some normal red blood cells.

Figure 5

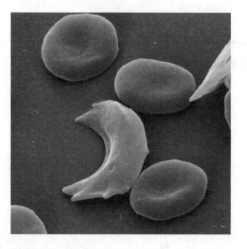

A person with sickle cell anaemia may experience breathlessness.
Suggest why they may experience this symptom.

....

....

....

....

....

....

[3 marks]

6 Blood flows around the body in arteries, veins and capillaries.

6.1 **Table 3** shows some of the features of these three different types of blood vessel.

Table 3

	Type of blood vessel		
	A	**B**	**C**
Walls	Thick, muscular	Very thin	Thin
Presence of valves	No	No	Yes
Pressure of blood in vessels	High	Low	Low

Identify blood vessels **A**, **B** and **C**.

A ....

B ....

C ....

[2 marks]

Figure 6 shows a human heart.

Figure 6

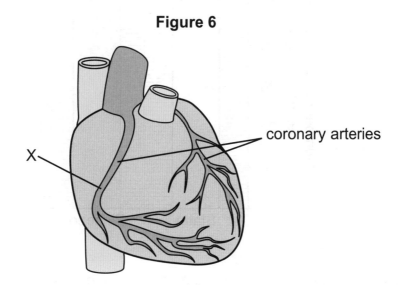

coronary arteries

X

6.2 Explain what would happen if the coronary artery was blocked at the point labelled **X**.

....

....

[2 marks]

Question 6 continues on the next page

Turn over ▶

A patient has fatty deposits in the walls of one of his coronary arteries.
The patient's doctor recommends that the patient is treated using a stent.

6.3 Explain how having a stent fitted could help the patient.

....

....

[1 mark]

Statins are a type of drug used to reduce the risk of coronary heart disease.

A new statin has been developed and was initially put through preclinical testing.
Following this, the drug was given to thirty healthy volunteers in a clinical trial.

A trial was then carried out on 2000 patients who had previously had a heart attack
— half were given the drug and half were given a placebo.

Figure 7 shows the results after five years of treatment.

Figure 7

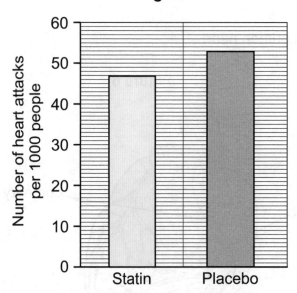

6.4 In preclinical testing, new drugs are tested on human cells and tissues and on
live animals.
Give **two** reasons why preclinical tests are carried out.

....

....

[2 marks]

6.5   During the clinical trial, what was the main reason for giving the drug to healthy human volunteers?

....
[1 mark]

6.6   Describe the results of the trial.

....

....
[1 mark]

6.7   Give **one** reason why the results of the trial could be considered valid.

....

....
[1 mark]

Turn over for the next question

Turn over ▶

7 A student did an experiment to investigate the effect of temperature on the action of the enzyme amylase. The method used is shown below.

---

1. Add a set volume of starch solution to a test tube and the same volume of amylase solution to another.

2. Place the test tubes in a water bath at 10 °C.

3. Allow the starch and amylase solutions to reach the temperature of the water bath, then mix them together and return the mixture to the water bath.

4. Take a small sample of the mixture every ten seconds and test for starch.

5. Stop the experiment when starch is no longer present in the sample.

6. Repeat the experiment at different temperatures.

7.1 What happens to the starch solution during the experiment?

....

[1 mark]

7.2 Give **one** variable that the student should have controlled during the experiment.

....

[1 mark]

7.3 Suggest how the student could have tested for the presence of starch in **Step 4**.

....

....

....

....

[3 marks]

Figure 8 shows a graph of the student's results.

Figure 8

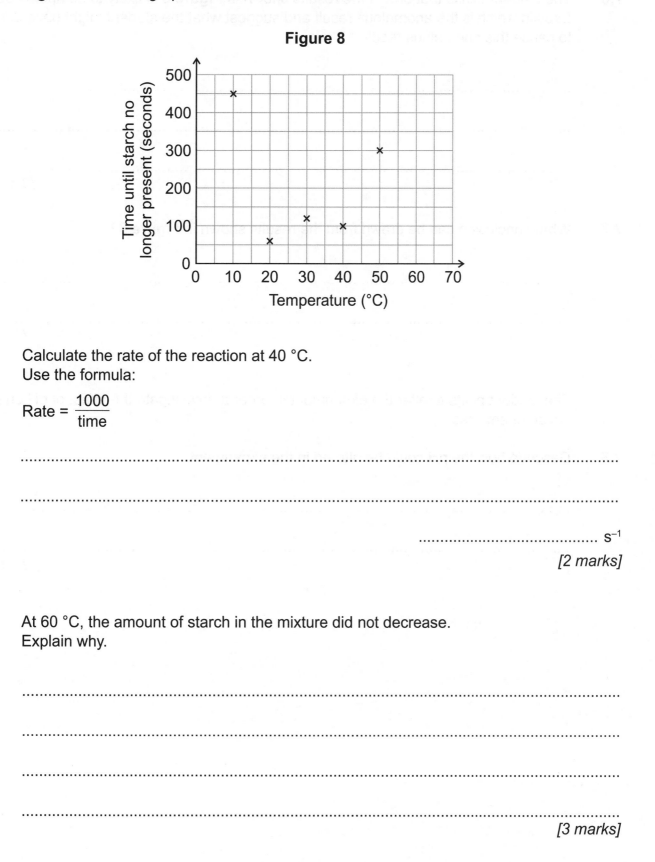

7.4 Calculate the rate of the reaction at 40 °C.
Use the formula:

$$\text{Rate} = \frac{1000}{\text{time}}$$

....

....

.... s⁻¹

[2 marks]

7.5 At 60 °C, the amount of starch in the mixture did not decrease.
Explain why.

....

....

....

....

[3 marks]

Question 7 continues on the next page

Turn over ▶

7.6 The student thinks that one of the results shown in **Figure 8** is likely to be anomalous. Explain which is the anomalous result and suggest what the student might have done to cause this anomalous result.

....

....

....

[3 marks]

7.7 What conclusion can be drawn from the results shown in **Figure 8**?

....

....

[1 mark]

The student plans to alter the experiment in order to investigate the effect of pH on the action of amylase.

7.8 Describe how the pH could be altered in the experiment.

....

....

[1 mark]

8 A scientist measured the rate of transpiration in two plants over 48 hours. The results are shown in **Figure 9**.

Figure 9

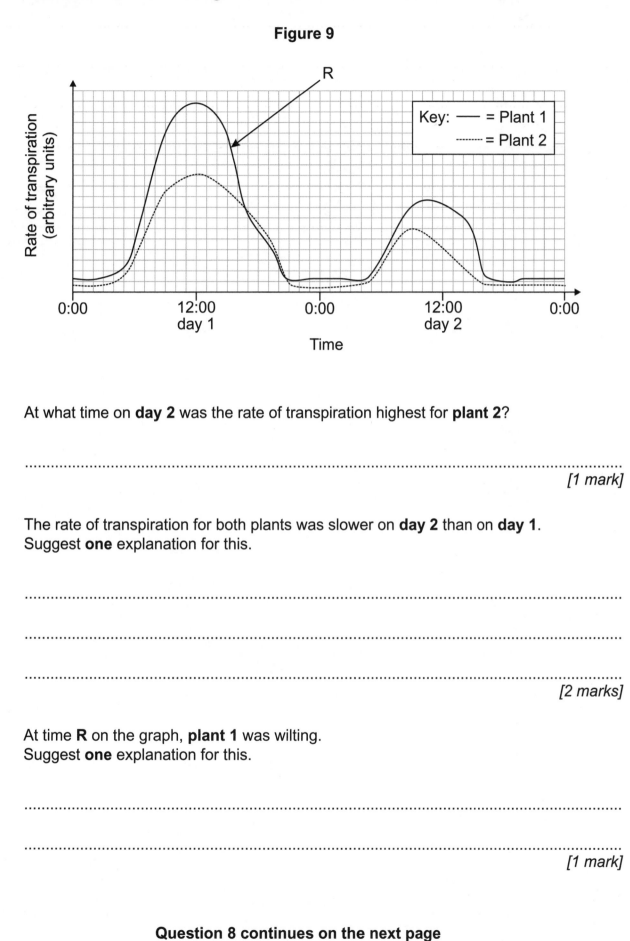

8.1 At what time on **day 2** was the rate of transpiration highest for **plant 2**?

....

[1 mark]

8.2 The rate of transpiration for both plants was slower on **day 2** than on **day 1**. Suggest **one** explanation for this.

....

....

....

[2 marks]

8.3 At time **R** on the graph, **plant 1** was wilting. Suggest **one** explanation for this.

....

....

[1 mark]

Question 8 continues on the next page

Turn over ▶

8.4 Describe how a transpiration stream moves water through a plant.

....

....

....

....

....

....

[3 marks]

9   Herbicides are chemicals that are used to kill unwanted plants.
       Some herbicides work by disrupting the cell cycle within plants.

       Describe the stages of the cell cycle and suggest why disrupting the cell cycle by using
       herbicides can kill plants.

....

....

....

....

....

....

....

....

....

....

....

....

....

....

                                                                                                          [6 marks]

Turn over for the next question

Turn over ▶

10 A student is investigating how his heart rate changes during and after exercise.
He measures his heart rate using a portable heart rate monitor.
He takes his resting heart rate before running around the school track
for two minutes. Then he rests again. His results are shown in **Table 4**.

Table 4

Time after first heart rate measurement taken (min)	First run — Heart rate (beats/min)
0	72
1	118
2	132
3	129
4	116
5	98
6	84
7	76
8	72
9	72

10.1 Complete **Figure 10** using the data from **Table 4**.
- Complete the *x*-axis. Include a label and use a suitable scale.
- Plot the heart rate.
- Draw a curve of best fit.

Figure 10

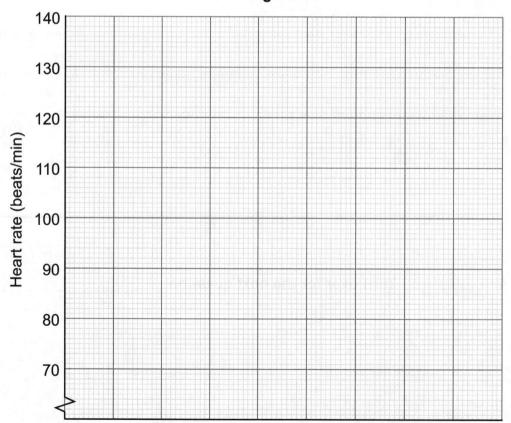

[4 marks]

10.2 Use your graph in **Figure 10** to estimate the student's heart rate after thirty seconds.

heart rate = ... (beats/min)

[1 mark]

10.3 Give the dependent variable in this experiment.

....

[1 mark]

10.4 Describe how the student's heart rate changes with exercise.
Explain why this change occurs.

....

....

....

....

....

[4 marks]

When the student first starts running he respires aerobically.

10.5 Complete the word equation for aerobic respiration.

.... + oxygen → carbon dioxide + ...

[2 marks]

10.6 As the student continues running, his muscles start to respire anaerobically.
Suggest why this causes his heart rate to be higher than normal for a while
after the exercise is finished.

....

....

....

....

[3 marks]

END OF QUESTIONS

GCSE Biology

Paper 2

Higher Tier

In addition to this paper you should have:
- A ruler.
- A calculator.

Centre name				
Centre number				
Candidate number				

Time allowed:
- 1 hour 45 minutes

Surname	
Other names	
Candidate signature	

Instructions to candidates
- Write your name and other details in the spaces provided above.
- Answer **all** questions in the spaces provided.
- Do all rough work on the paper.
- Cross out any work you do not want to be marked.

Information for candidates
- The marks available are given in brackets at the end of each question.
- There are 100 marks available for this paper.
- You are allowed to use a calculator.
- You should use good English and present your answers in a clear and organised way.
- For Questions 2.6 and 7.7 ensure that your answers have a clear and logical structure, include the right scientific terms, spelt correctly and include detailed, relevant information.

Advice to candidates
- In calculations show clearly how you worked out your answers.

For examiner's use

Q	Attempt Nº			Q	Attempt Nº		
	1	2	3		1	2	3
1				7			
2				8			
3				9			
4				10			
5				11			
6							
	Total						

1   **Figure 1** shows the amount of biomass contained within an area of plants.
It shows how much biomass from the plants is transferred to each trophic level
in a food chain.

Figure 1

plants	→	grasshoppers	→	mice	→	snakes
120 kg		12 kg		1.4 kg		0.15 kg

1.1   Plants are the producers in this food chain.
What is meant by the term 'producer'?

....

[1 mark]

Figure 2 shows four different pyramids of biomass.

Figure 2

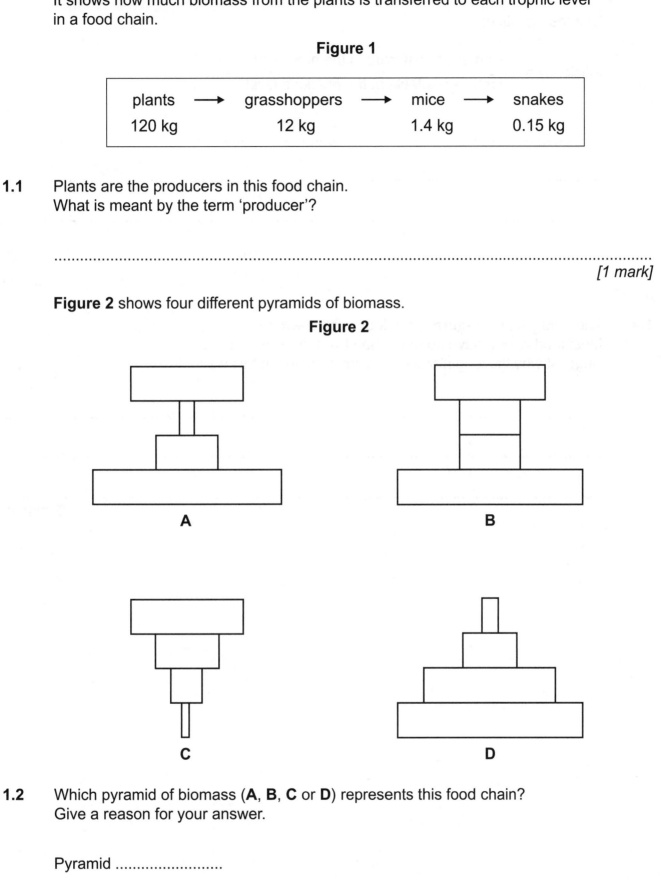

1.2   Which pyramid of biomass (**A**, **B**, **C** or **D**) represents this food chain?
Give a reason for your answer.

Pyramid ....

Reason ....

....

[2 marks]

Question 1 continues on the next page

Turn over ▶

1.3 Calculate the efficiency of biomass transfer between the grasshoppers and mice.

Use the equation:

$$\text{efficiency} = \frac{\text{biomass transferred to the next level}}{\text{biomass available at the previous level}} \times 100$$

....

....

....

Efficiency = ... %

[1 mark]

1.4 The food chain in **Figure 1** has four trophic levels.
Most food chains have no more than five trophic levels.
Suggest why the length of food chains is limited in this way.

....

....

....

[2 marks]

2   A student was investigating the distribution of buttercups
     in an area around his school.
     He counted the number of buttercups in 10 quadrats in five different fields.
     His quadrat measured 1 m². His results are shown in **Table 1**.

Table 1

Field	Mean number of buttercups per quadrat
A	10
B	35
C	21
D	37
E	21

2.1   What is the median of the data in **Table 1**?

....

[1 mark]

2.2   A week later, the student repeated his experiment in a sixth field, Field **F**.
           His results for each quadrat are shown below:

           6   15   9   14   20   5   3   11   10   7

Using this data, calculate the mean number of buttercups per m² in Field **F**.

....

....

Mean = ... buttercups per m²

[2 marks]

2.3   Field **F** measures 90 m by 120 m.
           Estimate the population of buttercups in Field **F**.

....

....

Estimated population = ... buttercups

[2 marks]

Question 2 continues on the next page

Turn over ▶

2.4 In some areas of the fields, the buttercups were closely packed together.
How could the student have estimated the area covered by the buttercups in a quadrat,
if they were difficult to count?

....

....

[1 mark]

The student observed that the distribution of buttercups changed across Field **A**.
Buttercups grow well in damp soil, so the student thinks that the change in the
distribution of buttercups is due to variability in the moisture level of the soil across
the field. The student wants to investigate this.

2.5 Suggest a hypothesis about the distribution of buttercups in Field **A**,
based on the student's observations.

....

....
[1 mark]

2.6 Describe how the student could investigate this hypothesis.

....

....

....

....

....

....

....

[4 marks]

3 A student grew three plants in a windowsill tray.
He then put the plants in a cardboard box with a cut-out hole.

Figure 3 shows the same plants before and after three days in the cardboard box.

Figure 3

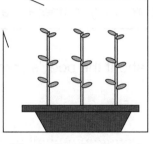 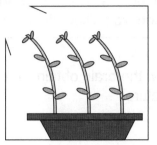

Start of experiment   After three days

3.1 Explain what caused the plants' response.

....

....

....

....

....

[3 marks]

3.2 Name the response shown by the plants in this experiment.

....

[1 mark]

3.3 The student removed one of the plants from the tray. He observed that the roots of the plant were growing downwards.
Name the stimulus that causes the roots of a plant to grow downwards.

....

[1 mark]

Turn over for the next question

Turn over ▶

4   **Figure 4** is an extract from a report by a lifeboat crew member.

Figure 4

> "We were very concerned when we received news of a man lost overboard tonight because the sea is extremely cold at this time of year. Fortunately, we found him quickly and were able to rescue him before he suffered any serious ill effects. His skin was very cold when we picked him up, but his core body temperature was normal."

4.1   Describe how the brain obtains information about the body's core temperature and skin temperature.

....

....

....

....

[2 marks]

4.2   Explain **one** way in which the man's body may have helped prevent his core temperature from falling whilst he was in the sea.

....

....

....

....

[2 marks]

5   ADH is a hormone involved in the regulation of the water content of the body.

5.1   From which gland is ADH released? Tick **one** box.

☐ pancreas   ☐ thyroid   ☐ adrenal gland   ☐ pituitary gland

[1 mark]

5.2   Describe what happens if the brain detects that the water content of the blood is too **low**.

....

....

[2 marks]

5.3   The drug ecstasy stimulates the release of ADH. Taking ecstasy can result in too much water entering the body cells, which can cause cell damage.
Suggest why taking ecstasy can lead to too much water entering cells from the blood.

....

....

....

[2 marks]

People suffering from kidney failure may be treated using a kidney dialysis machine.
Figure 5 shows a type of dialysis machine.

Figure 5

Dialysis fluid inlet

Blood inlet →   → Blood outlet

Dialysis fluid outlet   Tubes containing patient's blood

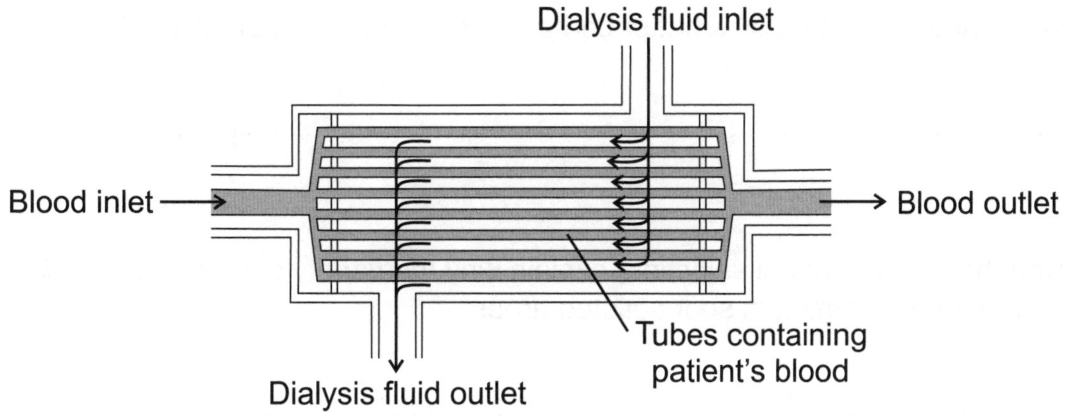

5.4   Explain how a dialysis machine works.

....

....

....

....

[3 marks]

Turn over for the next question

Turn over ▶

6   The peppered moth is an insect that lives on the trunks of trees in Britain.
The moths are prey for birds such as thrushes.

The peppered moth exists in two varieties:
* A light-coloured variety that is better camouflaged on tree trunks in unpolluted areas.
* A dark-coloured variety that is better camouflaged on sooty tree trunks in badly polluted areas.

Figures 6 and **7** show these two varieties of moths on different tree trunks.

Figure 6

Figure 7

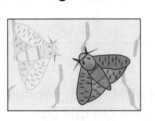
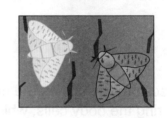

The dark variety of the moth was first recorded in the North of England in 1848.

It became increasingly common in polluted areas until the 1960s, when the number of soot covered trees declined because of the introduction of new laws.

6.1   The binomial name of the peppered moth is *Biston betularia*.
What is the moth's genus?

....
[1 mark]

6.2   Which variety of moth has a better chance of survival in a soot polluted area?

....
[1 mark]

6.3   Using the idea of natural selection, explain why the variety of moth given in **6.2** became more common in soot polluted areas.

....

....

....

....
[3 marks]

Figure 8 shows the percentages of dark- and light-coloured peppered moths in two different towns.

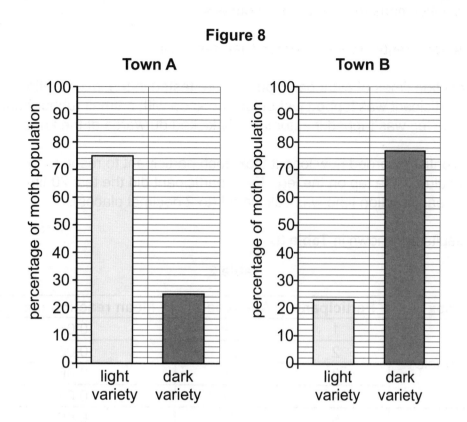

Figure 8

6.4 Which town is the most polluted, **A** or **B**?
Explain your answer.

[1 mark]

Turn over for the next question

7   A scientist was investigating the reflex actions of males and females.

The scientist made the following hypothesis:

'Males have faster reaction times than females.'

The reaction times of eight participants were tested in the investigation.
Each participant was tapped just below the knee with a small rubber hammer.
When the leg was tapped it automatically kicked outwards at the knee.

The scientist recorded how long it took each participant to respond to
the stimulus of the tap on the leg. Each participant did the test 20 times,
and a mean reaction time was calculated (to 2 decimal places).

The results are shown in **Table 2**.

Table 2

Sex	Participant	Age (years)	Mean reaction time (s)
Female	1	29	0.05
	2	26	0.06
	3	24	0.06
	4	27	0.04
Male	5	19	0.05
	6	22	0.04
	7	25	0.04
	8	20	0.05

7.1   How can you tell that the participants' response was a reflex?
Give **two** reasons.

....

....

....

....

[2 marks]

7.2   What was the dependent variable in this experiment?
Tick **one** box.

☐ age   ☐ stimulus   ☐ reaction time   ☐ sex

[1 mark]

7.3 What was the independent variable in this experiment?
Tick **one** box.

◻ age   ◻ stimulus   ◻ reaction time   ◻ sex

[1 mark]

7.4 **Figure 9** shows the mean reaction times for males and females in the investigation.

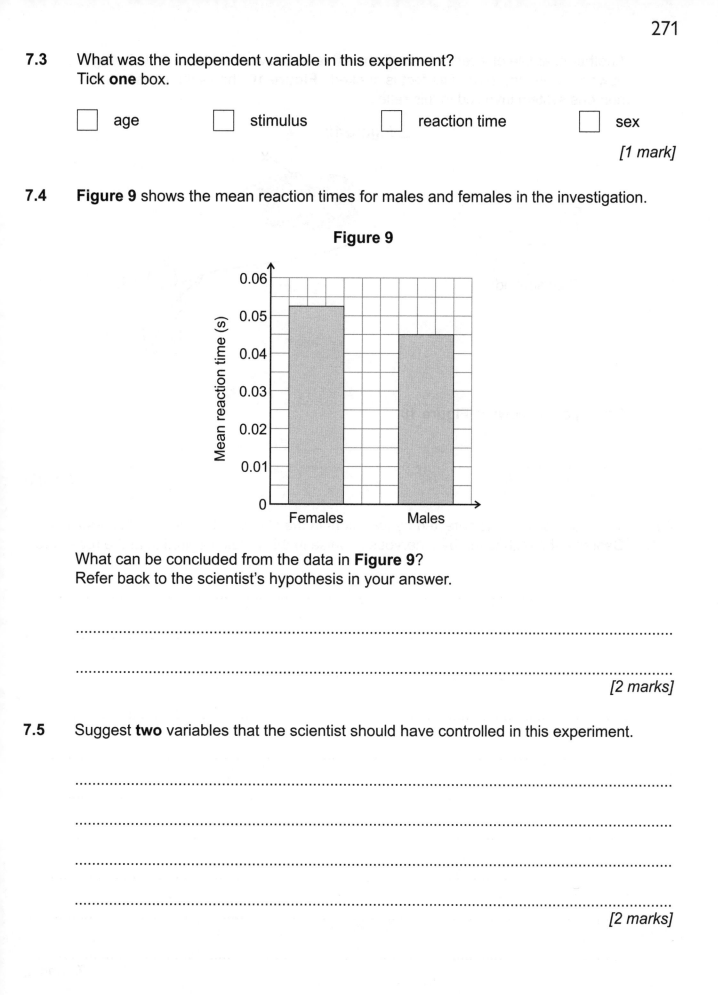

Figure 9

What can be concluded from the data in **Figure 9**?
Refer back to the scientist's hypothesis in your answer.

....

....

[2 marks]

7.5 Suggest **two** variables that the scientist should have controlled in this experiment.

....

....

....

....

[2 marks]

Question 7 continues on the next page

Turn over ▶

272

Another example of a reflex is the Babinski reflex, in which a baby curls its big toe upwards when the sole of its foot is stroked. **Figure 10** shows the parts of the nervous system involved in this reflex.

Figure 10

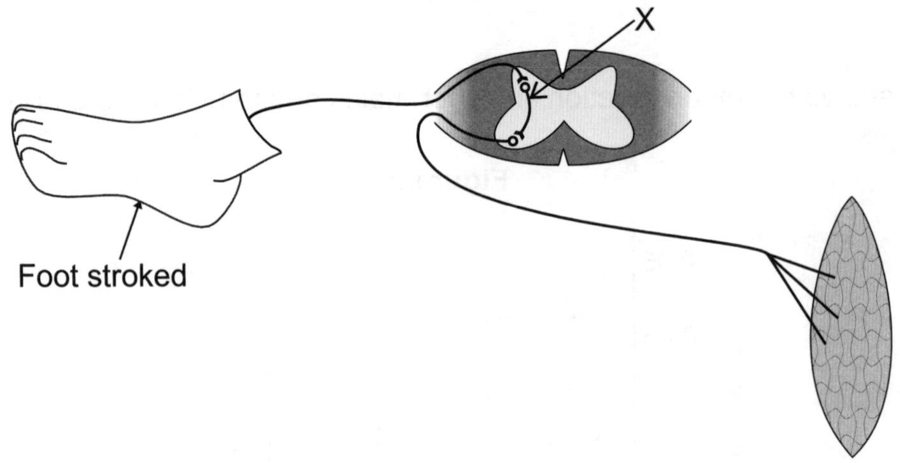

Foot stroked

X

7.6 Name part **X** shown in **Figure 10**.

....

[1 mark]

7.7 The touch stimulus is detected by receptors in the skin and causes a reflex response. Describe the path taken by a nervous impulse in this reflex, beginning at the receptors.

....

....

....

....

....

....

....

....

....

[6 marks]

8   Many people fear that cod supplies from the North Sea may run out in the near future. To prevent this, cod stocks need to be fished sustainably.

Figure 11 shows how the population of cod has changed between 1980 and 2005 in the North Sea, just off the coast of Norway.

Figure 11

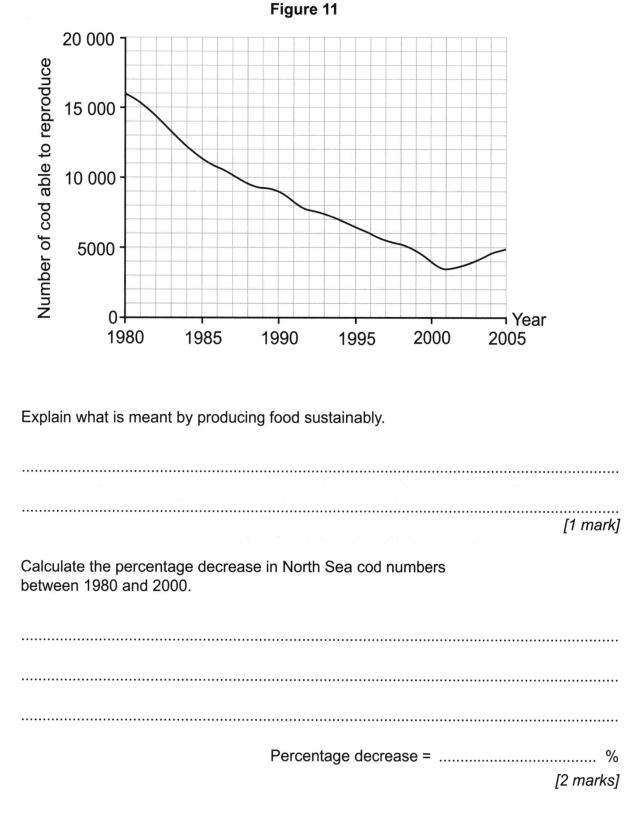

8.1   Explain what is meant by producing food sustainably.

....

....

[1 mark]

8.2   Calculate the percentage decrease in North Sea cod numbers between 1980 and 2000.

....

....

....

Percentage decrease = ... %

[2 marks]

Question 8 continues on the next page

Turn over ▶

8.3   Calculate the rate at which the cod population was decreasing between 1980 and 2000.

....

....

....

Rate = ... cod/year

[2 marks]

8.4   Describe the trend shown by **Figure 11**.
Suggest reasons for the trend you have described.

....

....

....

....

....

....

[3 marks]

An increasing demand for food has led scientists to look for new sustainable sources of food. An example of a sustainable food source is mycoprotein.

8.5   Name the fungus that is the main source of mycoprotein.

....

[1 mark]

8.6   Describe how mycoprotein is produced.

....

....

....

....

....

[3 marks]

9   Various research programmes aim to improve human health through research into the human genome.

9.1   What is meant by the term 'genome'?

....
[1 mark]

Cystic fibrosis is an inherited disorder caused by a recessive allele.

9.2   How could research into the human genome have the potential to help people with cystic fibrosis?

....

....
[1 mark]

A couple have a baby boy. The doctor tells them that the baby has inherited cystic fibrosis. Neither parent shows signs of the disorder.

9.3   Construct a Punnett square to show how the baby inherited cystic fibrosis. Use the diagram to work out the probability of any future child of the couple inheriting cystic fibrosis.

Use **F** to represent the dominant allele and **f** to represent the recessive allele.

Probability = ...
[4 marks]

Question 9 continues on the next page

Turn over ▶

9.4 Is the baby homozygous or heterozygous for cystic fibrosis?
Explain your answer.

....

....
[1 mark]

The doctor tells the couple that if they have another child, the fetus can be tested by embryonic screening to see if it will have cystic fibrosis.

Embryo screening can also be done during IVF treatment, so that doctors can select a healthy embryo to implant in the mother. The other embryos are discarded.

At the moment, UK regulations only allow embryo screening when there is "a significant risk of a serious genetic condition being present in the embryo."
This means that it is only allowed when a child of the person carrying the faulty allele would be likely to suffer from the disorder, and the disorder is serious.

9.5 Could embryos be screened for polydactyly under the current regulations?
Explain your answer.

....

....
[1 mark]

9.6 Suggest **one** reason why a person might be opposed to screening embryos for inherited conditions.

....

....
[1 mark]

10 Reproduction can be sexual or asexual.

10.1 Give **three** differences between sexual and asexual reproduction.

....

....

....

....

....

....

[3 marks]

In humans, sexual reproduction involves the reproductive system.

10.2 The male reproductive system includes the testes.
What hormone is produced by the testes?

....

[1 mark]

10.3 The female reproductive system includes the ovaries.

The ovaries produce the hormone oestrogen.
Describe the role of oestrogen in the menstrual cycle.

....

....

....

....

[2 marks]

Question 10 continues on the next page

Turn over ▶

Figure 12 shows the fluctuations in the levels of four different hormones during one 28 day menstrual cycle.

Figure 12

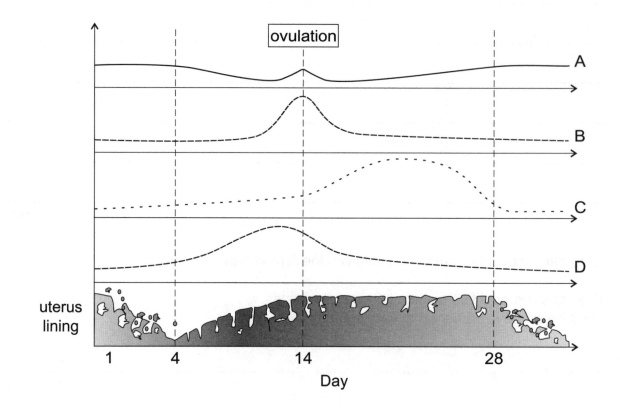

10.4 Which line in **Figure 12** represents progesterone?
Explain your answer.

Line ....

Explanation ....

....

....

[2 marks]

Some methods of contraception use reproductive hormones to control fertility.
One such method is the contraceptive implant, shown in **Figure 13**.

Figure 13

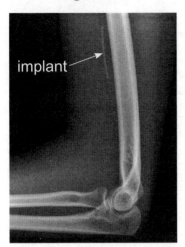

The contraceptive implant:

- is a small, plastic rod that is inserted by a doctor or nurse
- releases progesterone, which reduces fertility
- is effective for three years
- is over 99% effective at preventing pregnancy
- can cause side effects such as headaches and nausea
- can be made less effective by certain medications

Figure 14 shows a condom. The condom is a barrier method of contraception.

Figure 14

The condom:

- is worn over the penis during intercourse
- prevents sperm from entering the vagina
- can only be used once
- is 98% effective at preventing pregnancy when used correctly
- protects against sexually transmitted disease (STDs)

10.5   Use the information to evaluate the implant and condom as methods of contraception.
Give a conclusion of which you think is the better method of contraception.
Justify your conclusion.

....

....

....

....

....

....

....

....

[4 marks]

Turn over for the next question

Turn over ▶

11 **Figure 15** shows the carbon cycle.

Figure 15

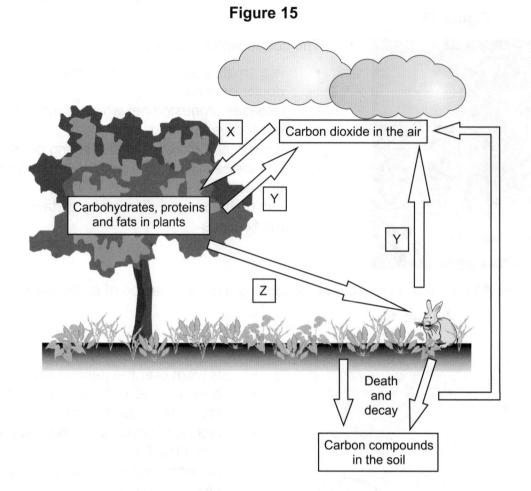

11.1 Describe what is occurring at points **X**, **Y** and **Z** in the cycle.

....

....

....

....

....

[3 marks]

11.2 How are microorganisms involved in the carbon cycle?

....

....

....

[2 marks]

A scientist was examining some data to see if there is a link between the global human population and the carbon dioxide concentration in the atmosphere.

Figure 16 shows the two graphs that the scientist examined.

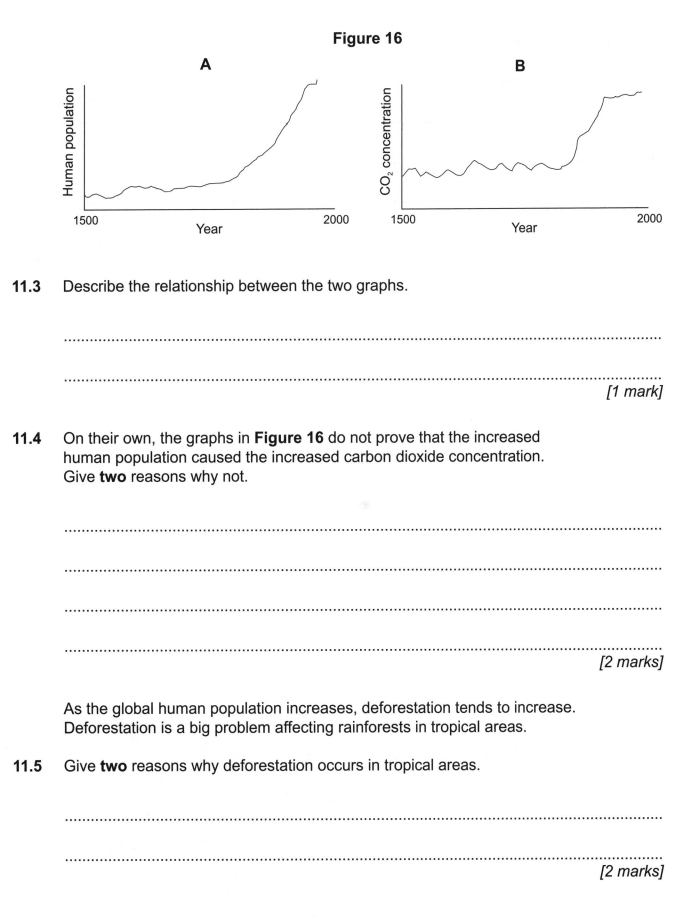

Figure 16

A

B

11.3 Describe the relationship between the two graphs.

....

....

[1 mark]

11.4 On their own, the graphs in **Figure 16** do not prove that the increased human population caused the increased carbon dioxide concentration. Give **two** reasons why not.

....

....

....

....

[2 marks]

As the global human population increases, deforestation tends to increase. Deforestation is a big problem affecting rainforests in tropical areas.

11.5 Give **two** reasons why deforestation occurs in tropical areas.

....

....

[2 marks]

Question 11 continues on the next page

Turn over ▶

282

11.6 Deforestation is one factor that can cause the amount of carbon dioxide in the atmosphere to increase. The rising concentration of carbon dioxide in our atmosphere has been linked to global warming.
Describe **two** possible biological consequences of global warming.

....

....

....

....

....

....

[2 marks]

END OF QUESTIONS

Topic 1 — Cell Biology

Page 18
Microscopy

Q1   real size = image size ÷ magnification
      = 2.4 mm ÷ 40
      = 0.06 mm *[1 mark]*
      0.06 × 1000 = **60 µm** *[1 mark]*

Page 21
Warm-Up Questions

1)   mitochondria

2)   Plant cells have a rigid cell wall, they have a permanent vacuole and they contain chloroplasts.

3)   Any two from: e.g. prokaryotic cells are smaller than eukaryotic cells. / Prokaryotic cells don't have mitochondria but eukaryotic cells do. / Prokaryotic cells don't have a true nucleus but eukaryotic cells do. / Prokaryotic cells have circular DNA but eukaryotic cells don't.

4)   electron microscope

5) 4.5×10^{-4} µm

Exam Questions

1   nucleus *[1 mark]*

Remember, DNA in prokaryotic cells floats freely in the cytoplasm — it's not stored in a nucleus.

2.1   C *[1 mark]*

2.2   They absorb light needed for photosynthesis to make food for the plant *[1 mark]*.

2.3   They're where proteins are made in the cell *[1 mark]*.

3.1   How to grade your answer:
      Level 0:   There is no relevant information. *[No marks]*
      Level 1:   There is a brief explanation of how to prepare a slide or how to use a light microscope. *[1 to 2 marks]*
      Level 2:   There is some explanation of how to prepare a slide and use a light microscope. *[3 to 4 marks]*
      Level 3:   There is a clear and detailed explanation of how to prepare a slide and use a light microscope. *[5 to 6 marks]*
      Here are some points your answer may include:
      To prepare a slide:
      Add a drop of water to the middle of a clean slide.
      Cut up an onion and separate it out into layers.
      Use tweezers to peel off some epidermal tissue from the bottom of one of the layers.
      Use tweezers to place the epidermal tissue into the water on the slide.
      Add a drop of iodine solution/stain.
      Place a cover slip on top by standing it upright on the slide, next to the water droplet, then carefully tilting and lowering it so it covers the onion tissue without trapping any air bubbles.

To use a light microscope:
Clip the slide onto the stage.
Select the lowest-powered objective lens.
Use the coarse adjustment knob to move the stage up to just below the objective lens (without looking down the eyepiece).
Look down the eyepiece and use the coarse adjustment knob to move the stage downwards until the image is roughly in focus.
Adjust the focus with the fine adjustment knob, until a clear image of the cells is visible.
To see the cells with greater magnification, swap to a higher-powered objective lens and refocus.

3.2   E.g. real size = 75 µm ÷ 1000 = 0.075 mm
      magnification = image size ÷ real size
      = 7.5 mm ÷ 0.075 mm = **× 100** *[2 marks for correct answer, otherwise 1 mark for correct working.]*

You could have converted the image size to µm here instead — the important thing is that both values have the same units before you stick them in the formula.

Page 27
Chromosomes and Mitosis

Q1 a)   11 ÷ (62 + 11) = 0.150...
         0.150... × 100 = **15%** *[1 mark]*

    b)   E.g. she could see the X-shaped chromosomes in the middle of the cells. / She could see the arms of the chromosomes being pulled apart *[1 mark]*.

Page 28
Binary Fission

Q1   Lots of nutrients *[1 mark]* and a warm environment *[1 mark]*.

Q2   2 hours = 60 × 2 = 120 minutes
      120 minutes + 40 minutes = 160 minutes
      160 ÷ 20 = 8 divisions *[1 mark]*
      $2^8 = 2 \times 2 \times 2 \times 2 \times 2 \times 2 \times 2 \times 2$
      = **256 cells** *[1 mark]*

Page 29
Warm-Up Questions

1)   It's the process by which a cell changes to become specialised for its job.

2)   The cell has a hair-like shape, which gives it a large surface area to absorb water and minerals from the soil.

3)   Copies of the plant can be made by taking stem cells from the meristem and growing them into new, genetically identical plants (clones).

4)   in the nucleus

5)   prokaryotic

Exam Questions

1.1   The amount of DNA is doubling *[1 mark]* so that there is one copy for each new cell *[1 mark]*.

1.2   The two new cells separate *[1 mark]*.

1.3   two *[1 mark]*

2.1 They could be grown into a particular type of cell, which can then be used to replace faulty cells *[1 mark]*.

2.2 Embryonic stem cells have the potential to develop into any kind of cell, whereas adult stem cells can only develop into certain types of cell *[1 mark]*.

2.3 E.g. bone marrow *[1 mark]*.

3 3 hours = $60 \times 3 = 180$ minutes
$180 \div 30 = 6$ divisions
$2^6 = 2 \times 2 \times 2 \times 2 \times 2 \times 2 = $ **64 cells** *[2 marks for correct answer, otherwise 1 mark for correct working.]*

Page 32
Culturing Microorganisms

Q1 a) A *[1 mark]*

b) diameter = 13 mm
radius = $13 \div 2 = 6.5$ mm *[1 mark]*
$\pi r^2 = \pi \times 6.5^2 = 132.7...$
= **133 mm²** *[1 mark]*

c) E.g. a paper disc soaked in sterile water *[1 mark]*.

Page 33
Warm-Up Questions

1) an inoculating loop / a sterile dropping pipette and spreader

2) To prevent contamination of a culture with unwanted microorganisms (that could affect results).

Exam Questions

1.1 B *[1 mark]*

1.2 To show that any difference in the growth of the bacteria is only due to the effect of the antiseptic *[1 mark]*.

2.1 radius = $15 \div 2 = 7.5$ mm
$\pi r^2 = \pi \times 56.25 = 176.7... = $ **177 mm²** *[2 marks for correct answer, otherwise 1 mark for correct working.]*

2.2 The strain of bacteria used in the experiment was resistant to antibiotic Z *[1 mark]*.

Page 34
Diffusion

Q1 a) The ink will diffuse / spread out through the water *[1 mark]*. This is because the ink particles will move from where there is a higher concentration of them (the drop of ink) to where there is a lower concentration of them (the surrounding water) *[1 mark]*.

b) The ink particles will diffuse / spread out faster *[1 mark]*.

Page 36
Osmosis

Q1 Water will move out of the piece of potato by osmosis *[1 mark]*, so its mass will decrease *[1 mark]*.

Page 38
Exchanging Substances

Q1 Surface area:
$(2 \times 2) \times 2 = 8$
$(2 \times 1) \times 4 = 8$
$8 + 8 = 16$ μm² *[1 mark]*
Volume:
$2 \times 2 \times 1 = 4$ μm³ *[1 mark]*
So the surface area to volume ratio
is 16 : 4, or **4 : 1** *[1 mark]*.

Page 40
More on Exchanging Substances

Q1 The flat shape of the leaf increases the area of the underside of the leaf (where gas exchange takes place) *[1 mark]*. This increases the rate at which carbon dioxide can diffuse into the leaf, and therefore the rate at which the plant can photosynthesise *[1 mark]*.

Q2 The damage to the villi is likely to reduce the surface for absorption *[1 mark]*. Therefore, less iron can be absorbed from the digested food in the small intestine into the blood *[1 mark]*.

Pages 42-43
Warm-Up Questions

1) The higher the temperature, the faster the rate of diffusion because the particles have more energy and so move around faster.

2) A partially permeable membrane only allows small molecules (e.g. water) to diffuse through it.

3) Osmosis and active transport.

4) They're thin, they have a large surface area, they have lots of blood vessels and they're often ventilated.

5) E.g. alveoli (in the lung) and villi (in the small intestine).

6) Any two from: e.g. it is made up of gill filaments which give a large surface area. / Each gill filament is covered in lamellae, which further increases the surface area. / The lamellae have a thin surface layer of cells. / The lamellae have lots of capillaries. / A large concentration gradient is maintained between the water and the blood.

Exam Questions

1 The time taken will decrease *[1 mark]*. There will be more ammonia gas particles at the end of the tube where they are injected, meaning a greater concentration gradient between that end and the end where the litmus paper is *[1 mark]*. This means an increased rate of diffusion, so the gas particles will reach the litmus paper more quickly *[1 mark]*.

2.1 The potato cylinder in tube D, because this tube contains the most concentrated sugar solution so this cylinder will have lost the most water *[1 mark]* by osmosis *[1 mark]*.

2.2 Tube A contained distilled water, so some of the water moved by osmosis into the potato cylinder *[1 mark]* from an area of high water concentration to an area of low water concentration *[1 mark]*.

3.1 By diffusion down their concentration gradients into the blood *[1 mark]*, and by active transport, against their concentration gradient *[1 mark]*.

3.2 E.g. they increase the surface area to maximise absorption *[1 mark]*. They have a thin wall/a single layer of surface cells to reduce the distance across which diffusion occurs *[1 mark]*. They have a good blood supply for the uptake of substances *[1 mark]*.

4.1 diffusion *[1 mark]*

The acid must by moving by diffusion here as it is moving from a region of higher concentration (outside the cubes) to a region of lower concentration (inside the cubes, which don't contain any acid to start with).

4.2 $(835 + 825 + 842 + 838) \div 4 =$ **835 s**
[2 marks for correct answer, otherwise 1 mark for correct working.]

4.3 Surface area: $(10 \times 10) \times 6 = 600$ mm^2
Volume: $10 \times 10 \times 10 = 1000$ mm^3
So the surface area to volume ratio is 600 : 1000, which simplifies to **3 : 5**
[3 marks for correct answer, otherwise 1 mark for correct surface area and 1 mark for correct volume.]

600 and 1000 are both divisible by 200. If you don't spot this straight away, you could simplify the ratio by first dividing both sides by 100, then by 2.

4.4 As the size of the gelatine cube increases, the time taken for the cube to become yellow increases *[1 mark]*. This is because there is a greater distance for the acid to travel in the bigger cubes / the bigger cubes have a smaller surface area to volume ratio *[1 mark]*, which decreases the rate of diffusion *[1 mark]*.

Topic 2 — Organisation

Page 49
Investigating Enzymatic Reactions

Q1 2 minutes $= 2 \times 60 = 120$ seconds
$36 \div 120 =$ **0.3 cm^3/s** *[1 mark]*

Pages 54-55
Warm-Up Questions

1) A group of organs working together to perform a particular function.

2) The pH at which the enzyme works best.

3) a) amylase
   b) protease
   c) lipase

Carbohydrases (e.g. amylase) break down carbohydrates, such as starch. Proteases break down proteins, and lipases break down lipids (fats).

4) a) (simple) sugars
   b) amino acids
   c) glycerol and fatty acids

5) stomach, pancreas, small intestine

6) E.g. break up the food using a pestle and mortar. Then transfer the ground up food to a beaker and add some distilled water. Next, stir the mixture with a glass rod, and finally filter the solution using a funnel lined with filter paper.

Exam Questions

1.1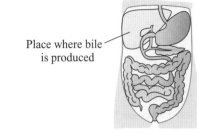
Place where bile is produced
[1 mark]

1.2 It neutralises the hydrochloric acid from the stomach *[1 mark]*.

1.3 It emulsifies fats *[1 mark]* to give a much bigger surface area of fat for the enzyme lipase to work on *[1 mark]*.

2.1 The enzyme has a specific shape which will only fit with one type of substrate *[1 mark]*.

2.2 It would break the bonds in the enzyme and change the shape of the enzyme's active site/denature the enzyme *[1 mark]*. This would mean the substrate would no longer fit into it so the enzyme wouldn't work anymore *[1 mark]*.

A similar thing happens when the pH or the temperature is too high — the bonds are disrupted and the shape of the active site may change.

3.1 Accept answers between 38 °C and 40 °C *[1 mark]*.

3.2 Enzyme B, because it has an unusually high optimum temperature which it would need to work in the hot vent *[1 mark]*.

4 The food sample contains starch *[1 mark]* and lipids *[1 mark]*, but no proteins *[1 mark]*.

5.1 To prevent the starch coming into contact with amylase in the syringe, which would have started the reaction before he had started the stop clock *[1 mark]*.

5.2 Rate $= 1000 \div 60 =$ **17 s^{-1} (2 s.f.)** *[1 mark]*

5.3 Repeat the experiment using buffers with a range of different pH values and compare the results *[1 mark]*.

Page 59
Circulatory System — Blood Vessels

Q1 2.175 l $\times 1000 = 2175$ ml *[1 mark]*
$2175 \div 8.7 =$ **250 ml/min** *[1 mark]*

Page 60
Circulatory System — Blood

Q1 They help the blood to clot at a wound *[1 mark]*.

Q2 To carry oxygen from the lungs to all the cells in the body *[1 mark]*.

Pages 61-62
Warm-Up Questions

1) bronchi

2) They supply oxygenated blood to the heart itself.

3) A device that is implanted under the skin and has a wire going to the heart. It produces an electric current to keep the heart beating regularly.

4) They carry blood back to the heart.

5) platelets

Exam Questions

1.1 $495 \div 12 =$ **41 breaths per minute** *[1 mark]*

You might be wondering why the answer has been rounded to 41 when the calculator said 41.25. That's because you can't get a quarter of a breath.

1.2 Resting heart rate is controlled by a group of cells in the right atrium wall that act as a pacemaker *[1 mark]*.

2.1 It is biconcave, which gives it a large surface area for absorbing oxygen *[1 mark]*.

2.2 E.g. it contains haemoglobin *[1 mark]* which binds with oxygen so it can be carried to the body tissues *[1 mark]*. / It has no nucleus *[1 mark]* so there is space to carry oxygen *[1 mark]*.

2.3 White blood cells *[1 mark]*. They defend the body against infection *[1 mark]*.

2.4 They have permeable walls *[1 mark]*, so substances can diffuse in and out *[1 mark]*. Their walls are usually only one cell thick *[1 mark]*, which increases the rate of diffusion by decreasing the distance over which it occurs *[1 mark]*.

2.5 $150 \text{ s} \div 60 = 2.5 \text{ min}$
$1155 \div 2.5 =$ **462 ml/min** *[2 marks for correct answer, otherwise 1 mark for correct working.]*

Make sure you read the question carefully — if you gave your answer in ml/second you wouldn't have got all the marks available.

3.1 A — aorta, B — vena cava, C — left atrium *[1 mark]*

3.2 It pumps blood around the body *[1 mark]*.

3.3 To prevent the backflow of blood *[1 mark]*.

3.4 How to grade your answer:

Level 0: There is no relevant information. *[No marks]*

Level 1: There are some relevant points describing how deoxygenated blood passes through the heart to reach the lungs but the answer is missing some detail. *[1 to 2 marks]*

Level 2: There is a clear, detailed description of how deoxygenated blood passes through the heart to reach the lungs. *[3 to 4 marks]*

Here are some points your answer may include:
Deoxygenated blood enters the right atrium through the vena cava.
The right atrium contracts.
The blood passes through a valve into the right ventricle.
The right ventricle contracts, forcing the blood through the pulmonary artery and out of the heart towards the lungs.

4.1 E.g. the vein has a bigger lumen/thinner wall/valves *[1 mark]*. / The artery has a smaller lumen/thicker wall/ no valves *[1 mark]*.

To answer this question, you needed to think about how the structure of veins and arteries differ — and how you could tell them apart by just looking at them.

4.2 The vein, because it has a thinner wall/less muscle in its wall/isn't as strong *[1 mark]*.

Page 66
Warm-Up Questions

1) the coronary arteries

2) a) a stent

b) E.g. complications during the operation, infection from surgery and developing a blood clot/thrombosis.

3) A mechanical device that is put into a person to pump blood if their own heart fails.

Exam Questions

1.1 fatty material *[1 mark]*

1.2 The fatty material causes the coronary arteries to become narrow, so blood flow to the heart muscle is restricted *[1 mark]*. This reduces (or stops) the delivery of oxygen to the heart muscle *[1 mark]*.

2.1 It could mean that blood flows in both directions rather than just forward *[1 mark]*, so the blood wouldn't circulate as effectively as normal *[1 mark]*.

2.2 Biological valves *[1 mark]* — these are replacement valves that can be taken from humans or other mammals *[1 mark]*.
Mechanical valves *[1 mark]* — these are man-made replacement valves *[1 mark]*.

2.3 E.g. it requires surgery, which could lead to bleeding/ infection. / There could be problems with blood clots *[1 mark]*.

3.1 Statins are drugs that can reduce the amount of 'bad' cholesterol present in the bloodstream *[1 mark]*. This slows down the rate of fatty deposits forming, which reduces the likelihood of coronary heart disease developing *[1 mark]*.

3.2 E.g. the patient has to remember to take them every day. / Statins can sometimes cause negative side effects. / The effect of taking statins isn't instant *[1 mark]*.

Page 72
Warm-Up Questions

1) The state of physical and mental wellbeing.

2) It can be spread from person to person or between people and animals.

3) E.g. money is needed to research/treat the diseases. / People with non-communicable diseases may be unable to work, which may reduce the country's economy.

4) The presence of certain substances in the body. / The presence of certain substances in the environment.

Exam Questions

1.1 A risk factor is something that is linked to an increase in the likelihood that a person will develop a certain disease during their lifetime *[1 mark]*.

1.2 E.g. smoking *[1 mark]*.

1.3 E.g. ionising radiation *[1 mark]*.

2.1 Uncontrolled cell division *[1 mark]*.

2.2 malignant *[1 mark]*

2.3 Tumour cells can break off and spread to other parts of the body by travelling in the bloodstream *[1 mark]*. The malignant cells then invade healthy tissues elsewhere in the body and form secondary tumours *[1 mark]*.

3.1 A disease that cannot spread between people or between animals and people *[1 mark]*.

3.2 Because of the problem with their immune system, their body is less likely to be able to defend itself against the pathogen that causes influenza *[1 mark]*.

Page 77
Measuring Transpiration and Stomata

Q1 Aloe vera, because the transpiration rate will be higher in the hot, dry area *[1 mark]*, so the aloe vera will have fewer stomata to help conserve water *[1 mark]*.

Pages 78-79
Warm-Up Questions

1) Meristem tissue is found at the growing tips of roots and shoots and is able to differentiate into lots of different types of plant cell.

2) palisade mesophyll tissue

3) False

4) light intensity, temperature, air flow, humidity

Exam Questions

1 spongy mesophyll tissue *[1 mark]*

2.1 xylem vessels *[1 mark]*

2.2 They are made of dead cells joined end to end *[1 mark]* with no end walls between them and therefore a hole down the middle *[1 mark]*. They're strengthened with a material called lignin *[1 mark]*.

2.3 transpiration *[1 mark]*

3.1 phloem *[1 mark]*

3.2 They are made of columns of elongated living cells with small pores in the end walls *[1 mark]* to allow cell sap to flow through *[1 mark]*.

3.3 translocation *[1 mark]*

4.1 The water level in the vase would decrease more slowly *[1 mark]*, as the rate of transpiration would be lower *[1 mark]*. This is because water molecules have less energy at lower temperatures, meaning they don't diffuse/evaporate as quickly from the leaves *[1 mark]*.

4.2 How to grade your answer:
Level 0: There is no relevant information. *[No marks]*
Level 1: The correct diagram is identified and the answer links the shape of the guard cell to the closing of the stomata at night. *[1 to 2 marks]*
Level 2: The correct diagram is identified and the answer clearly explains how the shape of the guard cell changes at night, allowing the stomata to close to reduce water loss when gas exchange is not required. *[3 to 4 marks]*
Here are some points your answer may include:
A, because the guard cell is most flaccid.
Flaccid guard cells mean that the stomata would be closed.
The stomata close at night as they don't need to be open for gas exchange as photosynthesis doesn't happen in the dark.
The closing of the stomata at night prevents water being lost through transpiration.

5.1 $(10 + 11 + 9) \div 3 = $ **10% *[2 marks for correct answer, otherwise 1 mark for correct working]***

5.2 The movement of air from the fan sweeps away water vapour, maintaining a low concentration of water outside the leaf *[1 mark]* and increasing the rate at which water is lost through diffusion *[1 mark]*. This means that the plants next to the fan would lose more water (and therefore more mass) than the plants in a still room in the same amount of time *[1 mark]*.

5.3 The rate of transpiration would be slower *[1 mark]* since most water loss occurs through the stomata, which are on the underside of the leaves *[1 mark]*.

5.4 E.g. you could put a new group of 3 basil plants in a separate room *[1 mark]* and increase the humidity in the room by misting/spraying the air with water *[1 mark]*.

If you've thought of another sensible way to increase or decrease the humidity around the plants, you'd still get the mark in the exam.

Topic 3 — Infection and Response

Page 86
Warm-Up Questions

1) A communicable disease is a disease that is easily spread.

2) E.g. measles, HIV and tobacco mosaic virus.

3) A red skin rash.

4) It causes purple or black spots to develop on the leaves, which can then turn yellow and drop off.

5) By sexual contact.

6) Vaccinations stop people from developing the disease, so that they cannot pass it on to someone else.

Exam Questions

1.1 Initial symptoms are flu-like *[1 mark]*.

1.2 Pain when the infected person urinates *[1 mark]*. Thick yellow or green discharge from the vagina or penis *[1 mark]*.

1.3 Any two from: e.g. fever / stomach cramps / vomiting / diarrhoea *[2 marks]*.

2.1 A microorganism that can cause disease *[1 mark]*.

2.2 The tobacco mosaic virus *[1 mark]*. It can reduce the growth of the plant *[1 mark]*.

2.3 By sexual contact *[1 mark]*, or by exchanging bodily fluids such as blood *[1 mark]*.

3.1 To prevent the contamination of food by disease-causing pathogens that may be on the chefs' hands *[1 mark]*.

3.2 Malaria is spread by vectors *[1 mark]* and not through contaminated food/surfaces / skin to skin contact *[1 mark]*.

3.3 E.g. mosquitoes are the vectors of malaria, so destroying mosquitoes will prevent malaria being spread between people *[1 mark]*.

Page 88
Fighting Disease — Vaccination

Q1 Basia's white blood cells recognise the antigens on the flu virus and rapidly produce antibodies, which kill the pathogen *[1 mark]*. Cassian's white blood cells don't recognise the antigens, so it takes a while for them to produce antibodies and he becomes ill in the meantime *[1 mark]*.

Pages 93-94
Warm-Up Questions

1) The skin acts as a barrier to pathogens and secretes antimicrobial substances that kill them.

2) To destroy pathogens that enter the body.

3) foxgloves

4) Whether the drug works and produces the effect you're looking for.

5) A placebo is a substance that's like the real drug but doesn't do anything.

6) Using a placebo allows the doctor to see the actual difference the drug makes (to a patient's illness/ symptoms).

Exam Questions

1.1 They trap particles that could contain pathogens *[1 mark]*.

1.2 They waft the mucus up to the back of the throat where it can be swallowed *[1 mark]*.

1.3 (hydrochloric) acid *[1 mark]*

2.1 human volunteers *[1 mark]*

Drugs are tested on human cells, live animals and human tissue in pre-clinical trials. If a drug makes it through the pre-clinical trials, it's then tested on human volunteers in a clinical trial.

2.2 In a double blind trial neither the patient nor the doctor *[1 mark]* knows who is receiving the drug and who is receiving the placebo until all the results have been gathered *[1 mark]*.

2.3 dosage *[1 mark]*, efficacy/how well the drug works *[1 mark]*

2.4 Peer review is where other scientists check the work to make sure it is valid/has been carried out rigorously *[1 mark]*. It's done help to prevent false claims being made about the results *[1 mark]*.

3.1 Engulfing foreign cells and digesting them / phagocytosis *[1 mark]*.

3.2 A particular antibody will only lock onto a specific type of antigen from one type of pathogen *[1 mark]*.

4.1 *Penicillium* mould / *Penicillium notatum* *[1 mark]*

4.2 Overuse of antibiotics may increase the rate of development of resistant strains of bacteria *[1 mark]*. This will make bacterial infections harder to treat in the future *[1 mark]*.

4.3 Antibiotics cannot kill viruses *[1 mark]*.

5.1 E.g. a painkiller/aspirin *[1 mark]*.

5.2 Rubella is a virus and viruses reproduce using your body cells *[1 mark]*, which makes it very difficult to develop drugs that destroy just the virus without killing the body's cells *[1 mark]*.

5.3 How to grade your answer:

Level 0: There is no relevant information. *[No marks]*

Level 1: There is a brief explanation of how vaccination against rubella can prevent a person catching the disease or how having a large proportion of vaccinated individuals in a population reduces the risk of rubella for people who are not vaccinated. *[1 to 2 marks]*

Level 2: There is some explanation of how vaccination against rubella can prevent a person catching the disease and how having a large proportion of vaccinated individuals in a population reduces the risk of rubella for people who are not vaccinated. *[3 to 4 marks]*

Level 3: There is a clear and detailed explanation of how vaccination against rubella can prevent a person catching the disease and how having a large proportion of vaccinated individuals in a population reduces the risk of rubella for people who are not vaccinated. *[5 to 6 marks]*

Here are some points your answer may include:
When a person is vaccinated against rubella, they are injected with dead or inactive rubella viruses.
The dead or inactive viruses carry antigens, which cause the body to produce antibodies to attack them.
If live rubella viruses infect the body after this, white blood cells can rapidly mass produce antibodies to defeat the virus.
If a large proportion of the population is vaccinated against rubella, then there are fewer people who are able to pass the disease on.
This means that even someone who hasn't been vaccinated is less likely to catch the disease.

5.4 E.g. they may be worried that they will have a bad reaction to a vaccine. / Vaccines don't always work and so the person might not be given immunity *[1 mark]*.

Page 97
Monoclonal Antibodies

Q1 The fluorescent antibodies will bind to the antigens on the bacteria *[1 mark]*, so any bacteria that are present in the sample will be detected / will glow *[1 mark]*.

Page 99
Warm-Up Questions

1) a (B-)lymphocyte

2) A (B-)lymphocyte and a tumour cell.

3) stunted growth

4) It acts as a physical defence, preventing pathogens from entering the plant.

Exam Questions

1   chlorosis *[1 mark]*

2.1   A waxy cuticle on leaves *[1 mark]*, cellulose cell walls *[1 mark]*, layers of dead cells around stems, e.g. bark *[1 mark]*.

2.2   Magnesium ions are needed for making chlorophyll, which is needed for photosynthesis *[1 mark]*.

2.3   Any two from: e.g. stunted growth / spots on the leaves / patches of decay / abnormal growths / malformed leaves or stems. *[2 marks — 1 mark for each correct answer.]*

3.1   A radioactive substance *[1 mark]*, a toxic drug *[1 mark]*, a chemical which stops cells growing and dividing *[1 mark]*.

3.2   The side effects of an antibody-based drug are lower than for standard treatment methods *[1 mark]*, because monoclonal antibodies target specific cells *[1 mark]*.

4   A will not turn blue if the woman is not pregnant *[1 mark]*, so B is included to show that the test has worked/the testing stick is not faulty if the woman is not pregnant *[1 mark]*.
If B turns blue, it shows that the urine has travelled all the way up the stick/past A on the stick *[1 mark]*.

Topic 4 — Bioenergetics

Page 106
Measuring the Rate of Photosynthesis

Q1   The light intensity becomes four times smaller *[1 mark]*.

Q2   light intensity $\propto \dfrac{1}{\text{distance}^2}$

$1 \div 15^2 = 0.00444...$ a.u. *[1 mark]*
$1 \div 5^2 = 0.04$ a.u. *[1 mark]*
$0.04 \div 0.00444... = 9$ *[1 mark]*

Pages 108-109
Warm-Up Questions

1) glucose

2) A limiting factor is something that stops photosynthesis from happening any faster.

3) If the temperature's too high, the plant's enzymes will be denatured, so the rate of photosynthesis rapidly decreases.

Remember, if the temperature is too high for an enzyme, the bonds holding it together may break. This can cause the shape of the enzyme's active site to change, denaturing the enzyme.

4) E.g. oxygen production.

5) light intensity $\propto \dfrac{1}{\text{distance}^2}$

6) To increase the plants' growth so that more/bigger tomatoes are produced and a bigger profit can be made from selling them.

Exam Questions

1.1   carbon dioxide + water *[1 mark]* $\overset{\text{light}}{\to}$ glucose + oxygen *[1 mark]*

1.2   cellulose *[1 mark]*

1.3   Any two from: e.g. for respiration. / For storage as lipids/ oils or fats. / For storage as insoluble starch. / For making amino acids, which are then made into proteins. *[2 marks]*

2.1   By counting the number of bubbles produced / by measuring the volume of gas produced, in a given time/ at regular intervals *[1 mark]*.

2.2   Dependent variable — rate of photosynthesis/number of bubbles in a given time/volume of gas in a given time *[1 mark]*.
Independent variable — light intensity *[1 mark]*.

2.3   E.g. carbon dioxide concentration in the water/ temperature/the plant being used *[1 mark]*.

3.1   At low light intensities, increasing the CO_2 concentration has no effect *[1 mark]*, but at higher light intensities, increasing the concentration of CO_2 increases the maximum rate of photosynthesis *[1 mark]*.

3.2   The rate of photosynthesis does not continue to increase because temperature or the level of carbon dioxide becomes the limiting factor *[1 mark]*.

You don't know if the temperature was kept constant or not, so either the level of carbon dioxide or temperature could have been the limiting factor here — there's no way of knowing.

4.1

[1 mark]

4.2   Plants need both chlorophyll and light to photosynthesise and produce starch — there is only chlorophyll in the green area of the plant *[1 mark]*, and light can only reach parts of the leaf not covered by black paper *[1 mark]*.

5   light intensity $= \dfrac{1}{d^2}$
$= \dfrac{1}{7.5^2}$
$= \mathbf{0.018}$ **a.u. (2 s.f.)**
[2 marks for correct answer, otherwise 1 mark for correct working.]

Page 113
Exercise

Q1 Running *[1 mark]*. It raises the pulse rate the most, so it is the most vigorous type of exercise *[1 mark]*. The more vigorous the exercise, the more anaerobic respiration will be taking place in the muscles *[1 mark]*. Anaerobic respiration produces lactic acid, so running will lead to the greatest build up of lactic acid in the blood *[1 mark]*.

Page 114
Warm-Up Questions

1) Any two from: e.g. to build up larger molecules from smaller ones. / To contract muscles. / To keep body temperature steady.

2) The sum of all of the reactions that happen in a cell or the body.

3) Glucose and oxygen.

4) fermentation

5) Breathing rate increases, breath volume increases and heart rate increases.

Exam Questions

1.1 To release energy *[1 mark]*.

1.2 Any two from: e.g. aerobic respiration uses oxygen, anaerobic respiration does not. / Glucose is broken down fully during aerobic respiration but is only partially broken down during anaerobic respiration. / Aerobic respiration doesn't produce lactic acid, anaerobic respiration does. / Aerobic respiration releases more energy than anaerobic respiration. *[2 marks]*

1.3 glucose + oxygen *[1 mark]* → carbon dioxide + water *[1 mark]*

2.1 glucose → lactic acid *[1 mark]*

2.2 During vigorous exercise, the body can't supply enough oxygen to the muscles *[1 mark]*. It uses anaerobic respiration to provide energy without using oxygen, which keeps the muscles going for longer *[1 mark]*.

3.1 Because during exercise the muscles need more energy from respiration *[1 mark]*, and this respiration requires oxygen *[1 mark]*.

3.2 Because there is an oxygen debt / oxygen is needed to react with the lactic acid that has built up *[1 mark]*.

Topic 5 — Homeostasis and Response

Page 119
Reflexes

Q1 A rapid, automatic response to a stimulus that doesn't involve the conscious part of the brain *[1 mark]*.

Q2 a) muscle *[1 mark]*

b) The heat stimulus is detected by receptors in the hand *[1 mark]*, which send impulses along a sensory neurone to the CNS *[1 mark]*. The impulses are transferred to a relay neurone *[1 mark]*. They are then transferred to a motor neurone and travel along it to the effector/muscle *[1 mark]*.

Page 120
Investigating Reaction Time

Q1 a) 242 + 256 + 253 + 249 + 235 = 1235 *[1 mark]*
   1235 ÷ 5 = **247 ms** *[1 mark]*

b) Any two from: e.g. the hand each person used to click the mouse / the computer equipment/programme used / the amount of energy drink they consumed / the type of energy drink used / the time between consuming the energy drink and taking the test *[2 marks]*.

Page 121
Warm-Up Questions

1) The maintenance of a stable internal environment in response to changes in both internal and external conditions.

2) E.g. body temperature, blood glucose level, water content.

3) synapse

4) sensory neurone, relay neurone, motor neurone

5) E.g. age / gender / drugs / caffeine.

Exam Questions

1.1 Stimulus: appearance of red triangle *[1 mark]*
   Receptors: cells in the eye / light receptor cells *[1 mark]*
   Effectors: muscles (in hand controlling mouse) *[1 mark]*

1.2 343 × 3 = 1029
   1029 − 328 − 346 = **355 ms** *[2 marks for the correct answer, otherwise 1 mark for the correct calculation]*

2.1 motor neurone *[1 mark]*

2.2 Muscle *[1 mark]*, which contracts to move the baby's finger *[1 mark]*.

2.3 When the electrical impulse reaches the end of the neurone, it stimulates the release of a chemical *[1 mark]*. The chemical diffuses across the synapse to activate an electrical impulse in the next neurone *[1 mark]*.

2.4 In a baby older than 6 months, the pathway will involve conscious parts of the brain, whereas in a newborn baby it won't. / In a baby older than 6 months, the response will not be produced as rapidly as in the newborn baby *[1 mark]*.

The response in the baby older than 6 months is not a reflex — it chooses whether it wants to grasp an object. Remember, reflexes are automatic — they don't involve conscious parts of the brain, which makes the response much faster.

Pages 128-129
Warm-Up Questions

1) cerebellum

2) cornea

3) The lenses refract the light rays so they focus on the retina.

4) The lens is the wrong shape / refracts the light too much or the eyeball is too long. So images of distant objects are brought into focus in front of the retina.

5) thermoregulatory centre

Exam Questions

1.1 A: cornea *[1 mark]*
B: pupil *[1 mark]*

1.2 To control the diameter of the pupil/the amount of light entering the eye *[1 mark]*.

1.3 Information is sent using impulses *[1 mark]*, via the optic nerve *[1 mark]*.

2.1 cerebral cortex *[1 mark]*

2.2 E.g. the doctor may be concerned that removing the tumour will cause physical damage to the brain *[1 mark]*. The doctor may also be concerned that removing the tumour will cause increased problems with brain function *[1 mark]*.

3.1 Vasoconstriction *[1 mark]*. Less blood flows through the blood vessels close to the surface of the skin *[1 mark]*. This reduces the transfer of energy from the skin to the environment, so helps to keep the body warm *[1 mark]*.

3.2 Sweat glands respond by stopping sweat production *[1 mark]*, because sweat transfers energy from the body to the environment when it evaporates *[1 mark]*.

3.3 Skin temperature will increase, so the sweat glands will respond by producing lots of sweat *[1 mark]*. Drinking water will help to restore the water balance in the body *[1 mark]*.

3.4 The blood vessels would widen/dilate / vasodilation would occur *[1 mark]*. This allows more blood to flow near to the surface of the skin *[1 mark]* so more energy can be transferred to the surroundings, cooling the body *[1 mark]*.

4.1 A, because the pupil is dilated/wider in this eye *[1 mark]*, which allows more light to enter the eye/reach the light receptors in the eye *[1 mark]*.

4.2 radial muscles *[1 mark]*

4.3 Reflex responses happen very quickly/are automatic *[1 mark]* so the eye can adjust quickly to prevent the retina being damaged by bright light *[1 mark]*.

5.1 The ciliary muscles relax *[1 mark]* allowing the suspensory ligaments to pull tight *[1 mark]*, which results in the lens becoming thinner/less rounded *[1 mark]*.

5.2 If the lens cannot form a rounded shape, light from nearby objects won't be refracted/bent enough to be focused on the retina *[1 mark]*. This means that people with presbyopia will be unable to focus on nearby objects *[1 mark]*.

Page 132
Controlling Blood Glucose

Q1 Curve 1, because the secretion rate is high when the blood glucose level is low / the secretion rate decreases as the blood glucose level rises *[1 mark]*. Glucagon increases the blood glucose level, so it is secreted when the blood glucose level becomes too low *[1 mark]*.

Page 134
Warm-Up Questions

1) In the blood.

2) E.g. pituitary gland, thyroid gland, adrenal gland, pancreas, testes.

3) A hormonal response.

4) Removes glucose from the blood. / Makes the liver turn glucose into glycogen for storage.

5) A condition in which the body becomes resistant to its own insulin.

Exam Questions

1.1 Organ A is the pancreas *[1 mark]*.
Organ B is the liver *[1 mark]*.

1.2 Eating carbohydrates *[1 mark]*.

1.3 The pancreas/organ A produces little or no insulin *[1 mark]*. This means that the liver/organ B is unable to remove glucose from the blood for storage *[1 mark]*. So the blood glucose level is able to rise to a dangerously high level *[1 mark]*.

1.4 It makes the liver/organ B turn glycogen into glucose for release into the blood *[1 mark]*.

2 The pituitary gland releases hormones that act on other glands, directing them to release hormones *[1 mark]*. If a pituitary hormone that acts on the thyroid gland is not released *[1 mark]*, then the thyroid gland may also stop releasing hormones, resulting in the symptoms described *[1 mark]*.

Page 136
The Kidneys

Q1 The kidneys will reabsorb less water *[1 mark]*, so too much water may be lost from the body in urine *[1 mark]*.

Page 138
Warm-Up Questions

1) The deamination of amino acids in the liver produces ammonia as a waste product. This is then converted into urea in the liver.

2) (excess) ions, (excess) water

3) ADH/anti-diuretic hormone

4) pituitary gland

5) It allows ions and waste substances to diffuse out of the blood into the dialysis fluid, but not large molecules like proteins (so they stay in the blood).

Exam Questions

1.1

Substances	Blood	Filtrate
glucose	✗	✓
urea	✗	✓
ions	✗	✓

[2 marks — 1 mark for each correct row of the table]

Water is also filtered out of the blood into the filtrate However, it's not all filtered out (otherwise the blood wouldn't be a liquid anymore) so the missing word in the table can't be water.

1.2 selective reabsorption *[1 mark]*

2.1 The urea diffuses out through the dialysis membrane / into the dialysis fluid *[1 mark]*, because the concentration of urea in the blood is higher than in the dialysis fluid / because the dialysis fluid contains no urea *[1 mark]*.

2.2 The dialysis fluid contains the same concentration of glucose as healthy blood *[1 mark]*, so there is no concentration gradient and no net movement of glucose *[1 mark]*.

2.3 E.g. she will not have to have dialysis sessions three times every week for hours each time *[1 mark]*. / A kidney transplant is cheaper than dialysis in the long term *[1 mark]*.

2.4 E.g. there are long waiting lists for kidneys. / There's a risk that the donor kidney will be rejected by the patient's immune system *[1 mark]*.

3 How to grade your answer:

Level 0: There is no relevant information. *[No marks]*

Level 1: There is a brief explanation of why the runner's urine was a darker colour than normal. *[1 to 2 marks]*

Level 2: There is some explanation of why the runner's urine was a darker colour than normal. *[3 to 4 marks]*

Level 3: There is a clear and detailed explanation of why the runner's urine was a darker colour than normal. *[5 to 6 marks]*

Here are some points your answer may include:
As the runner ran, she sweated, resulting in water loss and less water in her blood.
Receptors in her brain detected the decreased water content of her blood.
The coordination centre in the brain received this information and coordinated a response by the pituitary gland.
The pituitary gland released ADH (anti-diuretic hormone) into the blood.
The ADH caused the kidneys to reabsorb more water, resulting in less water being released in the runner's urine.
So the urine was more concentrated and appeared darker in colour.

Page 145
Warm-Up Questions

1) FSH/follicle-stimulating hormone

2) Any three from: e.g. progesterone-only pill / contraceptive implant / contraceptive injection / plastic IUD.

3) E.g. it doesn't always work. / It can be expensive. / Too many eggs can be stimulated, resulting in multiple pregnancies.

4) They stimulate several eggs to mature.

5) thyroid

Exam Questions

1.1 It inhibits it *[1 mark]*.

1.2 progesterone *[1 mark]*

1.3 day 14 *[1 mark]*

2.1 Keeping oestrogen levels permanently high inhibits production of FSH *[1 mark]*, so no eggs mature / so egg development and production stop *[1 mark]*.

2.2 E.g. by stimulating the production of thick cervical mucus *[1 mark]*, which prevents any sperm getting through and reaching the egg *[1 mark]*.

2.3 E.g. the contraceptive implant *[1 mark]*, as this is effective for three years once inserted and so does not have to be thought about on a daily basis *[1 mark]*. / The contraceptive injection *[1 mark]*, as this is effective for 2 to 3 months and so does not have to be thought about on a daily basis *[1 mark]*. / The contraceptive patch *[1 mark]*, as each patch lasts one week, so does not have to be thought about on a daily basis.

2.4 E.g. male/female sterilisation *[1 mark]*.

3 The cat's heart rate would increase *[1 mark]* because adrenaline is released *[1 mark]*. The increased heart rate increases the rate of delivery of glucose and oxygen *[1 mark]* to the brain and muscle cells *[1 mark]*, which prepares the cat to escape danger/the dog by fight or flight *[1 mark]*.

Page 149
Warm-Up Questions

1) auxin

2) More auxin accumulates on the side of the shoot that's in the shade. This causes the shaded side to elongate faster, so the shoot bends towards the light.

3) E.g. to stimulate seed germination / to control dormancy / to stimulate flowering / to grow larger fruit.

4) To control the time at which fruit ripens.

Exam Questions

1.1 auxin *[1 mark]*

1.2 She could use a rooting powder containing auxin *[1 mark]* to help the cutting produce roots rapidly and start growing as a new plant *[1 mark]*.

1.3 gibberellin *[1 mark]*

2.1 The shoot has grown upwards, away from gravity *[1 mark]*.

2.2 Auxin accumulated on the lower side of the shoot *[1 mark]*. This caused the lower side of the shoot to elongate faster, so the shoot bends upwards *[1 mark]*.

2.3 Any two from: e.g. the number of beans on the soil *[1 mark]* / the type of beans used *[1 mark]* / the amount of water in the soil *[1 mark]* / the depth of the soil *[1 mark]* / the temperature the beans are kept at *[1 mark]* / the length of time the beans are left for *[1 mark]*.

Topic 6 — Inheritance, Variation and Evolution

Page 153
The Structure of DNA and Protein Synthesis

Q1 a) Four *[1 mark]*.

  b) GAGGATGCACTA *[1 mark]*.

Page 156
Warm-Up Questions

1) chromosomes

2) A small section of DNA found on a chromosome that codes for a particular sequence of amino acids that are put together to make a specific protein.

3) E.g. it allows scientists to identify genes in the genome that are linked to different types of disease. Knowing which genes are linked to inherited diseases could help us to understand them better and could help us to develop effective treatments for them. Scientists can look at genomes to trace the migration of certain populations of people around the world.

4) A and T. C and G.

5) A mutation is a random change in an organism's DNA.

6) Mutations change the DNA base sequence. This can alter the amino acids that the bases code for. This can change the shape of the protein the amino acids make up, which can affect its function.

Exam Questions

1.1 A polymer made up of two strands. *[1 mark]*

1.2 Its genome. *[1 mark]*

Remember, an organism's genome is its entire set of genetic material. A gene is a short section of DNA and a chromosome is a really long structure, which contains genes.

1.3 DNA contains genes *[1 mark]*. Each gene codes for a particular sequence of amino acids *[1 mark]*, which are put together to make a specific protein *[1 mark]*.

2.1 A nucleotide consists of a sugar, a phosphate group and one 'base' *[1 mark]*.

2.2 The code from the GALC gene would be copied into mRNA. / A template would be made using the code in the GALC gene *[1 mark]*. The code would then be carried to a ribosome *[1 mark]*. Amino acids would be brought to the ribosome in the correct order by carrier molecules *[1 mark]*. The amino acids would then be joined together to make the correct enzyme *[1 mark]*.

2.3 The mutation in the GALC gene changes its base sequence *[1 mark]*. This alters the amino acids that the bases code for *[1 mark]*, which changes the shape of the enzyme and its active site *[1 mark]*. A change in the shape of the active site will affect the ability of the substrate to bind to it, altering enzyme activity *[1 mark]*.

2.4 Most mutations have very little or no effect on the production of a specific protein / change a specific protein to such a small extent that its function or appearance is unaffected *[1 mark]*.

Page 158
Meiosis

Q1 23 *[1 mark]*

Page 163
Warm-Up Questions

1) Because there are two parents, the offspring contain a mixture of their parents' genes. This mixture of genetic information produces variation.

2) two

3) asexual

4) XX

Exam Questions

1.1 asexual *[1 mark]*

1.2 They will be genetically identical *[1 mark]*.

Remember, asexual reproduction produces clones — offspring are exactly the same as the parent.

2.1 three *[1 mark]*

When a cell undergoes meiosis, each new cell ends up with half the number of chromosomes as in the original cell.

2.2 four *[1 mark]*

Remember, when a cell undergoes meiosis, four gametes are produced — it doesn't matter whether you're talking about human cells or mosquito cells.

2.3 Meiosis produces gametes that are genetically different to each other *[1 mark]*. A male gamete and a female gamete then combine at fertilisation *[1 mark]*, so the offspring inherits a mixture of chromosomes from both parents *[1 mark]*.

2.4 Any three from: e.g. only one parent is needed *[1 mark]*. / It uses less energy *[1 mark]*. / It is faster *[1 mark]*. / It's possible to produce many identical offspring *[1 mark]*.

2.5 The malarial parasite reproduces sexually whilst in the mosquito, which leads to genetic variation *[1 mark]*.

Page 167
More Genetic Diagrams

Q1

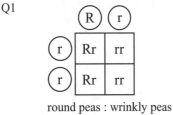

round peas : wrinkly peas
1 : 1

[1 mark for correct gametes, 1 mark for correct offspring genotypes and 1 mark for correct ratio.]

Pages 172-173
Warm-Up Questions

1) Different versions of the same gene.

2) The combination of alleles an organism has.

3) Because the allele which causes cystic fibrosis is recessive, so you have to have two recessive alleles to have the disorder. Heterozygous people have one dominant and one recessive allele.

4) It's a genetic disorder where a baby is born with extra fingers or toes.

5) Taking a cell from an embryo and analysing its genes in order to detect genetic disorders.

6) Scientists of the time didn't have the background knowledge to properly understand Mendel's findings because they didn't know about genes, DNA and chromosomes.

Exam Questions

1.1

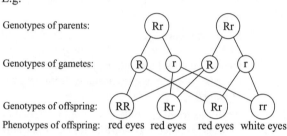

[1 mark for correct genotype of offspring, 1 mark for correct genotypes of gametes]

1.2 1 in 2 / 50% *[1 mark]*

1.3 One is unaffected *[1 mark]* and the other is a carrier of cystic fibrosis *[1 mark]*.

2.1 E.g.

Genotypes of parents: Rr Rr

Genotypes of gametes: R r R r

Genotypes of offspring: RR Rr Rr rr

Phenotypes of offspring: red eyes red eyes red eyes white eyes

[1 mark for correct genotypes of the parents, 1 mark for correct genotypes of offspring, 1 mark for correct phenotypes of offspring]

You could have drawn a Punnett square instead here.

2.2 1 in 4 / 25% *[1 mark]*

3 Dd *[1 mark]*. Polydactyly is a dominant disorder, so if she was DD all of her children would be affected *[1 mark]*.

4.1

female   male

Chromosomes of parents: XX XY

Chromosomes of gametes: X X X Y

Chromosomes of offspring: XX XX XY XY

Sex of offspring: female female male male

[1 mark for correct chromosomes in parents, 1 mark for correct chromosomes in offspring, 1 mark for correct sex of offspring]

4.2 Male children will not inherit the colour blindness allele because they don't inherit an X chromosome from their father *[1 mark]*.

4.3 0 / 0% *[1 mark]*

A daughter of this couple would inherit the recessive colour blindness allele from her father, but also a dominant allele from her mother, so she would not be colour blind.

5.1 AA, Aa *[1 mark]*

5.2 E.g.

Genotypes of parents: aa Aa

Genotypes of gametes: a a A a

Genotypes of offspring: Aa Aa aa aa

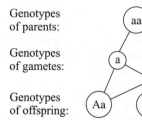

[1 mark for parent with genotype aa, 1 mark for parent with genotype Aa, 1 mark for correct genotypes of offspring]

5.3 50% *[1 mark]*

Offspring with the genotype aa will have albinism.

5.4 Fertilisation is random/the genetic diagram only shows the probability of the outcome, so the numbers of offspring produced will not always be exactly in those proportions *[1 mark]*.

Page 176
Evolution

Q1 There was a variety of tongue lengths in the moth population *[1 mark]*. Moths with longer tongues got more food/nectar and were more likely to survive *[1 mark]*. These moths were more likely to reproduce and pass on the genes responsible for their long tongues *[1 mark]*. So, over time, longer tongues became more common in the moth population *[1 mark]*.

Page 179
Warm-Up Questions

1) Differences between members of the same species that have been caused by the environment/conditions something lives in.

2) Simple life forms that first started to develop over three billion years ago.

3) Any three from: e.g. the environment changes too quickly. / A new predator kills all the individuals. / A new disease kills all the individuals. / They can't compete with another species for food. / A catastrophic event (e.g. a volcanic eruption or collision with an astroid) kills all the individuals.

4) It contradicted the common religious beliefs of the time that all life on earth was created by God. Darwin lacked the evidence that he needed to convince many other scientists. He also didn't have any explanation for why new beneficial characteristics appeared, or how they were passed on to offspring.

Exam Questions

1.1 The difference in weight must be caused by the environment *[1 mark]*, because the twins have exactly the same genes *[1 mark]*.

In this case, the environment can mean the amount of food each twin eats or the amount of exercise they each do.

1.2 No, because if they were caused by genes both twins should have the birthmark *[1 mark]*.

2.1 sexual reproduction/the combining of genes from two parents *[1 mark]*

2.2 Mutations change the sequence of DNA bases *[1 mark]*, which can change the protein produced by a gene *[1 mark]* and lead to new characteristics, increasing variation *[1 mark]*.

2.3 E.g. if the environment changes, some mutations may give individuals a phenotype that makes them more suited to the new environment *[1 mark]*. This would make them more likely to survive (than individuals without the phenotype) *[1 mark]*.

3 How to grade your answer:
   Level 0: There is no relevant information. *[No marks]*
   Level 1: There are some relevant points describing how the stingray has evolved but the answer is missing some detail. *[1 to 2 marks]*
   Level 2: There is a clear, detailed explanation of how the stingray has evolved through natural selection. *[3 to 4 marks]*
   Here are some points your answer may include:
   Ancestors of this stingray showed variation in their appearance.
   The stingrays that looked more like flat rocks were better camouflaged and so less likely to be seen and eaten by predators/more likely to survive.
   This means they were more likely to reproduce.
   As a result, the genes that caused the stingrays to look more like flat rocks were more likely to be passed on to the next generation.
   Over time, the flat rock appearance became more common in the population and the stingray evolved.

Page 180
Selective Breeding

Q1 Select rabbits with floppy ears *[1 mark]* and breed them together to produce offspring *[1 mark]*. Select offspring with floppy ears and breed them together *[1 mark]*. Repeat this over many generations until all of the offspring have floppy ears *[1 mark]*.

Page 185
Warm-Up Questions

1) E.g. to produce plants with large or unusual flowers.
2) Selective breeding reduces the gene pool. This causes an increased chance of organisms inheriting harmful genetic defects. There is also an increased chance that a population could be wiped out by a new disease.
3) E.g. insulin.
4) A few plant cells are put in a growth medium with hormones, and they then grow into new plants that are clones of the parent plant.

Exam Questions

1.1 E.g. to isolate/cut the gene out of the organism's DNA *[1 mark]*.
1.2 E.g. to improve the size/quality of their fruit. / To make them make them resistant to disease/insects/herbicides *[1 mark]*.
1.3 Any two from: e.g. some people are not convinced that GM crops are safe and are concerned that we might not fully understand the effects of eating them on human health. / Some people say that growing GM crops will negatively affect the number of wild flowers and insects that live in and around the crops. / There is concern that the transplanted genes could get out into the natural environment, which could lead to the creation of 'superweeds'. *[2 marks]*

2 The tall and dwarf wheat plants could be bred together *[1 mark]*. The best of the offspring/the offspring with the highest grain yield and highest bad weather resistance could then be bred together *[1 mark]*, and this process repeated over several generations *[1 mark]*.

3.1 Remove the nucleus from the unfertilised egg cell of a sheep *[1 mark]*. Insert a nucleus from an adult sheep's body cell into the empty egg cell *[1 mark]*. Stimulate the egg cell with an electric shock to make it divide *[1 mark]*. When the embryo is a ball of cells, implant it into the womb of a female sheep to develop *[1 mark]*.

3.2 Female. Dolly is a clone, so she must have exactly the same genetic material as her parent *[1 mark]*.

3.3 E.g. cloning can lead to a "reduced gene pool". / It's possible that cloned animals might not be as healthy as normal ones. / Some people worry that it may lead to humans being cloned in the future. *[1 mark]*

3.4 E.g. the study of animal clones could lead to greater understanding of the development of the embryo/ageing/age-related disorders *[1 mark]*.

Page 191
Classification

Q1 B and C *[1 mark]*.

Page 192
Warm-Up Questions

1) The microbes that cause decay can't survive in low oxygen conditions, so the dead organisms are preserved rather than decayed.
2) The two populations may be in different environments and so different characteristics will be beneficial. Natural selection will work differently in each population so that individuals with the beneficial characteristics are more likely to survive and reproduce.
3) Any one from: e.g. when the illness is only minor. / When the infection is being caused by a virus.
4) Taking the complete course makes sure that all the bacteria are destroyed. This means that there are none left to mutate and develop into antibiotic-resistant strains.
5) *fiber*

Exam Questions

1.1 Species C *[1 mark]*

1.2 Yes, you would expect Species D to look similar to Species E because they share a recent common ancestor, so they are closely related/have similar genes *[1 mark]*.

2.1 C, B, D, A *[2 marks for correct answer, otherwise 1 mark for three stages in the correct order]*

2.2 E.g. people in hospital are more likely to have weakened immune systems than people in the rest of society *[1 mark]*, and so are more likely to develop serious illness as a result of MRSA infection *[1 mark]*.

2.3 E.g. it can lead to infections becoming more widespread/difficult to control *[1 mark]*.

2.4 When antibiotics are used, resistant bacteria have an advantage over non-resistant bacteria *[1 mark]*, so they will increase in number meaning the resistance spreads *[1 mark]*. Reducing the use of antibiotics will slow/reduce the spread of antibiotic resistance *[1 mark]*.

Topic 7 — Ecology

Page 194
Competition

Q1 Any three from: light / space / water / mineral ions *[1 mark for each correct answer, up to 3 marks]*.

Q2 E.g. the frog population might increase as there might be more water spiders available for them to eat *[1 mark]* because there will be fewer sticklebacks to eat the water spiders / less competition for food *[1 mark]*. / The frog population might decrease as they are more likely to be eaten by pike *[1 mark]* because there will be fewer sticklebacks for the pikes to eat *[1 mark]*.

Page 197
Adaptations

Q1 a) A behavioural adaptation *[1 mark]*.

b) E.g. it has flippers *[1 mark]* so it can swim for food *[1 mark]*. / A thick layer of fat *[1 mark]* so it retains heat *[1 mark]*. / A low surface area to volume ratio *[1 mark]* so it retains heat *[1 mark]*.

Page 198
Food Chains

Q1 a) grass *[1 mark]*

b) three *[1 mark]*

c) grasshopper *[1 mark]*

d) The population of grasshoppers could increase *[1 mark]* as there's nothing to eat them *[1 mark]*. The population of snakes could decrease *[1 mark]* as there's nothing for them to eat *[1 mark]*.

Page 199
Warm-Up Questions

1) a community

2) The interaction of a community of living organisms (biotic) with the non-living (abiotic) parts of their environment.

3) Any four from: moisture level / light intensity / temperature / carbon dioxide level / wind intensity / wind direction / soil pH / mineral content of soil.

4) Structural adaptations are features of an organism's body structure that allow an organism to live in an environment.

5) A producer is an organism that makes its own food using energy from the Sun.

Exam Questions

1.1 tertiary consumer *[1 mark]*

1.2 The algae are producers *[1 mark]*. They are the source of biomass /energy for the food chain *[1 mark]*.

2.1 It doesn't sweat *[1 mark]*.

2.2 E.g. it lives in burrows *[1 mark]* so it can avoid the heat above ground *[1 mark]*. / It holds its tail over its head *[1 mark]* so it can shelter from the sun *[1 mark]*. / It lies in the shade *[1 mark]* so it can shelter from the sun *[1 mark]*. / It lies with its limbs spread out wide *[1 mark]* so it can lose more heat (as its surface area to volume ratio is increased) *[1 mark]*.

3.1 At first the population size of the cutthroat trout would decrease *[1 mark]*, as the lake trout would eat the cutthroat trout *[1 mark]*. This would lead to a decline in the population of the lake trout (as they'd have less to eat) *[1 mark]*, allowing an increase in the population of the cutthroat trout *[1 mark]*. The population size of the lake trout would then increase (as they'd have more to eat) and the cycle would start again *[1 mark]*.

3.2 Any two from: availability of food / competition for resources / new pathogens *[1 mark for each correct answer, up to 2 marks]*.

Page 200
Using Quadrats

Q1 $0.75 \times 4 = 3$ buttercups per m^2 *[1 mark]*.
$3 \times 1200 = $ **3600 buttercups in total** *[1 mark]*.

Pages 205-206
Warm-Up Questions

1) A line used to help find out how organisms are distributed across an area.

2) $(14 + 11 + 11 + 12 + 12) \div 5 = 12$

3) E.g. due to seasonal factors / geographic factors / human interaction.

4) To break down/decay dead matter and animal waste.

5) Through burning.

Exam Questions

1.1   eating *[1 mark]*

1.2   respiration *[1 mark]*

1.3   Detritus feeders and microorganisms break down/ decay the dead matter *[1 mark]* and return carbon to the air as carbon dioxide through respiration *[1 mark]*.

1.4   photosynthesis *[1 mark]*

2.1   By the process of transpiration / water evaporates from the plants *[1 mark]*.

2.2   Energy from the Sun evaporates water from the ocean *[1 mark]*, so the water molecule enters the atmosphere as water vapour *[1 mark]*. The warm water vapour rises, then cools and condenses into clouds *[1 mark]*. The water molecule then falls from the clouds as precipitation/rain/ snow/hail into a garden pond *[1 mark]*.

3.1   E.g. they could have placed quadrats at regular intervals *[1 mark]* along a transect/in a straight line from the wood to the opposite side of the field *[1 mark]*, and counted the number of poppies in each quadrat *[1 mark]*.

3.2   E.g. the number of poppies increases with increasing distance from the wood *[1 mark]*.

3.3   Any two from: e.g. moisture level / soil pH / soil mineral content / wind intensity / wind direction.
[2 marks — 1 mark for each correct answer.]

3.4   Species A = 47 squares out of 100
= (47 ÷ 100) × 100 = 47% *[1 mark]*
Species B = 48 squares out of 100
= (48 ÷ 100) × 100 = 48% *[1 mark]*

Remember, to calculate percentage cover of an organism in a quadrat you count the number of squares which are more than half covered by the organism.

3.5   E.g. because there may have been too many blades of grass to count each one individually / it's hard to count individual blades of grass *[1 mark]*.

4   How to grade your answer:
Level 0:   There is no relevant information. *[No marks]*
Level 1:   There is a brief description of one or two ways in which carbon stored in the vegetation could be returned to the atmosphere. *[1 to 2 marks]*
Level 2:   There is some description of more than two of the ways carbon stored in the vegetation could be returned to the atmosphere. *[3 to 4 marks]*
Level 3:   There is a clear and detailed description of all the ways carbon stored in the vegetation could be returned to the atmosphere. *[5 to 6 marks]*
Here are some points your answer may include:
Carbon stored in the small branches will be returned to the atmosphere as carbon dioxide when the branches are burnt.
The green plants could be eaten by animals, which will release some carbon as carbon dioxide during respiration.
The green plants could also be broken down by microorganisms/detritivores which will release carbon as carbon dioxide during respiration.
The wood that is taken away to be made into furniture will eventually return the carbon to the atmosphere through decay/burning when its lifespan as furniture is over.

Page 210
Investigating Decay

Q1   a) $\text{Rate} = \dfrac{1000}{\text{time}}$

$\text{Rate} = \dfrac{1000}{480} = $ **2.08 s^{-1}** *[1 mark]*

     b)   As the temperature increases, the rate of decay increases *[1 mark]*.

Page 211
Warm-Up Questions

1)   Compost is decomposed organic matter that is used as a natural fertiliser.

2)   Any two from: e.g. bacteria / fungi / detritus feeders.

3)   Any three from: e.g. temperature / water availability / oxygen availability / number of decay organisms.

4)   pink

5)   E.g. sodium carbonate.

Exam Questions

1.1   methane gas *[1 mark]*

1.2   The type of decay which produces biogas involves anaerobic respiration *[1 mark]*, which occurs when oxygen is not present *[1 mark]*.

1.3   E.g. heating / cooking / lighting / powering a turbine to generate electricity.

2.1   1000 ÷ 280 = **3.57 s^{-1} (3 s.f)** *[1 mark]*

2.2   E.g. the amount of milk used for each repeat *[1 mark]*. This could be controlled by using a measuring cylinder/ pipette to accurately measure the volume of milk used *[1 mark]*.

You could have also said the amount of phenolphathlein or lipase used.

2.3   E.g. judging when the solution has lost its pink colour *[1 mark]*. This effect of the error could be reduced by getting the same person to judge the colour change each time *[1 mark]*.

3   How to grade your answer:
Level 0:   There is no relevant information. *[No marks]*
Level 1:   There is a brief description of factors that could be changed to increase the rate of decomposition. *[1 to 2 marks]*
Level 2:   There is a description of factors that could be changed to increase the rate of decomposition and an explanation of how some of these factors affect the rate of decomposition. *[3 to 4 marks]*
Level 3:   There is a clear and detailed description of the factors that could be changed to increase the rate of decomposition and a full explanation of how each factor affects the rate of decomposition. *[5 to 6 marks]*

Here are some points your answer may include:
The gardener may need to change the temperature of her compost bin. A warm temperature will increase the rate of decomposition because the enzymes of the decay organisms will be able to work at a higher rate. However, if the temperature is too high, it will decrease the rate of decomposition. This is because the enzymes of the decay organisms will be destroyed and the decay organisms will die.

The gardener may need to increase the water content of her compost bin. A moist environment allows decay to happen faster because decay organisms need water to carry out their biological processes.

She may also need to increase the air flow through the compost bin. The more air flow, the greater the oxygen availability. This will increase the rate of decomposition by those microorganisms involved in decay that respire aerobically.

She could also consider adding additional decay microorganisms and detritus feeders to her compost bin, as the more of these organisms there are, the faster decomposition will take place.

Page 220
Warm-Up Questions

1) The variety of different species of organisms on Earth, or within an ecosystem.

2) E.g. carbon dioxide, methane.

3) E.g. to clear land for farming or to grow crops for biofuels.

4) Breeding programmes breed endangered animals in captivity to make sure the species survives if they die out in the wild. Individuals can sometimes be released into the wild to boost or re-establish a population.

5) Hedgerows and field margins can be reintroduced around single-crop fields. These provide a habitat for organisms that would otherwise be unable to live in the area.

Hedgerows and field margins mean that more species of wild plants can grow. Remember, plants are often the producers in food chains — so the more variety there is in the plants that are growing, the more organisms that will be able to survive in the area.

Exam Questions

1.1 E.g. smoke *[1 mark]*, acidic gases *[1 mark]*.

1.2 E.g. sewage/toxic chemicals from industry can pollute lakes/rivers/oceans. / Fertilisers/pesticides/herbicides/toxic chemicals used on land can be washed into water *[1 mark]*.

1.3 E.g. the human population size is increasing *[1 mark]*, people around the world are demanding a higher standard of living *[1 mark]*.

2.1 E.g. changes in species distributions *[1 mark]*, changes in migration patterns *[1 mark]*.

2.2 Governments have introduced regulations and programmes to reduce deforestation *[1 mark]*. They have also introduced regulations to limit the amount of carbon dioxide released by businesses *[1 mark]*.

3.1 When peat is drained, it comes into more contact with air and some microorganisms start to decompose it *[1 mark]*. This releases carbon dioxide *[1 mark]*. Carbon dioxide is also released when peat is burned as a fuel *[1 mark]*. Carbon dioxide is a greenhouse gas, which contributes to global warming *[1 mark]*.

3.2 E.g. destroying peat bogs reduces biodiversity *[1 mark]*, as it destroys the habitats of the organisms that live in the bog *[1 mark]*.

Page 223
Pyramids of Biomass

Q1 E.g.

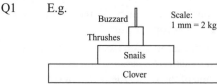

[2 marks for drawing all bars correctly to scale, otherwise 1 mark for any three bars drawn correctly to scale. 1 mark for all bars correctly labelled, 1 mark for a correct scale.]

Page 224
Biomass Transfer

Q1 Any two from: e.g. organisms don't always eat every single part of the organism they're consuming. / Organisms don't absorb all of the material in the food they ingest. / Some of the biomass is converted into other substances and released as waste. *[1 mark for each correct answer, up to 2 marks]*

Q2 a) 995 − 110 = **885 kg** *[1 mark]*

b) (110 ÷ 995) × 100 = **11.1%** *[1 mark]*

Page 227
Biotechnology

Q1 A plasmid could be removed from the bacterial cell and cut open with an enzyme *[1 mark]*. The rennin gene could be cut out of a cow chromosome using an enzyme *[1 mark]*. The plasmid and rennin gene could then be joined together and the plasmid re-inserted into the bacterial cell *[1 mark]*.

Page 229
Warm-Up Questions

1) Trophic levels are the different stages of a food chain.

2) Biomass is the mass of living material.

3) By reducing the number of fish that are caught in certain areas and preventing fish that are too small from being caught.

4) To reduce the transfer of energy from the livestock to the environment, which means more energy is available for growth. This increases the efficiency of farming / means more food can be produced from the same input of resources.

5) Golden Rice is a genetically engineered variety of rice which provides more nutritional value.

Exam Questions

1.1 $75 \times 1.5 =$ **112.5 g** *[1 mark]*

1.2 $(18 \div 112.5) \times 100 =$ **16%** *[1 mark]*

2.1   Food security is having enough food to feed a population *[1 mark]*.

2.2   Any two from: e.g. the increasing human population *[1 mark]*, because more people will require more food *[1 mark]*. / Increased demand for certain foods *[1 mark]* because this means that these food resources will become more scarce *[1 mark]*. / New pests/pathogens *[1 mark]* because these may result in the loss of crops and livestock *[1 mark]*. / Environmental conditions *[1 mark]* because these may result in the loss of crops and livestock *[1 mark]*. / High input costs of farming *[1 mark]* because these can make it too expensive for people in some countries to farm *[1 mark]*. / Conflicts in some parts of the world *[1 mark]* because they can affect the availability of food and water *[1 mark]*.

2.3   A larger mesh size will let unwanted species of fish escape *[1 mark]* reducing the number of fish that are caught accidentally and discarded *[1 mark]*. / A larger mesh size will allow smaller and younger fish to escape *[1 mark]*, allowing them to continue to breed and maintain the fish population *[1 mark]*.

3.1   To supply oxygen *[1 mark]* for fungus to respire aerobically *[1 mark]*.

3.2   E.g. to control the temperature inside the fermenter *[1 mark]* because if the temperature gets to high it will kill the fungus/denature the fungus's enzymes *[1 mark]*.

3.3   E.g. glucose syrup *[1 mark]* as this is a food source for the fungus *[1 mark]*.

Practice Paper 1

1.1   Any two from: e.g. it has a 'true' nucleus / it contains mitochondria / it doesn't have a cell wall / it doesn't contain plasmids *[2 marks]*.

1.2   E.g. most cells have a structure that is specialised for their function, so they will contain different subcellular structures *[1 mark]*.

1.3   cell membrane *[1 mark]*

1.4   *E. coli* bacteria *[1 mark]*

1.5   image size = magnification × real size
= 150 × 0.054
= **8.1 mm** *[2 marks for correct answer, otherwise 1 mark for correct working]*

1.6   How to grade your answer:
Level 0:   No relevant information is given. *[No marks]*
Level 1:   There is a brief comparison of plant and animal cells, including at least one similarity and one difference. *[1 to 2 marks]*
Level 2:   There is a comparison of plant and animal cells, including at least two similarities and two differences. Some descriptions of subcellular structures are included. *[3 to 4 marks]*
Level 3:   There is a detailed comparison of plant and animal cells, including at least three similarities and three differences. Detailed descriptions of subcellular structures are included. *[5 to 6 marks]*

Here are some points your answer may include:
Similarities:
Both plant and animal cells have a nucleus, which controls the cell's activities.
Both plant and animal cells contain cytoplasm, which is where most of the cell's chemical reactions take place.
Plant cells and animal cells both have a cell membrane, which controls what goes in and out of the cell.
Mitochondria are found in both plant cells and animal cells — these are where most of the reactions for aerobic respiration take place.
Both plant cells and animal cells have ribosomes, which are where proteins are made.
Differences:
Chloroplasts, the site of photosynthesis, are present in plant cells, but not in animal cells.
Plant cells have a cell wall, which supports and strengthens the cell, but animal cells do not.
Plant cells contain a permanent vacuole, containing cell sap, but animal cells do not.

2.1   It is a control *[1 mark]*. It shows that any difference between the growth of the bacteria is due to the effect of the antibiotics alone *[1 mark]*.

2.2   Any two from: e.g. used sterilised Petri dishes / used sterilised culture mediums / sterilised the inoculating loop used to transfer the bacteria (by passing it through a hot flame) / used a sterile dropping pipette and spreader / lightly taped on the lids of the Petri dishes after transferring the bacteria / stored the Petri dishes upside down *[2 marks]*.

2.3   Because harmful pathogens are more likely to grow above this temperature *[1 mark]*.

2.4   Antibiotic X:
4.4 cm ÷ 2 = 2.2 cm
$\pi \times 2.2^2 =$ **15 cm² (2 s.f.)** *[1 mark]*
Antibiotic Y:
3 cm ÷ 2 = 1.5 cm
$\pi \times 1.5^2 =$ **7.1 cm² (2 s.f.)** *[1 mark]*
The inhibition zone of antibiotic X is greater than the inhibition zone of antibiotic Y, so antibiotic X is more effective against the bacteria than antibiotic Y *[1 mark]*.

2.5   The bacteria could have developed resistance to the antibiotic *[1 mark]*.

3.1   By droplets from an infected person's sneeze or cough *[1 mark]*.

3.2   How to grade your answer:
Level 0:   There is no relevant information. *[No marks]*
Level 1:   There are some relevant points explaining how vaccination helps to protect the body against disease but the answer is missing some detail. *[1 to 2 marks]*
Level 2:   There is a clear, detailed explanation of how vaccination helps to protect the body against disease. *[3 to 4 marks]*
Here are some points your answer may include:
The body is injected with small amounts of dead or inactive pathogens (which are harmless).
The pathogens carry antigens, which cause the white blood cells in the body to produce antibodies.
Antibodies attack/kill the pathogens.
If live pathogens of the same type appear again, the white blood cells can rapidly mass-produce antibodies to kill the pathogens so the person doesn't get ill.

3.3 Any two from: e.g. stop the mosquitoes from breeding / protect people from mosquito bites using mosquito nets / protect people from mosquito bites by using insecticides (to kill the mosquitoes) *[2 marks]*.

3.4 malaria *[1 mark]*

3.5 3 days = 3 × 24 = 72 hours
72 ÷ 18 = 4 divisions
$2^4 = 2 \times 2 \times 2 \times 2 =$ **16 cells** *[2 marks for correct answer, otherwise 1 mark for correct working.]*

4.1 biuret solution *[1 mark]*

4.2 Benedict's solution *[1 mark]*

4.3 A *[1 mark]*

4.4 It is covered in many villi that provide a large surface area for diffusion (and active transport) to occur across *[1 mark]*. The villi have a thin wall/single layer of surface cells, which decreases the distance for diffusion to occur across *[1 mark]*. They also have a good blood supply to assist quick absorption *[1 mark]*.

4.5 Their blood sugar level will not rise very much or not rise at all *[1 mark]*. This is because a person with lactose intolerance has little or no lactase to break down the lactose in the drink, so there will be little or no sugar to be absorbed from the small intestine *[1 mark]*.

5.1 A group of different tissues that work together to perform a certain function *[1 mark]*.

5.2 A = oxygen, B = carbon dioxide *[1 mark]*
The job of the lungs is to transfer oxygen to the blood and remove waste carbon dioxide from it.

5.3 So that they have a good blood supply *[1 mark]* to maximise the rate of diffusion of the gases into and out of the alveoli *[1 mark]*.
A good blood supply makes sure that the concentration gradient between the blood and the air in the alveoli is maintained, which leads to a higher rate of diffusion.

5.4 E.g. the function of red blood cells is to transport oxygen to respiring cells *[1 mark]*. The sickle-shaped cells are more rigid than normal red blood cells and they are the wrong shape, which could result in them being unable to fit through the capillaries *[1 mark]*. This could reduce/block the blood supply to respiring cells, meaning that not enough oxygen is transported to the cells, causing breathlessness *[1 mark]*.
If you don't have enough oxygen for respiration, your breathing rate increases to get more oxygen into your blood. In a person with sickle cell anaemia, the lack of oxygen may cause their breathing rate to increase so much that they feel breathless.

6.1 A — artery, B — capillary, C — vein *[2 marks for all three correct, otherwise 1 mark for two correct.]*

6.2 The blood supply to the area below the blockage would be cut off/reduced *[1 mark]*. Not enough oxygen would reach this part of the heart muscle, resulting in cells being unable to respire/damage/death of the muscle tissue/a heart attack *[1 mark]*.

6.3 A stent will keep the coronary artery open, making sure that enough blood can reach the heart muscle *[1 mark]*.

6.4 Any two from: to test drug efficacy/to see whether the drug works and produces the desired effect. / To find out about the drug's toxicity/how harmful the drug is. / To find the best dosage of drug to use/the correct concentration and how often it should be taken *[2 marks]*.

6.5 To make sure it did not cause any harmful side effects when the body is working normally *[1 mark]*.

6.6 The statin decreased the risk of having a heart attack for people who had already had one attack *[1 mark]*.

6.7 E.g. a control/placebo was used *[1 mark]*.

7.1 It is broken down into sugars/maltose *[1 mark]*.

7.2 E.g. the concentration of starch / the concentration of amylase / the amount of mixing / the volume of the sample removed *[1 mark]*.

7.3 E.g. they could have added the sample to a drop of iodine solution (e.g. in a well of a spotting tile) *[1 mark]*. If starch was present the iodine solution would have changed to blue-black *[1 mark]*. If starch was no longer present, the iodine solution would have remained browny-orange *[1 mark]*.

7.4 Time of reaction at 40 °C = 100 s.
Rate = $1000 \div 100 =$ **10 s^{-1}** *[2 marks for correct answer, otherwise 1 mark for correct working.]*

7.5 The temperature was too high *[1 mark]*, causing the enzyme to denature / the shape of the enzyme's active site to change *[1 mark]*. This means the starch could no longer fit in the active site of the enzyme, so it could not be broken down *[1 mark]*.

7.6 The result for 20 °C is anomalous *[1 mark]* because the time taken until starch is no longer present is quicker than expected/quicker than at 30 or 40 °C *[1 mark]*. To cause this result, the student may not have used the correct volume of starch/amylase solution. / The student may have started timing the experiment too late. / The student may have stopped the experiment too early *[1 mark]*.

7.7 As temperature increases, the time until the starch is no longer present increases *[1 mark]*.

7.8 By using buffer solutions with a range of different pH values *[1 mark]*.

8.1 9:00 a.m. *[1 mark]*

8.2 E.g. day 2 was less bright, so the stomata weren't fully open and so less water could move out of the leaves. / Day 2 was colder, so the water evaporated/diffused more slowly. / Day 2 was less windy, so the water vapour was carried away more slowly, meaning that diffusion couldn't happen as quickly. / Day 2 was wetter/more humid, so there was a smaller diffusion gradient between the inside and outside of the leaf so diffusion couldn't happen as quickly *[1 mark for reason, 1 mark for explanation]*.
The rate of transpiration varies throughout the day due to the changing light intensity, but it can also be affected by the temperature, the air flow and the humidity around the leaves.

8.3 The plant has lost too much water/has lost water faster than it could be replaced through the roots *[1 mark]*.

8.4 Transpiration creates a slight shortage of water in the leaf *[1 mark]*. More water is drawn up from the rest of the plant through the xylem vessels to replace it *[1 mark]*. This in turn means that more water is drawn up from the roots, and so there's a constant transpiration stream of water through the plant *[1 mark]*.

9   How to grade your answer:

Level 0:   No relevant information is given. *[No marks]*

Level 1:   There is a basic description of at least two of the stages of the cell cycle or a suggestion of why disrupting the cell cycle may kill plants is stated. *[1 to 2 marks]*

Level 2:   There is a clear description of at least two stages of the cell cycle and a suggestion of why disrupting the cell cycle may kill plants is stated. *[3 to 4 marks]*

Level 3:   There is a detailed description of each stage of the cell cycle and a suggestion of why disrupting the cell cycle may kill plants is stated. *[5 to 6 marks]*

Here are some points your answer may include:

The cell cycle involves the division of cells to form two identical cells.

Before division takes place the cell grows and increases the amount of subcellular structures it has, such as mitochondria and ribosomes.

It then duplicates its DNA so there's one copy for each new cell.

Next, mitosis takes place. The chromosomes line up at the centre of the cell and cell fibres pull them apart.

The two arms of each chromosome go to opposite ends of the cell.

Membranes form around each of the sets of chromosomes to become the nuclei of the two new cells. Finally the cytoplasm and cell membrane divide so two identical daughter cells are formed.

Disrupting the cell cycle can kill plants as plants are multicellular organisms which use mitosis to grow and to replace damaged cells. If they can no longer do this, they may die.

10.1

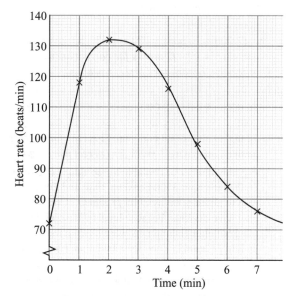

[1 mark for label and suitable scale for the x-axis, 2 marks for all points correctly plotted (or 1 mark for 8 points plotted correctly), 1 mark for a smooth curve of best fit.]

10.2   95 beats/min *[1 mark. Allow any value correctly read from 30 seconds on your own graph.]*

10.3   heart rate *[1 mark]*

10.4   The student's heart rate increases during exercise *[1 mark]*. This is because when he exercises he needs more energy, so he respires more *[1 mark]*. Increased respiration means that his cells need more oxygen *[1 mark]*, so his heart rate increases so that the blood flows more quickly to the cells to deliver oxygen *[1 mark]*.

10.5   glucose *[1 mark]* + oxygen → carbon dioxide + water *[1 mark]*

10.6   E.g. anaerobic respiration causes a build up of lactic acid in the muscles *[1 mark]*. After exercise, extra oxygen is needed to react with lactic acid / the lactic acid is transported in the blood from the muscles to the liver to be converted back to glucose *[1 mark]*, so the heart rate remains high to transport oxygen to the cells faster / to transport lactic acid away from the muscles to the liver faster *[1 mark]*.

Practice Paper 2

1.1   A producer is a photosynthetic organism that makes its own food using energy from the Sun *[1 mark]*.

1.2   D *[1 mark]*, because the biomass of the organisms decreases at each trophic level and the bars on this pyramid get smaller at each trophic level *[1 mark]*.

1.3   efficiency = (1.4 kg ÷ 12 kg) × 100
= 0.1166... × 100 = **12% (2 s.f.)** *[1 mark]*

1.4   Energy is lost at each level of a food chain *[1 mark]*. After about five levels, the amount of energy being passed on is not sufficient to support another level of organisms *[1 mark]*.

2.1   21 *[1 mark]*

To find the median, you write out all the results from lowest to highest, e.g. 10, 21, 21, 35, 37. 21 is in the middle of the list, so it is the median.

2.2   (6 + 15 + 9 + 14 + 20 + 5 + 3 + 11 + 10 + 7) ÷ 10
= 100 ÷ 10
= **10 buttercups per m² *[2 marks for correct answer, otherwise 1 mark for correct working.]***

2.3   90 × 120 = 10 800 m² *[1 mark]*
10 × 10 800 = **108 000 buttercups** *[1 mark]*
Allow incorrect value from 2.2.

2.4   He could have calculated the percentage cover *[1 mark]*.

2.5   E.g. more buttercups grow where there is a higher moisture level in the soil *[1 mark]*.

2.6   How to grade your answer:

Level 0:   There is no relevant information. *[No marks]*

Level 1:   There is a brief description of how the student could investigate whether the change in distribution of buttercups is due to variability in the moisture level of the soil. *[1 to 2 marks]*

Level 2:   There is a detailed description of how the student could investigate whether the change in distribution of buttercups is due to variability in the moisture level of the soil. *[3 to 4 marks]*

Here are some points your answer may include:
He could use a transect across Field A.
To do this he should mark out a line across the field.
Then he should record the number of buttercups in quadrats placed next to each other/at intervals along the line.
He should also measure the moisture level of the soil at each sampling point (e.g. with a probe).

3.1 Light coming through the hole in the box caused more auxin to accumulate on the shaded sides of the shoots *[1 mark]*. This made the cells on the shaded sides of the plants grow faster *[1 mark]*, so the shoots bent towards the light *[1 mark]*.

3.2 phototropism *[1 mark]*

3.3 gravity *[1 mark]*

4.1 The thermoregulatory centre in the brain contains receptors that monitor the temperature of blood flowing through the brain *[1 mark]*. It also receives impulses from temperature receptors in the skin, giving information about skin temperature *[1 mark]*.

4.2 E.g. blood vessels supplying skin capillaries would have constricted *[1 mark]* to reduce the amount of energy transferred from his skin to the environment *[1 mark]*. / He would have started to shiver *[1 mark]*. This needs respiration, which transfers some energy to warm the body *[1 mark]*.

5.1 pituitary gland *[1 mark]*

5.2 It sends a message to the pituitary gland to release more ADH *[1 mark]*, so more water is reabsorbed from the kidney tubules *[1 mark]*.

5.3 The increased level of ADH due to taking ecstasy causes the kidneys to reabsorb too much water into the blood *[1 mark]*. If the water content of the blood is higher than the body cells, water may enter the cells due to osmosis *[1 mark]*.

5.4 The person's blood flows between partially permeable membranes *[1 mark]*. The dialysis fluid contains the same concentration of glucose and dissolved ions as healthy blood, which ensures that glucose and other useful ions are not lost *[1 mark]*. Waste products/urea and excess ions and water are able to diffuse out of the blood into the dialysis fluid *[1 mark]*.

6.1 *Biston [1 mark]*

6.2 the dark variety *[1 mark]*

6.3 The dark variety is less likely to be eaten by predators in soot polluted areas (because they are better camouflaged) *[1 mark]* so they are more likely to survive to reproduce *[1 mark]*, meaning that the genes for the characteristics that made them successful / genes for dark colouring are more likely to be passed on to the next generation and become more common in the population *[1 mark]*.

6.4 Town B, because it contains a higher proportion of dark moths *[1 mark]*.

7.1 Their reaction time was very fast *[1 mark]*.
Their response was involuntary/automatic *[1 mark]*.

If you have to think about what response to give then it's not a reflex action.

7.2 reaction time *[1 mark]*

7.3 sex *[1 mark]*

7.4 The males in this experiment had a faster mean reaction time than the females *[1 mark]*, so the data supports the scientist's hypothesis *[1 mark]*.

7.5 Any two from: e.g. the age of the participants. / The strength of the tap on the knee. / Caffeine consumption of the participants prior to the investigation *[2 marks]*.

7.6 relay neurone *[1 mark]*

7.7 How to grade your answer:
Level 0: There is no relevant information. *[No marks]*
Level 1: There is a brief description of some parts of the path taken by a nervous impulse in the reflex. *[1 to 2 marks]*
Level 2: There is some description of the path taken by a nervous impulse in the reflex, but some detail is missing. *[3 to 4 marks]*
Level 3: There is a clear and detailed description of the path taken by a nervous impulse in the reflex. *[5 to 6 marks]*

Here are some points your answer may include:
The impulse travels along a sensory neurone to the central nervous system/spinal cord.
When the impulse reaches a synapse between the sensory neurone and a relay neurone, it triggers chemicals to be released.
These chemicals cause impulses to be sent along the relay neurone.
When the impulse reaches a synapse between the relay neurone and a motor neurone, chemicals are released again which cause impulses to be sent along the motor neurone.
The impulse then reaches the muscle, which contracts to curl the big toe upwards.

8.1 Producing enough food without using resources faster than they renew *[1 mark]*.

8.2 $4000 - 16\,000 = -12\,000$
$(-12\,000 \div 16\,000) \times 100 = -75\%$, so the percentage decrease is 75% *[2 marks for correct answer, otherwise 1 mark for correct working.]*

A negative value for percentage change indicates a decrease.

8.3 $16\,000 - 4000 = 12\,000$ cod
$2000 - 1980 = 20$ years
$12\,000 \div 20 =$ **6000 cod/year** *[2 marks for correct answer, otherwise 1 mark for correct working.]*

8.4 E.g. the number of cod able to reproduce declined from 16 000 to about 3500 between 1980 and 2001, then rose to about 5000 by 2005 *[1 mark]*. Cod numbers may have declined because levels of fishing increased / larger/better fishing nets were used so more cod were caught *[1 mark]*. They may have then risen because of the introduction of fishing quotas / restrictions on the type/size of nets that could be used *[1 mark]*.

8.5 *Fusarium [1 mark]*

8.6 E.g. the fungus is grown on glucose syrup *[1 mark]* in aerobic conditions *[1 mark]*. The fungal biomass is then harvested and purified to make mycoprotein *[1 mark]*.

9.1 The entire set of genetic material in an organism *[1 mark]*.

9.2 Knowing more about the cystic fibrosis gene could help us to understand the disorder better / develop effective treatments for it *[1 mark]*.

9.3 E.g.

mother's alleles

	F	f
F	FF	Ff
f	Ff	ff

father's alleles

ff offspring has cystic fibrosis.

Probability = 0.25 / 25% / 1:3 / 1 in 4 / ¼

[1 mark for correctly identifying parents' genotypes, 1 mark for correctly identifying possible genotypes of the offspring, 1 mark for correctly identifying cystic fibrosis genotype, 1 mark for identifying the correct probability of a child having cystic fibrosis.]

The parents must both be carriers, since neither of them show any sign of the disorder. This means they both have one copy of the recessive allele for cystic fibrosis — so they're both Ff.

9.4 Homozygous, because he has two alleles the same / both of his alleles are recessive *[1 mark]*.

9.5 No, because polydactyly isn't a significant health issue / embryos are only screened for serious genetic disorders *[1 mark]*.

People with polydactyly have extra fingers or toes, but it doesn't cause any other problems, so it isn't life threatening.

9.6 E.g. there may come a point where everyone wants to screen their embryos so they can pick the most 'desirable' one. / The rejected embryos are destroyed — they could have developed into humans *[1 mark]*.

10.1 Any three from: e.g. sexual reproduction involves the fusion of male and female gametes whereas asexual reproduction doesn't involve gametes. / Sexual reproduction involves two parents whereas asexual reproduction only involves one parent. / Sexual reproduction produces offspring that are genetically different to their parents whereas asexual reproduction produces offspring that are genetically identical to their parents (clones). / Sexual reproduction produces offspring that are genetically different to each other whereas asexual reproduction produces offspring that are genetically identical. *[3 marks]*

10.2 testosterone *[1 mark]*

10.3 It causes the lining of the uterus to grow *[1 mark]*. It also stimulates the release of luteinising hormone (LH) and inhibits the release of follicle stimulating hormone (FSH) *[1 mark]*.

10.4 C *[1 mark]* — e.g. because the level corresponds to the thickness of the uterus lining, which is maintained by progesterone *[1 mark]*.

There are a few different ways that you can tell that this line represents progesterone. As long as you're able to justify your answer, you'll get the marks.

10.5 Advantages of the implant: e.g. it works for three years / protection is always available / you do not have to remember to take a pill every day / it is highly effective. Disadvantages of the implant: e.g. it has to be inserted by a doctor or nurse which may be painful/inconvenient / if certain medications are taken, a different contraceptive method would have to be used / you could suffer from side effects / it does not protect against STDs.

Advantages of the condom: e.g. it protects against STDs / there are no side effects / it is highly effective if used correctly / it is not affected by medication. Disadvantages of the condom: e.g. it needs to be available at the time of intercourse / if it isn't used correctly it may not be effective / it can only be used once.

[3 marks for at least one advantage and one disadvantage of each method, otherwise 2 marks for at least two advantages or disadvantages of either method or 1 mark for one advantage or disadvantage of either method. 1 mark for giving a justified conclusion that refers to at least one advantage and one disadvantage of the chosen method.]

11.1 At point X, CO_2 is being removed from the atmosphere by photosynthesis *[1 mark]*. At point Y, CO_2 is being released into the atmosphere by plants and animals respiring *[1 mark]*. At point Z, carbon compounds in the plants are being transferred to animals as they eat the plants *[1 mark]*.

11.2 Microorganisms break down waste products and dead organisms *[1 mark]* and release carbon dioxide into the atmosphere as they respire *[1 mark]*.

11.3 The two sets of data show the same pattern/increase at the same time *[1 mark]*.

11.4 Any two from: e.g. the two things may follow similar patterns by chance. / Some other factor may have caused both increases. / The concentration of carbon dioxide varied even when human population was low/fairly constant. *[2 marks]*

11.5 Any two from: e.g. to increase the amount of land available for farming cattle. / To increase the amount of land available for rice crops. / To increase the amount of land available for growing crops from which biofuels are produced *[2 marks]*.

11.6 Any two from: e.g. habitats in low-lying areas will be lost due to rising sea levels *[1 mark]*. / The distribution of organisms could change due to changes in temperature and rainfall *[1 mark]*. / Biodiversity could be reduced *[1 mark]*. / There could be changes in migration patterns (e.g. some birds may migrate further north) *[1 mark]*.

Glossary

Abiotic factor	A non-living factor of the environment.
Accommodation	The ability to focus on near or distant objects by changing the shape of the lens in the eye.
Accurate result	A result that is very close to the true answer.
Active transport	The movement of particles against a concentration gradient (i.e. from an area of lower concentration to an area of higher concentration) using energy transferred during respiration.
Adaptation	A feature or characteristic that helps an organism to survive in its natural environment.
Aerobic respiration	Respiration taking place in the presence of oxygen.
Allele	An alternative version of a gene.
Alveolus	A tiny air sac in the lungs, where gas exchange occurs.
Amino acid	A small molecule that is a building block of proteins.
Anaerobic respiration	Respiration taking place in the absence of oxygen.
Anomalous result	A result that doesn't seem to fit with the rest of the data.
Antibiotic	A drug used to kill or prevent the growth of bacteria.
Antibiotic resistance	When bacteria aren't killed by an antibiotic.
Antibody	A protein produced by white blood cells in response to the presence of an antigen.
Antigen	A molecule on the surface of a cell or a pathogen. Foreign antigens trigger white blood cells to produce antibodies.
Antitoxin	A protein produced by white blood cells that counteracts toxins made by invading bacteria.
Artery	A blood vessel that carries blood away from the heart.
Asexual reproduction	Where organisms reproduce by mitosis to produce genetically identical offspring.
Auxin	A plant hormone that controls the growth of a plant in response to different stimuli.
Behavioural adaptation	A way in which an organism behaves that helps it to survive in its environment.
Bias	Prejudice towards or against something.
Binary fission	A type of simple cell division carried out by prokaryotic cells where the cell makes copies of its genetic material, before splitting into two daughter cells.
Binomial system	The system used in classification for naming organisms using a two-part Latin name.
Biodiversity	The variety of different species of organisms on Earth, or within an ecosystem.
Biomass	The mass of living material in an organism or a group of organisms.
Biotic factor	A living factor of the environment.

Glossary

Capillary	A type of blood vessel involved in the exchange of materials at tissues.
Carbohydrase	A type of digestive enzyme that catalyses the breakdown of a carbohydrate into sugars.
Cardiovascular disease	Disease of the heart or blood vessels.
Catalyst	A substance that increases the speed of a reaction, without being changed or used up.
Categoric data	Data that comes in distinct categories (e.g. flower colour or blood group).
Cell membrane	A membrane surrounding a cell, which holds it together and controls what goes in and out.
Cell wall	A structure surrounding some cell types, which gives strength and support.
Cellulose	A molecule which strengthens cell walls in plants and algae.
Central Nervous System (CNS)	The brain and spinal cord. It's where reflexes and actions are coordinated.
Chlorophyll	A green substance found in chloroplasts which absorbs light for photosynthesis.
Chloroplast	A structure found in plant cells and algae. It is the site of photosynthesis.
Chromosome	A long molecule of DNA found in the nucleus. Each chromosome carries many genes.
Clinical trial	A set of drug tests on human volunteers.
Clone	An organism that is genetically identical to another organism.
Communicable disease	A disease that can spread between individuals.
Community	The populations of different species living in a habitat.
Continuous data	Numerical data that can have any value within a range (e.g. length, volume or temperature).
Contraceptive	A method of preventing pregnancy, which can be hormonal or non-hormonal.
Control experiment	An experiment that's kept under the same conditions as the rest of an investigation, but doesn't have anything done to it.
Control variable	A variable in an experiment that is kept the same.
Coordination centre	An organ (e.g. the brain, spinal cord or pancreas) that processes information from receptors and organises a response from the effectors.
Coronary artery	A blood vessel which supplies blood to the heart muscle.
Coronary heart disease	A disease in which the coronary arteries are narrowed by the build up of fatty deposits.
Correlation	A relationship between two variables.
Cutting (plants)	A small piece of a plant (usually with a new bud on it) that can be grown into a new plant.
Cystic fibrosis	An inherited disorder of the cell membranes caused by a recessive allele.

Glossary

Cytoplasm	A gel-like substance in a cell where most of the chemical reactions take place.
Deforestation	The cutting down of forests (large areas of trees).
Dependent variable	The variable in an experiment that is measured.
Diabetes	A condition that affects the body's ability to control its blood glucose level.
Dialysis	A way of artificially filtering the blood to remove waste products and keep the concentration of dissolved ions in the blood at normal levels. It is used to treat patients with kidney failure.
Differentiation	The process by which a cell becomes specialised for its job.
Diffusion	The spreading out of particles from an area of higher concentration to an area of lower concentration.
Discrete data	Numerical data that can only take certain values (e.g. number of people).
Distribution	Where organisms are found in a particular area.
DNA	Deoxyribonucleic acid. The molecule in cells that stores genetic information.
Dominant allele	The allele for the characteristic that's shown by an organism if two different alleles are present for that characteristic.
Double-blind trial	A clinical trial where neither the doctors nor the patients know who has received the drug and who has received the placebo until all the results have been gathered.
Ecosystem	The interaction of a community of living organisms with the abiotic parts of their environment.
Effector	Either a muscle or gland which responds to nervous impulses.
Efficacy	Whether something, e.g. a drug, works or not.
Endothermic reaction	A reaction where energy is transferred from the environment.
Enzyme	A protein that acts as a biological catalyst.
Eukaryotic cell	A complex cell, such as a plant or animal cell.
Evolution	The changing of the inherited characteristics of a population over time.
Excretion	The removal of waste products from the body.
Exothermic reaction	A reaction that transfers energy to the environment.
Extinction	When no living individuals of a species remain.
Extremophile	An organism that's adapted to live in extreme conditions.
Family tree	A diagram that shows how a characteristic is inherited in a group of related people.
Fermentation	The process of anaerobic respiration in yeast cells.
Fertilisation	The fusion of male and female gametes during sexual reproduction.

Glossary

Fertility	The ability to conceive a child.
Fishing quota	A limit on the number and size of fish that can be caught in a certain area.
Food security	Having enough food to feed the population.
Fossil	The remains of an organism from many years ago, which is found in rock.
Fossil record	The history of life on Earth preserved as fossils.
Functional adaptation	Something that goes on inside an organism's body that helps it to survive in its environment.
Gamete	A sex cell, e.g. an egg cell or a sperm cell in animals.
Gene	A short section of DNA, found on a chromosome, which contains the instructions needed to make a protein (and so controls the development of a characteristic).
Genetic engineering	The process of cutting out a useful gene from one organism's genome and inserting it into another organism's cell(s).
Genetically modified (GM) crop	A crop which has had its genes modified through genetic engineering.
Genome	All of the genetic material in an organism.
Genotype	What alleles you have, e.g. Tt.
Geotropism	See gravitropism.
Gibberellin	A type of plant hormone that stimulates seed germination, stem growth and flowering.
Gland	An organ that hormones are produced and secreted from.
Global warming	The rise in the average global temperature.
Glucagon	A hormone produced and secreted by the pancreas when blood glucose level is too low.
Glycogen	A molecule that acts as a store of glucose in liver and muscle cells.
Gravitropism	The growth of a plant in response to gravity. Also known as geotropism.
Guard cell	A type of cell found on either side of a stoma. A pair of these cells control the stoma's size.
Habitat	The place where an organism lives.
Haemoglobin	A red pigment found in red blood cells that carries oxygen.
Hazard	Something that has the potential to cause harm (e.g. fire, electricity, etc.).
Heterozygous	Where an organism has two alleles for a particular gene that are different.
Homeostasis	The regulation of conditions inside your body (and cells) to maintain a stable internal environment, in response to changes in both internal and external conditions.
Homozygous	Where an organism has two alleles for a particular gene that are the same.
Hormone	A chemical messenger which travels in the blood to activate target cells.

Glossary

Hybridoma	A cell made by fusing a mouse lymphocyte with a tumour cell, which is used to produce lots of monoclonal antibodies.
Hyperopia	Long-sightedness.
Hypothesis	A possible explanation for a scientific observation.
Inbreeding	When closely related animals or plants are bred together.
Independent variable	The variable in an experiment that is changed.
Inherited disorder	A disorder caused by a faulty allele, which can be passed on to an individual's offspring.
Insulin	A hormone produced and secreted by the pancreas when blood glucose level is too high.
Interdependence	Where, in a community, each species depends on other species for things such as food, shelter, pollination and seed dispersal.
IVF	*In vitro* fertilisation. The artificial fertilisation of eggs in the lab.
Limiting factor	A factor which prevents a reaction from going any faster.
Lipase	A type of digestive enzyme that catalyses the breakdown of lipids into fatty acids and glycerol.
Mean (average)	A type of average found by adding up all the data and dividing by the number of values.
Median (average)	The middle value in a set of data when the values are put in order of size.
Meiosis	A type of cell division where a cell divides twice to produce four genetically different gametes. It occurs in the reproductive organs.
Menstrual cycle	A monthly sequence of events during which the body prepares the lining of the uterus (womb) in case it receives a fertilised egg, and releases an egg from an ovary. The uterus lining then breaks down if the egg has not been fertilised.
Meristem tissue	Tissue found at the growing tips of plant shoots and roots that is able to differentiate.
Metabolism	All the chemical reactions that happen in a cell or the body.
Mitochondria	Structures in a cell which are the site of most of the reactions for aerobic respiration.
Mitosis	A type of cell division where a cell reproduces itself by splitting to form two identical offspring.
Mode (average)	The most common value in a set of data.
Monoclonal antibodies	Antibodies produced from lots of clones of a single white blood cell. This means that all the antibodies are identical and will only target one specific antigen.
Motor neurone	A nerve cell that carries electrical impulses from the CNS to effectors.
MRSA	A strain of antibiotic-resistant bacteria. (Meticillin-resistant *Staphylococcus aureus*.)
Mutation	A random change in an organism's DNA.
Mycoprotein	Protein produced by fungi, in particular *Fusarium*.

Glossary

Myopia	Short-sightedness.
Natural selection	The process by which species evolve.
Negative feedback	A mechanism that restores a level back to optimum in a system.
Nervous system	The organ system in animals that allows them to respond to changes in their environment.
Neurone	A nerve cell. Neurones transmit information around the body, including to and from the CNS.
Non-communicable disease	A disease that cannot spread between individuals.
Nucleotide	A repeating unit in DNA and RNA that consists of a sugar, a phosphate group and a base.
Nucleus (of a cell)	A structure found in animal and plant cells which contains the genetic material.
Obesity	A condition where a person has an excessive amount of body fat, to the point where it poses a risk to their health.
Optimum dose	The dose of a drug that is most effective and has few side effects.
Optimum level (in the body)	A level of something (e.g. water, ions or glucose) that enables the body to work at its best.
Organ	A group of different tissues that work together to perform a certain function.
Organ system	A group of organs working together to perform a particular function.
Osmosis	The movement of water molecules across a partially permeable membrane from a region of higher water concentration to a region of lower water concentration.
Oxygen debt	The amount of extra oxygen your body needs after exercise to react with the build up of lactic acid and remove it from cells.
Partially permeable membrane	A membrane with tiny holes in it, which lets some molecules through it but not others.
Pathogen	A microorganism that causes disease, e.g. a bacterium, virus, protist or fungus.
Peer review	The process where scientists check each other's results and explanations to make sure they're scientific.
Permanent vacuole	A structure in plant cells that contains cell sap.
Phagocytosis	The process by which white blood cells engulf foreign cells and digest them.
Phenotype	The characteristics you have, e.g. brown eyes.
Phloem	A type of plant tissue which transports dissolved sugars around the plant.
Photosynthesis	The process by which plants use energy to convert carbon dioxide and water into glucose and oxygen.
Phototropism	The growth of a plant in response to light.
Placebo	A substance that is like a drug being tested, but which doesn't do anything.

Glossary

Plasma	The liquid component of blood, which carries blood cells and other substances around the body.
Platelet	A small fragment of a cell found in the blood, which helps blood to clot at a wound.
Polydactyly	An inherited disorder, caused by a dominant allele, where a person has extra fingers or toes.
Precise result	A result that is close to the mean.
Predator	An animal that hunts and kills other animals for food.
Prey	An animal that is hunted and killed by another animal for food.
Primary consumer	An organism in a food chain that feeds on a producer.
Producer	An organism at the start of a food chain that makes its own food using energy from the Sun.
Prokaryotic cell	A small, simple cell, e.g. a bacterium.
Protease	A type of digestive enzyme that catalyses the breakdown of proteins into amino acids.
Protein	A large biological molecule made up of long chains of amino acids.
Protist	A type of pathogen. Protists are often transferred to other organisms by a vector.
Punnett square	A type of genetic diagram.
Pyramid of biomass	A diagram to represent the biomass at each stage of a food chain.
Quadrat	A square frame enclosing a known area. It is used to study the distribution of organisms.
Random error	A difference in the results of an experiment caused by things like human error in measuring.
Range	The difference between the smallest and largest values in a set of data.
Receptor	A group of cells that are sensitive to a stimulus (e.g. receptor cells in the eye detect light).
Recessive allele	An allele whose characteristic only appears in an organism if there are two copies present.
Reflex	A fast, automatic response to a stimulus.
Relay neurone	A nerve cell that carries electrical impulses from sensory neurones to motor neurones.
Repeatable result	A result that will come out the same if the experiment is repeated by the same person using the same method and equipment.
Reproducible result	A result that will come out the same if someone different does the experiment, or a slightly different method or piece of equipment is used.
Respiration	The process of breaking down glucose to transfer energy, which occurs in every cell.
Ribosome	A structure in a cell, where proteins are made.
Risk	The chance that a hazard will cause harm.
Risk factor	Something that is linked to an increased likelihood that a person will develop a certain disease.

Glossary

Secondary consumer	An organism in a food chain that eats a primary consumer.
Selective breeding (artificial selection)	When humans artificially select the plants or animals that are going to breed, so that the genes for particular characteristics remain in the population.
Sensory neurone	A nerve cell that carries electrical impulses from a receptor in a sense organ to the CNS.
Sex chromosome (humans)	One of the 23rd pair of chromosomes, X or Y. Together they determine whether an individual is male or female.
Sexual reproduction	Where two gametes combine at fertilisation to produce a genetically different new individual.
Speciation	The development of a new species.
Species	A group of similar organisms that can reproduce to give fertile offspring.
Stable community	A community where all the species and environmental factors are in balance, so that the population sizes are roughly constant.
Statins	A group of medicinal drugs that are used to decrease the risk of heart and circulatory disease.
Stem cell	An undifferentiated cell which has the ability to become one of many different types of cell, or to produce more stem cells.
Stent	A wire mesh tube that's inserted inside an artery to help keep it open.
Stimulus	A change in the environment.
Stoma	A tiny hole in the surface of a leaf.
Structural adaptation	A feature of an organism's body structure that helps it to survive in its environment.
Synapse	The connection between two neurones.
Systematic error	An error that is consistently made every time throughout an experiment.
Tertiary consumer	An organism in a food chain that eats a secondary consumer.
Theory	A hypothesis which has been accepted by the scientific community because there is good evidence to back it up.
Thermoregulatory centre	An area of the brain which controls and monitors body temperature.
Tissue	A group of similar cells that work together to carry out a particular function.
Tissue culture (plants)	A method of cloning plants in which a few plant cells are put on a growth medium containing hormones and allowed to grow into new plants.
Toxicity	How harmful something is, e.g. a drug.
Toxin	A poison. Toxins are often produced by bacteria.
Transect	A line which can be used to study the distribution of organisms across an area.

Glossary

Translocation	The movement of dissolved sugars around a plant.
Transpiration stream	The movement of water from a plant's roots, through the xylem and out of the leaves.
Trophic level	A stage in a food chain.
Tumour	A growth of abnormal cells.
Uncertainty	The amount of error your results might have.
Urea	A waste product produced from the breakdown of amino acids in the liver.
Vaccination	The injection of dead or inactive microorganisms, in order to produce an immune response that will help to protect you against a particular pathogen in the future.
Valid result	A result that is repeatable, reproducible and answers the original question.
Valve	A structure within the heart or a vein which prevents blood flowing in the wrong direction.
Variable	A factor in an investigation that can change or be changed (e.g. temperature or concentration).
Variation	The differences that exist between individuals.
Vasoconstriction	When blood vessels supplying the skin capillaries constrict (get narrower).
Vasodilation	When blood vessels supplying the skin capillaries dilate (get wider).
Vector (in genetic engineering)	Something used to transfer DNA into a cell, e.g. a virus or a bacterial plasmid.
Vector (in disease)	An organism that transfers a disease from one animal or plant to another, which doesn't get the disease itself.
Vein	A blood vessel that carries blood to the heart.
Virus	A tiny pathogen that can only replicate within host body cells.
White blood cell	A blood cell that is part of the immune system, defending the body against disease.
Xylem	A type of plant tissue which transports water and mineral ions around the plant.
Zero error	A type of systematic error caused by using a piece of equipment that isn't zeroed properly.

Index

Index

Index

Index